SELECT EDITIONS
LARGE TYPE

CONTENTS

Ethan Bright, a budding musician, had promised to write a song for Anna, his new bride. But work and life and the daily struggle of everything that happens to two people over time somehow got in the way. Years later, Ethan still hasn't written that promised song. Now it might be too late, and a song is the one thing that might still make a difference.

They are totally different: a rootless young girl from a broken, troubled family, and a firmly rooted young guy from a family tightly tied to the soil. But they marry anyhow, and learn and grow, and somehow make their marriage work. This is a story of people facing real life, and about how getting through that life changes us in ways we could never imagine.

THE FINAL NOTE

KEVIN ALAN MILNE

A YOUNG romance threatens to burn out over time, extinguished by the demands of job and dreams misplaced.

Prelude

I AM a sane person . . . I think. Which is why I feel terrible for going to her house and screaming at the top of my lungs like a raving lunatic. I wasn't even intoxicated, unless you count being drunk with rage, in which case my insobriety was well beyond legal limits.

"You ruined our family!" I yelled. "You and your stupid thumbs and your stupid phone!"

Okay, maybe that last part sounds a little crazy, but in context I swear it made perfect sense.

"Mr. Bright, I'll give you exactly two seconds to leave before I call the police! She's already apologized. There's nothing more to say!" That was the mother.

But I wasn't there to talk to the mother. I was there for her daughter, the twentysomething college student. She was standing between her mom and dad on the front porch, a few steps up from where I stood. The way she was holding herself made it look like she was freezing to death, even though it was a warm summer evening; I'm sure she was just doing that to keep from falling apart.

I'd already berated her once, earlier in the day. This was round two, and despite her mother's threats, I was just getting started.

"Really? Because I've got plenty to say! But first I want to show you something." I was carrying a briefcase. In one swift move I swung it in front of me, rested it on my thigh, and flipped it open.

"Oh, Lord, he brought a gun!" the mother screamed. She and her husband both jumped in front of their daughter instinctively.

"Oh, stop it," I barked. "I just want to show you what you took from me." I waved a fistful of the briefcase's contents.

"Paper?" That was the dad.

"Notes!" I shouted back. "The kind you can hold. These notes are meant to be cherished and read over and over again, not like your stupid texting that you read one moment and delete the next."

"What?" That was Ashley, the perpetrator.

"This morning," I reminded her, "before you ran off, you said your boyfriend sent you a 'note.' What he sent you was a two-bit text message, and like an idiot you answered it.

So I wanted to show you what real notes look like. Thoughtful, meaningful correspondence. The kind of communication that started—and probably saved—my marriage. Love notes! And I don't ever want you to forget what they look like, because this is what you took from me!"

The mom and dad were speechless. Ashley bowed her head and went back to holding herself, weeping audibly in the night.

What happened next is hard to explain. I glanced at the wad of papers in my hand. In that brief instant, memories came flooding back, from the very first note that Anna gave me, right down to the very last. The notes hadn't come as often in recent years, but that was mostly my own fault. And I was going to change. I swear. I *swore* to Anna that things would be different.

I broke a promise; she paid the price.

I looked back up at the family, and suddenly everything I'd wanted to scream at them—*at her*—just vanished. Why had I let my hatred drag me away from Anna?

"I'm so sorry," breathed Ashley.

I didn't want to hear it. I wanted to be mad. I wanted her to live with the guilt of what she'd done. I wanted her to be as miserable as I was. But mostly, I just wanted to get away and go be with the dying body of my wife. "You should be." I turned abruptly and left.

Thirty minutes later I was sitting next to Anna's bed in the ICU. She didn't know I was there. Physically she was lying right there on the bed, living on borrowed time through the wonder of modern medical machinery. But the part of her that really mattered? For all I knew, it was already gone.

"Anna"—my voice cracked—"I'm back."

There was no reply. I didn't expect one, but I kept trying.

"Can you hear me? Honey, are you there? I ran home, but I'm back now. Hope is doing fine. Your brother is watching her. Grandpa Bright is there, too. They're all praying for you.

"I found something," I told her. "It's my briefcase. The one you got me when they moved me into management. I've been loading it up with your notes. I brought them all with me. I thought maybe you'd like it if I read them to you. . . ." I wanted to cry.

No, that's being dishonest. I *did* cry, especially when I stumbled upon her original note to me. It wasn't a love note, but it certainly paved the way for love to grow. Reading the words she'd written took me back to another time and place. A different country, a foreign language. A hope, a prayer, and a guitar. Back then we were young and naive. Everything seemed possible. We fell in love.

We hardly knew what love was, but it didn't matter, because we had each other and we were happy. We were dirt poor, but it didn't matter, because we had each other and we were happy. In time we discovered that not everything in life goes as planned, but even then it didn't matter. We still had each other. And we were still happy.

All of which is a very long way of saying *I screwed up*.

I let the most important things in life take a backseat. I somehow lost sight of—maybe even forgot—just how good things had been in the beginning, back when life was simple . . . and perfect.

Anna's notes reminded me of everything we'd had and everything I was about to lose. I wished I could tell her how sorry I was. Actually, I did tell her as she was lying there, but she didn't hear.

"Remember how it used to be?" I asked her. "I thought ours was a fairy-tale once-upon-a-time story. Where is our happily ever after? How did I let this happen? I wish we could back up and do it all over again. Maybe then I'd get it right."

LONG before our lives fell apart, my wife dreamed of writing and illustrating books. It didn't exactly pan out. My dream was writing music, which was also a bust. But in the end none of those things mattered. The only things of consequence were the moments we had together and the memories we shared. Maybe that's why it's so important for me to tell our story, no matter how much it hurts. We once had something great, and I don't want to ever forget it. Nor would I want to lose sight of where I went wrong, lest I make the same mistake again and lose the precious few things I have left.

Not long ago my grandfather—who owns all the blame for getting me hooked on music as a kid—encouraged me to not just tell my story but to write it down so the memories remain fresh. "Writing your story is just like writing a song," he explained. "Start with the first verse, and take it one note at a time."

If Grandpa's counsel is right, then I've already messed up. I have taken a giant leap to the bitter end. But I suppose even a dismal tune like mine can easily be rewound.

FIRST VERSE:
Solo, Allegretto Scherzando

Chapter 1

"LET'S start at the very beginning. A very good place to start." Julie Andrews sang those words in *The Sound of Music* just before she and the kids broke into their famous do-re-mi's. When concerned friends have asked how my life got to the point it's at now, I tell them simply that, like Captain von Trapp and his musical wife, it all began quite wonderfully in Austria with a song and a guitar, but somehow it ended up in San Francisco . . . with nothing.

A lot has transpired since Austria. But if we're to follow my grandfather's (and Fräulein Maria's) admonition, then the snowcapped Alps of Europe's cultural heart is a very good place to start. That was *the beginning,* the place where I received my first note.

I'd just graduated from the University of Rochester's Eastman School of Music and was on my way overseas for graduate studies at the University of Music and Performing Arts in Vienna, Austria, when Grandpa Bright announced he was loaning me Karl.

Karl was the name of Grandpa's guitar, though why he'd given it a name was anyone's guess. Karl was the instrument I'd been openly coveting since I first heard Grandpa play it when I was a kid. Not only did Karl sound great, but it carried a certain mystique among the Bright family, mostly because Grandpa was so tight-lipped about how he'd acquired it and why he'd named it Karl. All he would say was that he owed his life to that old guitar.

I was more than a little surprised when he lent it to me. I was also deeply honored. But it was nonetheless fitting that Grandpa's beloved six-string should accompany me on my journey to Austria. We all knew he'd gotten it there while serving in the war. We just didn't know how. So going back to Austria, where Herbert Bright and Karl the guitar first met, was like a dream come true.

After settling into my two-year music

program in Austria's capital city, I began soaking up as much as I could of the sights, sounds, and culture of my new surroundings. There were frequent visits to the opera houses, countless hours staring at the intricate details of St. Stephen's Cathedral and Karlskirche, and more than a few excursions to the Imperial Palace—the home of the Habsburgs, rulers of the Austrian empire for more than six hundred years. I saw the Lipizzaner horses, the Vienna Boy's Choir, the Sigmund Freud Museum, and enough castle ruins to last a lifetime.

Unfortunately, tourist activities cost money, which was something I didn't have a lot of. And so, on the day before Christmas, I realized that I was flat broke. I'd secured loans to cover the big-ticket items, such as tuition and housing, so that wasn't a worry. But funds to simply exist? Those coffers were empty.

Other students might have called their parents for financial assistance, but that wasn't an option for me. My mom couldn't help, because she was "gone." That's how Dad explained it to me when I was five and she didn't come home from the hospital. And my dad? Well, after Mom left, he sort of died, too. Not physically, but in every other way—stopped going to work, lost his job, slept most of the time, started drinking heavily. After three months of depression, he decided that raising a child by himself was more than he could handle, so he handed me over to my grandparents.

Dad pulled out of his tailspin a few years later. He never asked to take me back, though. In fact, I rarely saw him.

Following where my mother had gone, Grandma Bright "left" just before I turned seven, so Grandpa and I learned to look out for each other. Grandpa was a psychologist, but his passion was music, and he shared everything he knew about it with me. Sometimes we'd listen to the radio and he'd have me write down the lyrics that spoke to me the loudest. Other times we'd learn about the classical masters. But more often than not, we'd sit and play the guitar.

Grandpa began teaching me how to play as soon as I moved in with him and Grandma. By the time I was ten, I was pretty good, and by the time I was thirteen, the student had become the teacher. Eventually I got my own guitar, though not as nice as Karl, and together we would write songs and play music until the wee hours of the night. It was those late nights playing music with Grandpa that convinced me my future was tied to the musical arts.

Although my childhood wasn't perfect, I survived, but only thanks to Grandpa. So, naturally, Grandpa is the one who got the call when I spent myself into the poorhouse in Austria.

"You spent *how much?*" he asked after I explained my predicament.

I was on a pay phone, spending my last pocket change at two dollars per minute, so I had to speak quickly. "All of it," I repeated. "I'm really sorry. Can you wire enough money to tide me over?"

I knew I was in trouble when Grandpa suddenly switched to his thoughtful psychologist voice. "I would, but I think this will be a good growing opportunity for you. Here's my advice. Use Karl."

The automated female voice of the pay phone chimed in: *"Nocheine Minute."* One minute left.

"What is that supposed to mean?"

"Why don't you play the guitar for money? I'm sure tourists will appreciate music from a skilled street musician."

I'd seen grungy musicians playing at tourist locations, sometimes to good-sized crowds, but I'd assumed those were just deadbeats trying to siphon liquor change from people's pockets. "Really?"

"Ethan, why do people visit Austria? For music! It's the heart of classical music in all the world. They want to hear music everywhere. I'm willing to wager that if they hear you play, they'll pay."

"Dreissig Sekunden." Thirty seconds.

"You got yourself into this mess, and I think it'll do you some good to get yourself out. If you want to stay in Austria, you'll find a way to make it happen. If you don't, call me back and I'll arrange a flight back to the States—which you can pay me back for."

The phone beeped three times in my ear. I had just enough time to say, "Good-bye, Grandpa," and then it clicked off.

THE next day, following an afternoon practicum at the university, I hauled Karl down to Stephansplatz, an upscale pedestrian area surrounding St. Stephen's Cathedral, in the center of the city. I'd seen musicians there before, and I figured it was as good a place as any for a solo performance.

I laid a piece of cardboard on the ground to protect my backside, then sat down. I made sure Karl was tuned; then I propped the hard-shell case open in front of me. It wasn't a hat, but there was ample room for donations. Finally, I closed my eyes and started to play.

I loved playing that guitar. Karl wasn't the most stunning instrument to look at. Its wood was heavily worn from decades of use. But what mattered was the sound, and in that it was a masterpiece.

I began with "Clair de Lune," a piece by Claude Debussy that I'd learned when I was sixteen. When I was done, I lifted my eyes to see the crowd's reaction. Only . . . there wasn't a crowd.

No money in the guitar case, either.

The only person there was a man in his early twenties. "Dat was wery *güt*," he said with a heavy Austrian accent. "You are *Amerikaner, ya?*"

"How could you tell?"

He shrugged. "You look it. May I offer adwice?"

"Okay."

"Do you know songs dat are more . . . eh . . . *femiliare?*"

"Familiar?"

"*Ja.* Und faster. Wit more *zing.*"

"Um . . . sure." Mentally I raced through the list of songs I'd prepared. They were plenty difficult, but they lacked zing. Then my mind landed on one of the earliest neo-classical pieces I'd ever learned. "I got it," I said. "'Bohemian Rhapsody,' by Queen."

He smiled with a nod. "Dat should do it."

I started into the song. It was slow at first, but clean and crisp, with enough notes to make it interesting. I kept my eyes open to better assess the response. Sure enough, people stopped to listen. And as the tempo flared, the crowd of onlookers grew. And grew.

Before the song ended, at least five people dropped money in the case. When the last note sounded, another three lined up to reward my efforts. I thanked them all with a courteous nod or smile.

"Vell," said the man, "I tink you found your moneymaker."

"*I tink* you may be right," I replied. "Thank you."

I could see at a glance that there was at least two hundred and fifty schillings in the case. *Twenty-five dollars! From one song!*

From that moment on, finances were no longer a problem. Several days a week I would lug Karl to various tourist sites in the city. Sometimes the crowds were thin. But then there were days that money flowed from pockets like air from a flute.

I soon discovered that three or four compelling songs were plenty for one "show." To make sure I maintained sufficient zing, I always ended with "Bohemian Rhapsody." That one always seemed to draw out loose change.

I continued playing and studying right on into spring. During the summer session my class load was light, allowing me more time to make money as a street musician. By the start of my second, and final, school year in September, I had enough saved that I could cut back to playing once per week.

By my second Christmas, I was in the

thick of my master's project, which kept me busy through the end of the semester in April. That left me with just one course and a summer practicum before graduation ceremonies in August. I'd been in college for six straight years—four in Rochester and two in Vienna—so it was hard to believe the end was so near. Time had flown by.

Then, in the middle of June, the passage of time suddenly shifted. In fact, it seemed to stop altogether. But it was actually just a side effect of a strange illness I'd contracted. Physical symptoms included high blood pressure, shortness of breath, fever, and occasional chills. Heart palpitations came and went, too.

I knew what I had was rare—lovesickness of such severity only comes around once in a lifetime.

I also knew that the *cause* and the *cure* were one and the same: Annaliese Burke.

Chapter 2

I GUESSED as soon as they got on the tramcar and sat down right behind me that one of them—the one whose hair wasn't in braids—

was an American tourist. It was her faded USC T-shirt and Bermuda shorts that gave her away. Her friend was harder to place. Both women were in their early twenties, and neither unattractive.

"Where to next?" the American asked, but she didn't give her friend a chance to answer. "Oh, my gosh! Look at that building! It's got to be, like, three hundred years old!"

"Probably older," the other woman responded flatly. Her English was impeccable, showing just the slightest hint of an accent. "Most of them are. Remember, we're not still in California."

I listened as the tourist asked questions about everything she saw, while her friend tried hard to be enthusiastic with her answers.

Three stops away from my apartment, the American let out an excited squeal. "Ooooh, there it is! We have to stop and see it!"

"It's just a garbage incinerator. And it stinks."

"It's not *just* a garbage incinerator. It was designed by Friedens-reich Hundertwasser. It's legendary! A perfect complement of art and industry, beauty and function. We have to stop."

I knew what building she was referring to. I rode past it every day. Its mosaic-tiled smokestack was encompassed by several large protrusions along its length, including one that resembled a four-story golden egg. The roofline sported an odd arrangement of peaks and angles, each topped with spheres that glistened in the sun.

"Ich bin aber müde," whined the friend under her breath.

"What did you say?"

"Nichts. Forget it. If you really want to stop, fine. We'll stop."

I felt a hand tapping my shoulder. "Excuse me," said the American. "Sir, do you speak English?"

I turned and looked at her. She had beautiful light brown hair, penetrating eyes, and an inviting smile. I nodded.

"Good. Did you hear what my friend just said in German?"

I smiled awkwardly. "My German's not the best, but I'm pretty sure she said she's tired."

The American's eyes lit up. "You're from the U.S.! Imagine that." She turned to her friend. "Tired? Really? Our trip is exactly one day old and you're already pooped?"

The woman smiled weakly. "Jet lag?"

"I know this stuff is boring to you because you grew up here. So why don't you run off and take a nap. I'll just go see it by myself and then catch up in time to change my clothes before dinner."

"Can you find your way back?"

"Probably not, but I'll figure something out."

That's when my first heart palpitations began. "I could get you wherever you need to go. I mean, if you'd like. I'm a student here." I forced a smile before adding, "I'm Ethan, by the way."

The woman turned once more to her friend. "Magda, this is my *new* best friend, Ethan, who will be escorting me to view an iconic Hundertwasser." She stuck out her hand as she turned back to me. "Pleased to meet you, Ethan. I'm Annaliese Burke. I go by Anna."

"You're not going over there alone with this *stranger.*" Magda glowered. "He could be a crazy person. A psycho."

"So you'll come, then?"

Magda cursed softly in German, then mumbled, "Yes, I'll come."

Anna turned to me again with a grin. "You're still invited, too, if you're interested. I'm willing to bet I can tell you at least twenty things about that building that you never knew."

"How could I pass up an offer like that?"

People have since asked me how my wife and I met. I discovered that "eavesdropping on a tramcar near an artistic waste incinerator" only spawned more questions. Instead, I learned to say simply, "In Europe." I would add that I helped show her around Vienna while I was a student there and that the rest, as they say, is history.

Incidentally, history had a lot to do with Anna and me. Specifically, art history. She was a recently graduated art history major whose purpose in traveling abroad was to experience Europe's rich artistic past firsthand. Anna spent two hours studying the strange factory, pointing out intricate nuances in its unique design and artistic form.

I spent two hours studying Anna's form and the intricacies of her physical graces. She was a beauty. Flowing hair. Brilliant blue eyes. Soft neck. Gentle hands. Perfect legs. When she walked, she glided. When she smiled, it was sincere. When she spoke, she did so with passion. And when she caught me staring at her rather than Hundertwasser's creation? She acted humble and flattered.

Once Anna decided she'd seen enough of the garbage dump, we found a café with umbrella tables, not too far from the Leopold Museum of Modern Art, where we could sip drinks and chat.

Anna was stirring the ice cubes in her Limonade with a straw. "So let me get this straight," she said. "You've got a degree in music theory, but you don't want to teach music. You earned a minor in guitar performance, but you don't want to play professionally. And now you're finishing a master's in music, and you don't plan on doing anything with that, either?"

"It's not that I won't benefit from what I've learned along the way," I told her. "It's just that what I want to do can't be taught in the classroom."

"Ooh, sounds exciting. Care to share?"

"You promise not to laugh?"

"Cross my heart," she said.

I don't know why I felt comfortable telling

Anna my future plans, a woman I'd known all of three hours. "I want to write songs."

"And what's wrong with that? Sounds like a perfect career for a well-educated musician like yourself. What type of songs? Classical music? Or were you thinking something more contemporary?"

"Uhh . . . contemporary. I'm sort of partial to rock ballads, but I'll probably dabble in country songs, too."

"Good for you, Ethan. If that's your dream, then go for it." She tilted her head. "But if that's what you've always wanted to do, why go to school for so long?"

"To fine-tune my music skills? To expand my horizons? To get out of Podunk? Take your pick."

She chuckled. "That sounds eerily familiar."

It turned out that Anna's educational background wasn't so different from my own. She'd always been passionate about art, particularly painting, so it wasn't a surprise to anyone when she graduated from USC with a degree in art history. Yet what she really wanted to do was write and illustrate children's books.

We talked and laughed for another thirty minutes before Magda finally called it quits. "My parents are taking us out to eat in half an hour. If we don't go now, we'll be late."

Not wanting our time together to end, I rode with the women to Magda's apartment building. Anna pulled Magda aside to speak to her in private. When she turned back to me, she was beaming. "We're both in agreement: You're *not* a crazy psycho. You may have noticed that Magda's heart isn't into playing tour guide. We're leaving Vienna soon, but until then, she wouldn't mind if I had someone else to show me the sights. How about it?"

My heart palpitations returned instantly. And chills. And shortness of breath. Anna wanted to see Vienna with *me*.

"Consider me yours," I said, not realizing how that might sound.

She didn't skip a beat. "Thanks . . . I think I will." She paused. "Can you be here at nine? I want to get an early start."

"The sooner the better." I didn't care if I sounded a little too eager. I *was* eager. I was thrilled. My heart was pounding.

Anna was going to see Vienna. With *me!*

THE NEXT MORNING, I arrived at Magda's apartment building promptly at 8:59.

Anna was already waiting for me near the front door. "You sure you've got time for me today?" she asked. "I hope you're not skipping something important, like school."

I tried not to grin too sheepishly. "I called in sick. Besides, it's just one class today. It's no biggie. Really."

"Good," she responded.

The first half of the day was spent looking at a church. It was called Karlskirche, and she seemed to know everything about it—who had commissioned it to be built and when, who designed it. She could look at one gilded pillar for fifteen minutes. When I asked her what she saw in it, she replied, "What do you see—or hear—when you play Mozart's *Requiem* or *The Magic Flute?*"

"Easy. Pure genius."

She winked. "Exactly."

We shared an Italian gelato from a street vendor, then hopped a subway out to Schönbrunn Palace, the 1,441-room summer home of the former Imperial family. We were in and out in just under two hours.

At dusk Anna inquired about my availability for the following day. My practicum—which I couldn't miss—was over by ten thirty, so we agreed to meet for lunch, followed by more sightseeing.

We followed that same basic pattern every day thereafter. We would meet as soon as my classes were through, explore the city together, say good night, then start all over again the next day. I didn't care that I'd already seen all of the places a hundred times; they were infinitely more interesting with Anna.

By the end of day nine, we'd covered all of the must-sees, so I began taking her to places like Zentralfriedhof, the massive cemetery where Austria's musical luminaries, such as Mozart, Beethoven, and Strauss, are memorialized. Or Schatzkammer, the Imperial treasury that houses the Holy Lance, believed by some to be the lance that pierced Jesus's side.

The only times we saw Magda were when she occasionally joined us for dinner. But on day thirteen—the day before Anna and Magda were skipping town to explore Paris, Berlin, Budapest, and Venice—Magda suddenly decided that it was unfair that she'd "neglected" her friend, so she didn't leave our side the entire day.

Her timing couldn't have been worse. I had been carefully strategizing about how, on our last night together, I was going to finally man up and steal a kiss from the most amazing woman on Earth. What I ended up with was a long shopping trip with our Austrian third wheel so she could pick up supplies for their trip. And when the sun started to set, Magda was adamant that they turn in early so as to rest up for their long journey.

When we parted ways outside Magda's apartment building, Magda gave me a sturdy handshake. *"Auf Wiedersehen,* Ethan."

I sensed that Anna wasn't ready to say good-bye, but at Magda's prodding she gave me a quick hug. "Thanks for everything."

I couldn't formulate a decent response, so I just nodded. The moment passed, and they were gone. *I'll never see her again.* Two weeks trying to charm Annaliese Burke, and what did I have to show for it? Nothing. *Nada. Gar nichts.*

No "I'll write!" or "Gee, it was fun spending so much time with you, and I sure hope to see you again." No indication that she expected our paths to cross in the future, let alone an address to look her up at when I got to the States. Heck, I didn't even know which town she was from, only that it was somewhere in rural Idaho.

All of a sudden I really did feel sick.

I stood for a moment by the curb, hoping beyond hope that oh, I don't know, maybe she'd run out at the last second and jump into my outstretched arms. The door remained closed.

Annaliese Burke was officially a memory.

BROKE. That's what I was after playing tour guide for two weeks. The only thing to do was tune Karl and head back out on the street.

July is the peak month for tourism in Vienna. However, competition from street performers was greatest at the big cathedrals and civic buildings downtown, so I tended to stake out locations where I could have an audience all to myself. My favorite place to play was the Basilisk House, which happened to be the oldest building in town. I didn't make quite as much money there, but the acoustics were excellent, and the history of the place made it ideal for dreaming about Anna and wallowing in self-pity.

The Basilisk House earned its name from the sandstone basilisk figure protruding from the second-story façade. Medieval legend has it that a horrible monster, hatched from the rotten egg of a chicken-toad, lived in the nearby well and killed people by looking at them. One day an apprentice baker, who was smitten with the baker's beautiful daughter, elected to prove his love through an act of bravery. He confronted *der Basilisk*. When the monster attacked, the apprentice averted his eyes and cleverly held up a mirror. Repelled by its own appearance, the creature instantly turned to stone.

Each time I sat in front of the historic old building, I thought about the legend. Anna was the baker's daughter. But what was I? The brave young apprentice? I wish. More likely, I was the geeky minstrel across the street who was never mentioned in the tale because all he ever did was admire the fair maiden from afar.

On a July evening, two weeks after Anna's departure, business in the shadow of the basilisk was unusually good. A group from Ireland had come to visit, but their tour bus was having mechanical problems. While they waited for it to be fixed, they doled out the equivalent of more than a hundred dollars in my guitar case. It was already getting late when they left.

As I was putting Karl away, I heard steps approaching quickly.

"Ethan?" It was a woman, her local accent slight but detectable.

My head jerked up. "Magda? What are you doing here?"

She rolled her eyes. "Believe me, I didn't want to come."

"Then why—"

"Because *I* wanted to hear you play."

Magda's mouth hadn't moved. The words came from someone standing right behind me whose voice was even more familiar.

I turned. There was Anna—*the baker's daughter*—smiling nervously as she stepped out from behind a car. "Hi," she said softly.

It was all I could do to form an intelligent response. I spotted the basilisk looming overhead. It reminded me that this was my chance. I could still be the apprentice, if only

I was willing to be brave. I blurted out, "You are so incredibly beautiful."

Her cheeks turned crimson. "I missed you, too."

I asked her the same question I'd already posed to Magda. "What are you doing here? I didn't think you were coming back."

"We weren't planning on it. But there were two trains to choose from to get to Hungary, and one of them came through Vienna."

"So how long is your layover?"

She checked her watch. "About thirty minutes left," she said.

My heart sank. "The train station is twenty minutes from here."

"I know. I'm sorry. I tried calling your apartment as soon as we got in. Your roommate said you were probably out playing the guitar. He gave us a list of the places you've been playing at the most, so we've been making the rounds. This was our last stop."

"You found me just in time to—what?— say good-bye again?"

Anna joined Magda on the other side of the guitar case. "No, just in time to hear you play the guitar. All those days we spent together, and I never heard you play."

I picked up Karl. "Anything special you'd like to hear?"

"Make it something memorable. I want a song that I'll recognize so I can listen to it in the future and think of you."

Staring at her beautiful face, a melody came to mind, and I knew that was the one for her. I began plucking the notes to perhaps the most romantic of classical tunes, Pachelbel's "Canon in D." I let my fingers feel their way from string to string, not looking up until I was halfway through the melody. Anna was still there, smiling, apparently pleased with what she heard. Magda was smiling, too. A small group of five or six others gathered around to listen.

When the notes reached their maximum velocity, people clapped. Then the crowd dispersed. Only Anna and Magda remained.

"You're amazing," Anna said.

"So are you." My voice cracked just a little.

Magda rolled her eyes again. "We have to get going."

Anna shot her a look. "I know. But first I have to give this fine musician a tip." From the pocket of her jeans, she pulled out a small slip of paper. Standing over the guitar case, she was about to drop the paper in with the money, but instead she took a step closer to me and slid the note beneath the strings of my guitar. Her fingers brushed mine for just a moment, sending a welcome shiver up my arm. "There," she told Magda. "Now we can go catch our train."

"Wait!" I shouted. "Will I see you again?"

Anna motioned to the "tip" she'd left in my guitar. "I hope so." She waved, then turned the corner and was gone.

I carefully unfolded the paper. It was a napkin, folded in fourths. When I reached the center, there was a brief handwritten message.

It was a note that would change everything.

Ethan,

I can't tell you how much I enjoyed spending time with you in Vienna. To me you've been the best part of Europe! On July 23 I will have one final stop in Austria. I know it's out of the way, but if you'd like to see me as much as I'd like to see you, meet me at 10:00 a.m. at the birthplace of Austria's most famous musical prodigy.

Hope to see you there! Anna

P.S.—If you're unsure which musical prodigy, just hum a few bars of Falco's greatest hit and it will come to you!

I knew all four words of Falco's song by heart, and I sang them happily as I folded up the note. *"Ooh, rock me Amadeus!"*

I WAS up early on July 23 and at Vienna's Südbahnhof by five a.m. There was a train leaving at five thirty, but it had lots of stops and wouldn't have gotten me to Salzburg until nine forty-five, which was cutting it close. But an express train was departing at six o'clock, which would put me in Salzburg by nine. The choice was a no-brainer: arrive at my destination with plenty of time to meet Anna at ten.

I'd brought Karl along, thinking that Anna might want to hear another song. On boarding, I stowed Karl on the luggage rack overhead, sat down, and anxiously checked my watch.

"Five fifty-five," I whispered to myself, anxious to get rolling.

A minute later a loud commotion erupted

on the platform. A stout train conductor was waving and shouting to another conductor a few cars up. "I'll stay here! You call for help! Hold the train!"

Hold the train? *"Wun-der-bar,"* I moaned aloud.

Seven minutes later an ambulance rolled onto the platform with sirens screaming. Twenty minutes later the ambulance was still there. Another half hour and our train was still motionless at the station. I wanted to scream. Now I was officially late.

After five more minutes the woman sitting across from me asked her husband to go find out what was taking so long. He returned to inform us that an elderly woman from Switzerland had passed out in her cabin and cut her head. But the woman was adamant that she was staying on the train and returning home to Switzerland. Fifteen minutes later the "express" train finally started to roll. By then I knew my date with Anna was sunk. The soonest I could get to Mozart's house was ten forty-five, nearly an hour after our scheduled rendezvous, and by then she would be gone.

It was a few minutes after eleven when I

finally arrived at the birthplace of Wolfgang Amadeus Mozart. I quickly scanned the crowd of people who were admiring the historic site from ground level, but none of them were Anna. Then I went inside and checked every room of the third-floor museum, but she wasn't there, either. After redoing the entire search once more from the start, I finally concluded that she was, in fact, gone.

Can't blame her. She'd given me a chance, and I blew it.

I picked up my guitar case and walked toward the center of town, kicking myself. Why didn't I just get on the slower train that left at five thirty? I wondered how Anna reacted when she realized that I hadn't come. Was she indifferent? Was she mildly disappointed? Or was she like me, heartbroken over what might have been?

It seemed unlikely that I would ever know.

AFTER getting a quick bite to eat at a deli, I decided to kill time waiting for the next train back to Vienna by trying to make a few bucks. I found a good spot at the base of Horse Fountain, a famous statue in the middle of Residenzplatz, and began playing. It wasn't long before a decent-sized group had gathered around to listen.

The fourth and final song of my set was the ever popular "Bohemian Rhapsody." I closed my eyes and thought of Anna. I tried to remember every detail about her as I lost myself in the song. There were a million things about her that I would miss. Her gentle voice. Her even gentler eyes. Her easy laugh. Her honest heart.

My eyes were still closed as the song was winding down. Small flurries of clapping erupted from all around. A voice called out above the dying din. "I'm not sure you deserve a tip for that, sir. Since when does Queen qualify as classical music?"

The comment yanked me immediately to my feet. "Anna!" I shouted, completely ignoring the onlookers. "You're here!"

"You're late."

I put down Karl without taking my eyes off of her. "Too late?"

"That depends on how good your excuse is . . . and whether or not you'll join me on the *Sound of Music* self-guided tour."

I tried to match her mock seriousness. "Okay, then first let me assure you that I had every intention of being on time but was waylaid by a very old woman who needed medical assistance."

"You stopped to help her? How noble."

"Well, no. . . . Actually, I was praying that she'd get off the train as quickly as possible so we could get moving. But, if absolutely necessary, I would have helped her, too . . . probably."

Anna laughed. "At least you're honest."

"Thanks. Now, about *The Sound of Music*. Is there really a self-guided tour?"

She unrolled a small pamphlet. "Sure is. Are you game?"

"I wouldn't miss it." I paused. "What about Magda?"

"Aww, you miss her. I'll let her know the next time I see her."

"When will that be?"

"Tomorrow, in Venice. She's on her way there now, along with most of my luggage. Our train came through Salzburg just before ten this morning. I got off; she stayed on."

"I didn't think Salzburg was on your itinerary."

The way she was smiling lit up my heart. "It wasn't. I gave up a day in Venice so I could spend one here. I had no interest in Salzburg." She inched closer. "I came to meet someone. A *guy*, if you must know. A guy who I couldn't stop thinking about."

I moved closer, too. "A super nice, really handsome guy?"

"As a matter of fact, he is. And he's someone who I was sure would want to see me again, even if it was only for a few hours."

"Did he show up?"

"Sadly, no. He stood me up. Too bad for me; he was something special." She threw up her hands. "Oh, well. At least *you're* here."

What a tease. "Yeah, lucky me."

We spent the next couple of hours walking from site to site around town. My favorite was the Abbey, where we sang a rousing rendition of "How Do You Solve a Problem Like Maria?" But mostly we just talked. And laughed. And teased.

We stopped by the train station and paid to have them hold Karl. That freed up my hand for when Anna decided to hold it.

In the afternoon we found a cabdriver to drive us the thirty or so miles to Bertchtesgaden, a small town just across the border in Germany. From there we took a tour bus up to the Eagle's Nest, Hitler's Bavarian hide-out. It was a sobering experience to walk the same halls as one of history's greatest fiends.

To lighten the mood, we scoured the compound's many restrooms, looking for one that might be missing a door handle. My grandpa claimed to have been part of the brigade that took over the Eagle's Nest in 1945. He also insisted that he'd helped himself to one of Hitler's bathroom door handles as a souvenir.

Much to our disappointment, the restrooms that were open to the public had all of their handles accounted for.

Anna and I returned to Salzburg, where we enjoyed a candlelit dinner at a Tirolean restaurant. Then it was time to make our way back to the train station to catch Anna's southbound line.

While waiting for her train to board, I fetched my guitar from the luggage hold. Anna wanted to hear "her song," the "Canon in D."

Before I played, she scooted closer on the bench we were sharing. "Ethan, how far would you go to see me again?"

"When?" I asked excitedly.

"No, I mean just hypothetically."

"Well, that depends. On how far away you are."

Her smile said my answer was the right one.

Anna's train was boarding, but there was still enough time to play the canon one time through. While my fingers were working the guitar, Anna's fingers took a moment to scribble something on a piece of paper. When the song finished, she stood up in front of me and slid the paper through the guitar strings, the same as she'd done in front of the Basilisk House. Only this time she leaned over and added a soft peck on each of my cheeks, followed by a perfect, pensive kiss on the lips. Standing up, she adjusted her backpack and began walking toward platform number 6.

I quickly grabbed the note. It took me all of two seconds to read.

Octavius Burke—Moscow

I recognized the name as that of her father. "Moscow?" I called. "You want me to find you in Russia?"

Anna turned. "Is that too far for you, Mr. Bright?"

"No, but . . . why *Moscow?*"

"It's a little place I like to call home. Good ol' Moscow, Idaho."

"And you're sure it won't be hard to find Octavius?"

"It shouldn't be hard. He's the only one in the entire state, the last time we checked. Find him and you'll find me."

Chapter 3

THE rest of the summer passed much slower than I would have liked. I could hardly wait to embark on the important business of locating Anna Burke. Eventually I was officially declared a Master of Music. While my peers were interviewing for teaching positions at universities, conducting musical theater in Paris or New York, or playing in renowned orchestras, I was flying back to my grandfather's home in the quiet coastal town of Garibaldi, Oregon—population 881.

I stayed one week, which was the amount of time it took to persuade Grandpa to loan me his beat-up truck for a trip to Idaho.

"You just got here and now you want to run off again?" he asked when I raised the question over dinner on my first night home. "What's Idaho got that Oregon doesn't?"

"Would you believe it if I said there's a shortage of professionally trained guitarists there?"

"*Pfft.* I'm neither young nor naive, Ethan."

And so I admitted to having met an exceptional woman from the Potato State and that I wanted to go see her.

"How long do you plan on being there?"

"Depends on how it goes. Maybe a week or two."

"I'll think about it."

I knew he'd end up letting me go . . . eventually. He didn't admit it, but I think he really missed having me around. On the evening of my sixth day there, he gave in. The next morning, I was gone.

By six o'clock that night, I rolled into Moscow, across the border from Pullman, Washington. The welcome sign coming into town said there were twenty thousand residents. Based on what Anna had described, I'd expected to see nothing but farmland. What I found was a vibrant town with a charming university at its core.

It took me only five minutes to find a 7-Eleven with a public phone book. The cashier was more than happy to offer basic directions to the address of Octavius Burke. Ten minutes later I parked in front of a two-level home on Ponderosa Drive.

My stomach did somersaults as I waited for the door to open. When it finally did, I was greeted by a tall man with wire-rimmed glasses. His mop of graying hair curled just above the shoulder. He examined me from head to toe. "Can I help you?"

I felt like a teenager arriving for a prom. "Hello. Is Anna home?"

"Perhaps. Is she expecting you?"

"Probably not."

"Then may I ask what your business is?"

"I guess you could say I'm just following up on some unfinished business from Austria."

The man's demeanor softened considerably. "So you're Ethan?"

"I am. You must be Mr. Burke."

He nodded again. "Octavius."

"Anna told me a lot about you," I lied. "All good, I might add."

That put a smile on his face. He motioned for me to come inside, then closed the door and asked me to wait there. He called out, "Annaliese! There's someone here to see you."

"Who is it?"

Octavius turned his head and looked at me, flashing a mischievous smile; then he called back over his shoulder, "Oh, nobody important." He whispered to me, "If I mentioned your name, I bet it would take twenty minutes of hair-doing and makeup before she'd be ready to be seen. Better off just surprising her."

I suddenly liked Octavius Burke very much.

A moment later a door opened on the second floor and out came Anna, looking as gorgeous as ever in a maroon sweatshirt, gray pajama pants, and a pair of fluffy pink slippers. When she saw me, she did a double-take. By the look on her face, she regretted her choice of evening attire. But she just walked confidently down the stairs as though she knew I wouldn't care what she was wearing.

Anna gave me a friendly hug. "You came," she said.

I chuckled. "Did you think I wouldn't?"

"I hoped, but it's been almost a month and a half, so who's to say you didn't forget about me? Wasn't your graduation two weeks ago? After a week passed, I started to worry."

"Actually, graduation was only eight days ago. And once I was back in Oregon, it took me longer than expected to scrounge up wheels to drive out here. Before I went to Europe, I sold everything I had, including my car. Convincing my grandfather to lend me his truck was like getting Magda to visit the Hundertwasser garbage dump. He caved in last night, and I hit the road this morning."

She tilted her head at an angle. "So it wasn't two weeks ago?"

"Maybe you have me confused with that other guy who stood you up in Salzburg."

"That's probably it. Oh, well, at least one of you made it here."

OCTAVIUS and Anna lived alone. Julia, Anna's mother, had succumbed to cervical cancer when Anna was a freshman in high school. The fact that we'd both lost our moms earlier than anyone should was one of the things that had helped us really connect back in Austria. Her older brothers were already out of the house. Lance, the oldest, was living on the opposite end of the state, where he taught junior-high shop class as a means to fund his exotic summer adventures. The middle sibling, Stuart, was some sort of techno geek running his own start-up company in Silicon Valley.

Octavius surprised me by offering Stuart's old bedroom, directly across the hall from Anna's. "As long as you're in there," he told me, "and Anna's in her room, then everything is copasetic. Call me old-fashioned, but this is my house and we play by my rules."

I made up my mind immediately to follow the house rules. If anything serious were ever to come of my relationship with Anna, I wouldn't want to be on anything but good terms with her father. "Understood," I said. "And thank you."

I intended to stay with the Burkes for only a few days. However, when a few days were up, Anna convinced me to stay for a few more. And then a few more. Moscow, Idaho, was certainly not Vienna, but on her home turf it was Anna's turn to play tour guide. Each day, she took me to see something new—the university where Octavius was a philosophy instructor, an apple orchard, white-water rafting, a farmer's market, and an alpaca ranch.

Anna took me to meet the countless friends and family she had in the area. In the evenings, we would try new places to eat, walk along the river, or simply sit in the park and talk.

At the two-week mark Octavius shocked me by offering Stuart's room on a longer-term basis. "You've earned my trust," he said. "I don't know what your immediate plans are, but if you need a place to stay while you're figuring things out, you're welcome here."

"Thank you," I said coolly. "I'll think about it." *As if there's anything to think about.*

The next day, Anna and I caravanned back to Oregon to return my grandfather's truck. We stayed nearly a week, allowing Anna time to get to know Grandpa Bright and a couple of my aunts and allowing me time to pack up my few personal belongings. On the morning of our sixth day there, we said good-bye, loaded the boxes into Anna's Jetta, and returned to Moscow.

I had no car and very little money, but at least I had a place to stay. *And I had Anna.*

Knowing that I had to do something to start earning money like a respectable adult, I registered as a substitute music teacher with the local school districts. Between that and private guitar lessons, I was able to afford my own transportation very quickly, which was a huge relief. Soon I was making enough to afford a single-room apartment. Octavius assured me I was welcome to stay, but I knew I needed to be on my own, if only for the self-respect.

While I was busy teaching, Anna spent her days taking courses in writing, publishing, and children's literature at the university. She was still very determined that she was going to write and illustrate children's books as a career. In the evenings we often got together to nudge one another along in the pursuit of our artistic dreams—she would sit on one end of the sofa, thinking up catchy story lines, while I sat on the other end with Karl, trying to write pop hits. Periodically we'd stop to share notes and a quick kiss.

Anna and I grew steadily closer. She described our comfort level with one another as "uncommonly natural." We just seemed to fit, kind of like a two-part harmony. It wasn't very long—a few months, tops—before we began openly discussing the possibility that our relationship might have the makings of something special.

By my fifth month in Moscow, a short seven months after meeting Anna, I decided that the time for speculation about what our future might hold was over. One night at Anna's house, after Octavius had gone to bed, I grabbed the globe on his desk in the study and brought it to Anna on the living-room floor.

"Do you remember what you asked me before you got on the train for Venice?"

"Of course. I asked how far you'd travel to see me again."

"And my answer?"

"Depends on where I am."

"Exactly. And I still feel that way. More so, actually."

Anna wrinkled her nose. "So what's with the globe?"

"That, Ms. Burke, is just to help you keep

in mind how big the world is. Because I want you to know that wherever you are, that's where I want to be."

Her eyes smiled at the comment. "I'm here now."

"The thing is," I continued, straight-faced, "I'm more than a little interested in how far *you'd* go."

She chuckled dryly. "Why? You going somewhere?"

I raised my eyebrows but didn't say anything.

Anna sat straight up. "Oh, my gosh. Are you? Where?"

"Well, that depends."

She politely played along. "Okay. Depends on what?"

"On how far you'd go to be with me. Would you search the world to find me? To find true love?"

"Is that what we have?"

"I think so." I paused to let that sink in. "Do you?"

With her eyes locked on mine, she calmly stated, "Yes."

"Then how far would you go?" I repeated.

"As far as I have to."

I smiled and spun the globe. "Would you go all the way to Miami?"

"Absolutely."

I spun it again. "How about Rome?"

"Definitely. I'd love to go back there."

"Berlin?"

"Sure."

"What if I said I was going to Australia? Would you go?"

"Without question."

I spun the globe one more time. "Anna, I am going to one of those places, but it wouldn't be the same without you there."

"Which one?" she asked, then added, "Don't say, 'It depends.'"

"But it does. First, it depends on which of the cities that I mentioned sounds the most interesting to you."

She considered the matter. "I've been to Europe already, so . . . I think Miami would top the list. I've never been to Florida."

"Okay. Then second, it depends on . . ." I let the words trail off as I deftly scooted closer, positioning myself on a single knee right beside her. "On whether," I continued, "you agree to marry me."

For a minute I feared her eyes were going

to pop right out of her head. And her eyes got even bigger when I produced a small engagement ring from my jeans pocket. Then she began to tear up, whether out of happiness or eyestrain, I wasn't sure.

Anna took a moment to compose herself while wiping her eyes. "Yes, but why are we going to Florida?"

I grinned. "We have to go somewhere on our honeymoon, right?"

She whispered, "Florida is perfect."

"Florida was my first choice, too, because I think I can afford to take us there without major debt. So thanks for that."

She said, "We can go to Boise, for all I care. It doesn't matter, as long as we're together."

SECOND VERSE:
Duet, Adagio Dolcissimo

Chapter 4

THE wedding happened six months later at an old church near the university campus in Moscow. Only a handful of my family could make it to Idaho, but the ones who mattered most were there—Grandpa Bright, aunts Jo and Beth, and my cousin Seth, who was also my best man. To everyone's astonishment my dad made an appearance, too. He talked to me only briefly, offering whatever fatherly wisdom he could, but it was a kind gesture on his part.

In contrast to my limited family support, the church was packed to overflowing with Anna's friends and family, who'd come to celebrate the occasion. Her mother's side of the family was thrilled that she chose to wear her mom's elegant white wedding dress.

Anna was a rare sight, with her long satin train and flowing hair. Once she started walking down the aisle with Octavius, to the sound of a violin quartet playing the "Canon in D," I couldn't take my eyes off of her.

The minister gave a brief sermon on the sanctity of marriage, but I was too wrapped up in admiring the woman who was about to be my wife to catch many of the details. I do, however, remember vowing before God and the congregation that I would love, comfort, and honor Anna always, no matter what.

That evening, after the reception, we

caught a late commuter to Boise and from there boarded a red-eye to Florida. I added a vow or two to the ones I'd made earlier at the church. "There's only one way I could ever express how much I love you," I told her. "I'm going to write a song just for you."

"That's sweet. I'm also counting on you serenading me at least once a week on the guitar."

"Only once a week? Easy."

"For the rest of our lives?"

I smiled and kissed her. "Forever."

"So when will this song of yours be done?" Before I could answer, her eyes lit up. "You can work on my song for the next year, then sing it to me one year from today, on our first anniversary!"

"So it's settled, then: I owe you a song one year from today. But I want to request an anniversary present, too."

"Okay."

"I'd like a painting. An original Annaliese Bright. On canvas."

She tapped the tip of my nose with her finger. "Consider it done."

Anna eventually fell asleep. I stayed awake long enough to write down a few of my thoughts from the most important day of my life, but the only thing I could find to write on was the white throw-up bag in the seat pocket in front of me. It occurred to me that I'd made many promises in the last twenty-four hours. I flipped the bag over and itemized each of them.

Promised Octavius:
- that I will always put Anna's happiness ahead of my own.
- that I will take care of her.
- that I will never break his little girl's heart.

Promised Grandpa Bright:
- that I will always treat Anna as a treasure. "For where your treasure is, there will your heart be also."

Promised my dad:
- that I will learn to be forgiving, even when it's hard.

Promised Aunt Jo:
- that I will remember to put the toilet seat down.

Promised God, "in witness thereof by those in attendance," that I will love, comfort, and honor my wife:

- in sickness and in health
- for richer or for poorer
- for better or for worse
- in sadness and in joy
- to cherish and continually bestow my heart's deepest devotion upon her
- to love her and none other, as long as we both shall live.

Promised Anna:

- that I will serenade her on the guitar at least once a week.
- to write a song just for her and sing it to her on our first anniversary.
- that my love for her will be greater with each new tomorrow.

Satisfied that the list was complete, I tucked the vomit bag in my carry-on and leaned back. Anna was leaning against the window, oblivious to the world around her. Yet even as she slept, I could see the makings of a beautiful smile on her lips.

After my mom died when I was a kid, I

often wondered where heaven was located, assuming that's where my mother had "gone." But my final thought that night on the airplane, before succumbing to the lull of jet engines, was that I'd finally found heaven. It was right beside me in Anna's perfect smile.

THOUGH our flight ended in Miami, our resort was in West Palm Beach. When we arrived late in the morning, exhausted from a long night of travel, the beach at our back door seemed the perfect place to sit and relax. We lounged on the white sand for almost an hour, planning out the rest of our week. Hanging out at the beach was a top priority, but we also wanted to see the sights. Our list included parasailing, deep-sea fishing, driving south to explore the Keys, an airboat tour in the Everglades, and a trip to a gator farm.

We grabbed a late lunch at a beachside cabana, then went back to our room and unpacked. The bulkiest of our belongings was Grandpa's guitar. Anna insisted that I bring it along so I could play for her late at night on the beach. I took Karl from its case and plucked out a medley of classical pieces, followed by a country song I'd recently written; then I laid down for a much-needed nap.

When I awoke, Anna was curled up beside me, sleeping. Next to my side of the bed, propped up against the nightstand, was Karl.

Tucked beneath the strings of the guitar was a small pink envelope. On the front, written in Anna's distinctive hand, were the words "True Love Note." On either side of the inscription, she'd drawn a pair of musical notes.

Hey Hubby! Do you like the sound of that? I can hardly believe we're actually married! What a trip, huh?

As the envelope states, I've named this a "True Love Note." I know how much you love playing musical notes, and I've always had an affinity for writing love notes, so this is my attempt at bringing those two things together.

So here's the deal: Every time you play the guitar for me, I promise to leave you a True Love Note in your guitar. Yes, I know that means at least once a week (you promised!). They won't always be long, but they will always be true. And they'll always be a reminder to you that you are truly loved.

You've made me so happy, and I can't wait for that happiness to expand as we grow old together.

In every way possible, I am yours.

Anna

OCTAVIUS was kind enough to move all of Anna's belongings from his place to ours while we were in Florida. He also surprised us with a brand-new queen-size sleigh bed, complete with warm flannel sheets and a thick feather duvet.

Once September rolled around, substitute teaching and a part-time job at a music store kept me busy about four days a week. The other three days were spent writing lyrics and melodies from the comfort of our tiny living room. It was working out so well that in the first few months of marriage, I'd already composed eight songs.

Anna worked evenings at a department store. Not her dream job, but it was enough to help cover the bills, and it left her mornings free to focus on writing and illustrating children's books. Anna kept all of the completed artwork on the top shelf of her closet in special binders. The books were progressing so well that she expected to have them polished enough to send out to publishers by the end of the year.

The newness of marriage made it seem as though nothing would ever go wrong. It was as perfect a beginning to our new life together as I could have imagined.

I played the guitar for Anna at least once a week, as I'd promised, and in return I received a *True Love Note* woven into the strings of my guitar, to be found the next time I played. Sometimes the notes were pages long, and other times they were a sentence or two. But *I love you more today than yesterday* was enough.

I'd diligently lived up to all of my other marriage-day promises, too. Well, maybe I left the toilet seat up a few times.

Wouldn't it be great if the honeymoon period never ended? If everything stayed divine and unbelievably dreamy forever? But eventually, every marriage succumbs to the realities of life.

Our formal honeymoon in Florida ended on a Sunday. The honeymoon period ended almost four months later on a Friday.

A page was made over the intercom at the middle school where I was substituting. "Mr. Bright, to the office, please."

When I got there, the school secretary was waiting anxiously with a phone outstretched in her hand. She mouthed, *It's your wife.*

"It's me. What's going on?"

"It's my fault," she whimpered. "I thought I turned the oven off."

"What happened?"

"The chicken *burned*, Ethan."

"Sweetie, it's okay. I don't care that you burned the chicken. We can spare a few bucks tonight to go out for dinner."

The wailing intensified. "It's not the ch-chicken! It's everything else! I th-thought I'd t-turned it off when I ran to the store. And when I c-came back—"

"Anna, what happened?"

She took a breath, then said, "It's gone, Ethan. Our furniture, our clothes, the apartment—it's all gone. The fire spread so fast."

My mind was reeling. I tried focusing on

the key words. *Chicken. Fire. Apartment. Burned. Everything.*

"The bed from your dad?"

"Gone."

"Your stories and artwork?"

She cried loudly, then mustered another sorrowful "Gone."

"What about Grandpa's guitar? And all of my songs?"

"The guitar was near the f-front door. I was able to grab it. But your sheet music was on the n-nightstand." Anna broke into another fresh round of sobbing. "I'm . . . *so* . . . sorry."

"But you're safe, right? You're not hurt?"

"I smell like smoke, but I'm fine. Can you come home?"

The vice principal filled in for me in the classroom so I could go be with Anna and survey the damage.

The property manager was on the scene talking to Anna when I approached. "The building is covered with its own fire policy," he told me. "But do you have any sort of renter's insurance to cover your things? Your wife wasn't sure."

"No," I whispered as I wrapped my arms

around Anna. I held her as tight as I could. "I meant to, but it slipped my mind."

Anna sobbed some more. Not only was everything we owned gone, but without insurance we had no way to replace it.

We were both shaking when we left the apartment. All of our hard work—*our dreams*—had literally gone up in smoke. I didn't blame Anna for "burning the chicken" any more than she blamed me for not getting insurance, but the fact remained that we suddenly had nothing, and the thought of it shook us to the very core.

But the trauma of the day was not over. Once we were alone in my car, Anna fumbled around in her purse. "This isn't how it was supposed to turn out."

"You mean extra crispy? No kidding."

"No, I mean *today*. It's all wrong."

"What could be wrong with losing everything you own?"

She ignored me. "When it didn't come this week, I feared the worst." She'd found whatever she was looking for, but her hand remained in her purse, trembling. "I don't know how to say this, Ethan. This clearly isn't the best time for mistakes of this sort."

"For crying out loud, our house just burned down. What could be worse than that?" It was the first time I'd spoken to Anna in a way that was anything less than adoring. I regretted it instantly.

Her free hand shot up to her face as a new wave of tears began.

I gently apologized, and she seemed to settle back down. "Please," I said, "just tell me what's wrong so I can help."

She steadied herself. "The thing . . . Ethan . . . is that . . . there is more in the oven than just some lousy chicken." She withdrew her hand from the purse and dropped an odd-looking stick on my lap.

I just stared at it. "So rather than keeping an eye on the chicken, you were . . ."

"Taking a pregnancy test. I couldn't wait to find out, so I found a stall in the grocery-store bathroom and sat there waiting for the results. After I saw the plus sign on that test, everything is a blur. I ended up back at the apartment, and there was smoke coming out of the windows. I grabbed your guitar, but that was all I could get to."

"It's going to be fine," I assured her.

But in the back of my mind, all I could think was, *The honeymoon is definitely over.*

OCTAVIUS WAS MORE than happy to let us move back into his house. He didn't even charge us rent, so we could save our money for all the things we didn't have—clothes, bed, furniture, art supplies, bedding, dishes, towels, just to rattle off a few.

The shock over the fire eventually faded enough that we were able to focus our attention on Anna's pregnancy. Thankfully, she wasn't sick at all, so her spirits remained high. At night we would lie awake in bed trying to sort through the details of our sudden state of pre-parenthood. I tended to focus on what I viewed as the more pressing, tactical concerns: *How soon can we move back into a place of our own? How much does a baby cost?*

Though she didn't dismiss the practical realities, Anna stewed more on things like who the baby would look like, would it be a boy or a girl, and would it prefer Dad's music or Mom's art?

"He, or she, might not be artistic at all," I pointed out late one night. "He could end up like your brother, a brainiac techno-gadget whose only creative outlet is programming video games."

She gasped. "Can you imagine us raising a little Stuart?" Though it was already well past midnight, she climbed out of bed.

"Where are you going?"

"I have some fun ideas for paintings of animals to hang in the nursery—assuming our baby *has* a nursery. They'll be bright and bold and daring, just like our child. I want to start working on them while the images are fresh in my mind. You just go to sleep."

"Anna," I called before she slipped out through the bedroom door. "You're really liking the idea of being a mom, aren't you?"

She glided back to the bed and gave me a final kiss good night. "I'm scared," she admitted, "but I couldn't be happier."

Both of us were determined to pitch in to make things work. I accepted every substitute teaching job that came up. I also took on more hours at the music store and added three additional students to my regimen of private lessons on the weekend. Anna bumped up to almost thirty hours a week at the department store.

I noticed a steady decline in the number of True Love Notes I was receiving from Anna, but only because the frequency of my guitar serenades had dropped. Whereas during the early months of our marriage I would play for her almost daily, by the twelfth week of her pregnancy, I felt good if I pulled out Karl twice in a seven-day stretch. But every time I did, she left me a note without fail.

Although we still felt as poor as dirt, we found a two-bedroom apartment and moved back out on our own. In order to tuck away a little money for after the baby arrived, I added four more hours of private guitar lessons to my weekend schedule.

It felt like Anna and I hardly saw each other. Sometimes, late at night, she would say that I'd taken on too much.

"It's only temporary until the baby comes," I would tell her. "Just to make sure we've got enough money to get by."

"Just until the baby comes?"

"I promise."

Honestly, I intended to keep that promise. Unfortunately, I didn't get the chance. Before the end of the fifth month of the pregnancy, Anna miscarried. The baby never came.

FOR ME THE MISCARRIAGE was an unfortunate event. For Anna it was an emotional avalanche. Sure, the pregnancy was a bit of an "oops," but as the pregnancy progressed, she'd started to view and define herself as a mother. She'd narrowed down a long list of baby names to a handful of her favorites, and she'd painted enough watercolor animals to fill Noah's Ark. But now that was all just wasted effort. One day everything was perfect, and the next day all of her fantasies of motherhood were yanked away.

The obstetrician's explanation was, "Sometimes these things just happen." Without health coverage to defray the costs, the unsuccessful pregnancy sucked up every cent in our savings account. To deal with the loss, we settled back into a routine that included heavy doses of "me time," during which both of us refocused our efforts on our elusive dreams of writing songs and children's books.

I was happy to see Anna spending more time on her artwork. I didn't say anything when she'd sequester herself in our apartment's second bedroom—the one we'd planned for a nursery but that now served as her art studio—until all hours of the night.

When I came home from work on the day of our first anniversary, I was surprised to find candles lit throughout the apartment Anna was waiting for me, wearing a beautiful red dress and, more important, a smile that spanned her entire face. It was the same smile I'd fallen in love with back in Austria, the same one that reminded me of heaven. Ever since the fire, and even more so after the miscarriage, that particular smile had been noticeably absent from her repertoire of expressions.

I bent down to give her a kiss. "I think you look more beautiful tonight than ever before. But I guess I didn't get the memo that we were having a fancy dinner. Something smells terrific."

She let out a muffled laugh. "It's called Chicken Fuego."

"Fuego? Doesn't that mean fire?"

"Uh huh. *Fire chicken,* to commemorate our sizzling first year together. But unlike the last time, this recipe is heavy on the fire sauce but light on the actual fire."

"We could always go to the store for a while and see if anything ignites while we're gone."

"Hmm. Do we have renter's insurance yet?"

I let out a laugh as I stared in awe at the woman sitting across from me. "You're incredible, Anna. I love you so much."

"I know you do. And for some crazy reason I feel the same way about you. Which is why I have something to show you. I was going to save it for later, but now I can't wait." She stood up and grabbed my hand, then pulled me into our bedroom. On the wall above our bed was a large framed oil painting. "So? What do you think? It's your very own, original, Annaliese Bright. On canvas."

The painting was a stunning portrayal of her and me on the night I proposed. It showed us sitting on the floor holding hands, curled in perfect symmetry around a globe. The way we sat, with our bodies and legs curving in opposing directions around each other, it gave the appearance of a human yin and yang. Where one ended, the other began, each giving rise to and completing the other.

"It's the most amazing thing I've ever seen," I said at length. "Is this what you've been working on late at night?"

She nodded excitedly. "It's been so hard

keeping it a secret from you, but . . . well, I wanted to keep my promise."

My heart sank. I'd been so preoccupied that I'd failed to keep my end of the bargain. Though I'd written plenty of good songs, she'd heard all of them, and none of them were written especially for her.

"It's okay," she said gently. "It's been a rough year, and you've been beyond busy. Don't feel bad that you didn't write me a song."

"But I promised," I said lamely.

A serious look crossed her face. "I know. And there are other things you promised. I'd like to talk about them while we eat."

I nodded, and we returned to the kitchen. While we were eating Chicken Fuego, Anna surprised me again by sliding a white airplane vomit bag across the table. I recognized it instantly.

"Where did you find this? I thought it burned up."

"I was taking Karl out of its case about a month ago to leave you a note, but the button for the shoulder strap caught on a piece of the padding. It pulled it right out. This was tucked in there behind it."

"That's right! I completely forgot. I put it there, thinking it would be safe." I scanned the words I'd written three hundred and sixty-five days earlier, the list of wedding-day promises. I took the time to read each one before responding. "Well . . . some of these I think I've done okay on. Not perfect, but pretty good. For the things I vowed during the ceremony, I believe I've kept each of them. Same goes for what I promised your dad."

"What about the things you promised *me?*" she asked softly.

I read those silently again. Promised that I will serenade her on the guitar at least once a week. Promised to write a song just for her and sing it to her on our first anniversary. Promised that my love for her will be greater with each new tomorrow.

I met her gaze. "Well . . . one out of three's not bad, right?"

"Nice try."

"I can do better. I should be able to start playing for you again. At night, before we go to sleep. And as for your special song, I won't work on anything else until it's done. Okay?"

She crossed her arms. "I've been thinking.

And I've decided that I want you to hold off. I know you love me, and I know eventually those feelings will spill over into a song that's just for me. But until then, I'd rather you focus your attention on something else."

I sat up. "Do you have something specific in mind?"

Anna reached across the table for my hands. Once she had them, she squeezed gently. "I want us *both* to focus on having a baby."

I resisted the urge to pull my hands back. "Are you sure?"

She nodded resolutely. "I know it's crazy, given where we're at financially. But I want to find a way to make it work. If that means I work full-time and spend less time on my books, I'm okay with that. And if I have to wait longer to get my song, that's okay, too. It's just that I know I want to be a mom. And I don't want to put it off."

I stared into the face of my best friend and said, as sincerely as I could, "I'm with you one hundred percent."

ANNA had no idea that I was even looking for a new job. Rather than get her hopes up prematurely, I decided to wait until there was something positive to report. That moment came about six weeks after our one-year anniversary.

"I have an interview," I announced one evening.

"A new job?" Her eyes betrayed her excitement. We both knew that the best way to embark on starting a family would be with steady employment, complete with an insurance plan and maternity coverage. We knew our budget couldn't take another hit.

"Yep. It's time to join the big boys in corporate America."

"Corporate America has openings for classical guitarists? I had no idea."

"Cute. I stumbled across a marketing firm that's looking to hire what they're calling a 'creative marketing specialist.' The posting says the candidate needs some musical training."

"And what exactly is a creative marketing specialist?"

"Basically, entry-level jingle writing. It's helping the marketing team come up with slogans for customers and then putting them to a catchy tune. It's like writing really short songs. I spoke with the hiring manager, and he's willing to give me an interview. But . . ."

Anna tilted her head. "What's the catch?"

"He wants to make a final decision by the end of the week, which means I have to be ready for the interview in three days."

"Aren't you ready now?"

"Yes, but it's in San Francisco. They won't pay to fly me in. If I want the interview, I have to start driving tomorrow morning."

Now she was on cloud nine. "Oh, we *have* to make this happen!"

"So you wouldn't mind moving if I got the job?"

"Mind? What self-respecting USC grad would say no to going back to Cali?"

The next morning at four, Anna and I piled into her Jetta and started driving south. Two days later we pulled into San Francisco.

My interview was scheduled for the following day at ten a.m. When I entered the firm's lobby, I was met by a dozen other men and women who were applying for the same position. The hiring manager, Mark Lloyd, swept into the room at ten o'clock. He was in his mid thirties, with thick hair and a confident demeanor.

"Hello, and thank you all for coming," Mark said. "You are the final group to be interviewed. But please understand that there is only one opening and roughly forty interviewees."

He glanced at his notepad. "You'll each get a twenty-minute interview with either me or my boss. At the conclusion of your interview, we'll tell you if we'd like you to move on to the next round. Any questions?" When there were none, he checked his notes once more. "All right. Then we'll go alphabetically. Ethan Bright, you'll be with me. Brittany Davis, follow us and I'll escort you to Mr. Schleger's office."

My twenty-minute interview went as well as I could have expected. At the end of it, Mark stood, shook my hand, and then told me he'd like me to proceed to the next step of the hiring process.

It took them two hours to get through the first round of interviews. By then there were four people left—two other men, and a chatty blonde who was "totally, like, going to freak out" if she got the job. Mark treated us to lunch, and then we started round two.

Mark explained, "We're going to go back

to a conference room where we have a piano. You don't have to use it, but it's there if you want. Our creative team will be in the room observing. When it's your turn, I'll introduce you to everyone. Then I'll give you the name of one of our customers and tell you a little bit about them. You'll have five minutes to come up with a jingle to be used for that customer's radio advertising."

When it was my turn to go, I felt oddly at ease as I took a seat. After brief introductions Mark reiterated that I would have precisely five minutes to come up with a jingle, and then he asked once more if I had any questions.

"Yes, two," I responded. "First, do you have a guitar? I can work with the piano, but my mind thinks best with a guitar in hand."

He shot a glance at a female employee. She nodded, then left the room. "Susan prefers to work with a guitar, too. She'll lend you hers."

"Great. My other question is about singing. What's more important to you, that I come up with a good jingle or that I sing it well?"

"You won't find many good singers here,"

Mark said. "We're definitely more interested in your *jingleability*. We have professional singers we contract with for the actual recordings."

Susan returned with a twelve-string Martin electric–acoustic.

"All right," continued Mark. "The company we'd like you to jingle is called Nick Jensen Auto Body. They specialize in repairing cars that have been damaged in accidents. They have a growing number of shops in California, and they're trying to create a brand name for themselves. So your job is to come up with something catchy to help them accomplish that." He looked at his watch and said, "You may begin."

For the first thirty seconds I just sat there. Soon my armpits began sweating. That's when I knew I was in trouble. My fingers began plucking nervously at the strings of the guitar. It wasn't until they'd been moving for half a minute that I realized I was playing Queen's "Bohemian Rhapsody," my old staple from Vienna.

I decided just to let my fingers keep playing. At least it seemed to have everyone's attention. A few heads were bobbing.

Mark announced that I had one minute left. I racked my brain, trying to think of something . . . *anything*, but nothing came. With thirty seconds remaining, I remembered the advice Anna had given me earlier: *Remember that the best jingles are the simple ones—simple words that are sung in a memorable way. Even a company's name can be interesting if it's got the right music.*

Mark mouthed the words, *Fifteen seconds!*

The company's name. Just then my fingers reached the end of a key stanza in the song. I strummed the last chord as loud as I could and then implemented Anna's advice. "*Nick . . . Jensen . . . Auto . . . Body . . .*" I sang, plucking one string of the chord for each syllable. I held out the last note as long as I could, and as it started to fade, I added quickly, "*Collision repair . . . in the* nick *of time!*" The words bounced from high to low through a warm major key.

All around the table, men and women exchanged excited glances. Mark finally stood up.

"Mr. Bright, if you don't mind, we'd like you to move to California to join our team."

"You mean, I got the job? Just like that?"

"Just like that." As he explained later, it wasn't the words I'd chosen for the jingle that impressed them so much as how the words *felt* with the music. "The whole package just worked. And the killer guitar performance didn't hurt, either," he added.

Two weeks later we waved good-bye to Octavius as we drove out of Moscow, Idaho, for a brand-new life in sunny California—a life that included a full-time salaried job.

Chapter 5

WHEN I was in fifth grade, my dad showed up one day insisting that I join youth basketball. It eventually became clear that this was his attempt to steer me away from "artsy" pursuits like playing the guitar. Not surprisingly, he never saw a single game.

Frankly, I was glad he never watched me play, because I was terrible at it. But I did learn from the experience. Notably, I remember struggling to make a simple layup.

The coach pulled me aside one day and gave me some excellent advice. "You're thinking too hard. Stop thinking and just have fun."

I made the very next layup, to thunderous applause from Grandpa, who was watching from the stands.

Six months after moving to California, I gave the same basic advice to Anna. "Sweetie, we must be thinking too hard. Let's stop *thinking* and just have fun."

She fiddled with the pregnancy test in her hand. It was the sixth such test in as many months. "Maybe I just *can't* get pregnant. What if the miscarriage permanently messed me up?"

"Or *maybe* our heads are getting in the way. I honestly think we just need to relax a bit. Slow down and have fun." I poked her in the ribs. "Let's not force it, and see what happens."

Apparently, that was the trick. Five weeks later I was in my office at work when the call came.

"Guess who's finally expecting!" she practically screamed.

I played dumb. Anna would say I wasn't playing. "Expecting what, hon?"

"What else? A baby!"

"Could it be . . . you?"

"Yes, genius. It's me!"

"That's awesome! I'm so happy for you—for *us*. And you took the pregnancy test without burning down the condo?"

"Amazing, huh? I'm getting good at this pregnancy thing."

She should have knocked on wood.

At sixteen weeks Anna had another miscarriage.

Emotionally, going through this for a second time was a major blow to both of us, though our individual coping mechanisms were quite dissimilar. Whereas Anna refused to do much of anything but cry for the better part of two weeks, I dealt with it by drowning myself in long hours at work. Ironically, my perceived dedication to the company's success turned out to be a boon for my career. When management saw how hard I was working, they rewarded me with a promotion, replacing Mark, who had accepted a new position.

Once Anna got all of her tears out, she gradually returned to her happy self. She busied herself with a part-time job at a craft store. In her free time she rekindled her dream of getting published by sending her books out for evaluation. Sadly, three months after shipping mock-ups and manuscripts to nearly one hundred publishers, she'd received nearly one hundred rejection letters.

One night over dinner, she announced that she was throwing in the towel for good. "And since I won't be painting or writing anymore, I want to try to get pregnant again," she said calmly.

Aren't two failures enough? But I shrugged and said, "Okay . . . maybe third time's the charm."

THIS time around, Anna was bound and determined to do everything in her power to go full term, which included an obstetric consultation before we even started trying to conceive.

It took several tests, but eventually the lady doctor had a prognosis. "Your cervix is incompetent."

"So are some doctors," I muttered under my breath.

Anna scowled. "Don't mind my husband."

The doctor waved it off. "Oh, I don't mind. Mr. Bright, cervical incompetence means the cervix has difficulty holding the weight of a fetus on its own. With some assistance I think you stand a reasonable chance to reach full term. The plan will be to perform what's called a cerclage in week fourteen—basically, sewing the cervix shut. Then we'd remove the sutures once the fetus is fully developed. This should give your body the extra support it needs to carry into week thirty-six or thirty-seven, which should be plenty."

The smile on Anna's face was one of hopeful optimism.

Six weeks later Anna was taking a pregnancy test. The results were positive.

Fourteen weeks later the doctor performed the cerclage, which caused an alarming amount of spotting. Two weeks later the spotting stopped. One week later the spotting resumed.

Three days after that, Anna miscarried for the third time.

OUR next two years in California were frightfully similar to the first two. I worked hard establishing a name for myself at the marketing firm, while Anna worked hard getting pregnant. Twice.

Both pregnancies ended prematurely.

Eventually, I think we both became numb to it all.

In the middle of our sixth year there, Anna woke me up one night. She'd obviously been crying. "One more time," she said. "I want to get pregnant one more time."

"What's the use? We already know what the outcome will be."

Anna flicked on a light. Then she pointed up at the painting above our bed; the one of us encircling a globe. "You said you'd search the world to find me. Where I want to be in the world is a place that includes children. It's the one dream I'm not ready to give up on."

She was as beautiful as ever, but her heart seemed more frail than in years past. A lot of that was a result of five miscarriages. But part of her hurt, I knew, was caused by me, through many little acts of thoughtlessness— leaving the house without kissing her good-bye because I was in a rush, staying late at work when I knew she needed me at home, or watching a show to wind down after a long day when she wanted me to play her a song on the guitar. Little things. But sometimes little things, when added together, aren't so little.

She then asked a question she should have never had to ask. "Do you blame me, Ethan, for losing so many babies?"

"Heavens, no!"

"You don't ever consider the possibility that if you'd married someone else, you could already be a father by now?"

"Of course not. I wouldn't want to be married to anyone else."

"Okay," she said slowly, "but even if you don't want to be married to someone else, are you sure you want to be married to *me?*"

"Where is this coming from, Anna? I love *you,* pure and simple."

Finally her face relaxed. "You promised me you'd serenade me on the guitar. That was all you needed to do to say you love me. But since you hardly play anymore, I guess I need to hear the actual words now and again."

"Anna, I'm sorry. I love you like crazy. I'll do better. And if you're still willing to keep trying for a baby, then I'm all for it, too."

She hugged me tight. "I was hoping you'd say that."

One month later Anna left a note in my guitar informing me that she was pregnant for the sixth time.

We were careful not to get too excited about it. Anna waited until she was two months along before going to see a doctor. That's when we learned this pregnancy was going to be a little different.

"Twins!" Anna shouted when I walked in after work on the day of her ultrasound. "You should have come with me, Ethan! Two little hearts beating side by side right there on the screen."

Given her history of miscarriages, combined with the added risk of carrying twins, the doctor took extra measures, including bed rest starting with month three. Throughout it all, Anna remained upbeat, telling herself it would all be worth it in the end.

When we moved into the seventh month, her modest optimism changed to hopeful enthusiasm. "We're gonna make it this time," she declared one morning. "We're going to be parents."

The excitement of parenthood was growing each day. Grandpa Bright called frequently. Octavius called often, too.

In the middle of the seventh month, Anna's brother Stuart and his wife, Heather, came by for an unexpected visit.

"Did Dad send you to check on me?" Anna asked.

"I just wanted to share my good news in person," Stuart replied.

Heather rolled her eyes. "*You* were our primary purpose for coming, Anna. But we do have some really good news, so we thought as long as we're here that you'd like to hear it in person."

"What's up? I want to hear all about it."

"Why don't we wait," Heather offered, "until you've had a chance to bring us up to speed on the pregnancy."

"What's to tell? I just lay here all day in bed, waiting to pop these kids out. Now c'mon, what's your big news?"

"Okay, here it is. . . . I'm retiring!" Stuart threw his arms in the air like he'd scored a touchdown.

"What do you mean?" I asked. "You're like, thirty-five years old. You can't just retire."

"Thirty-four, actually. And I just did. Yesterday."

"Isn't it terrific?" said an ecstatic Heather. "We feel so lucky. Almost like we won the lottery!"

"*Did* you win the lottery?" I pressed. "How else could you just up and quit your job?"

"Didn't quit, exactly," Stuart replied. "We sold our start-up to a big technology firm. I'm going to be a full-time dad for a while."

"Wow," I said, stunned by the news. "How much did it go for?"

"Three hundred."

"Thousand? That doesn't sound like it will last you long."

"*Million,* Ethan. This is big-time."

My jaw dropped to the floor. "Don't you have like a twenty percent stake in the company?"

"Twenty-five percent, making my take an even seventy-five million. Of course, they're going to tax the heck out of it, but I don't care. We'll still have plenty."

I don't think I said another word during the rest of their visit. Sure, I was happy for their success, but at the same time, I suddenly felt woefully inadequate. Was I jealous? Absolutely.

I silently vowed that I was going to make

sure that Anna and our two little babies had everything they wanted.

Two weeks later we received some very good news of our own: We'd hit the eight-month mark, and the doctor was ready to remove the sutures that were holding Anna's cervix together. To everyone's amazement the cervix held even after the procedure. Then we reached eight and a half months, and the doctor decided the safest thing for Anna and the babies was to deliver.

On a drizzly Wednesday morning we held our breath and drove to the hospital for a planned C-section. Thirty minutes after prep the medical team delivered a perfect, beautiful little girl. A minute or two later another girl was pulled from Anna's womb.

Two girls! Two healthy, beautiful little girls!

In that instant, I felt like the richest man in the world. "Did you see them, Anna? They're here! They made it! You did it!"

"*We* did it. *Together.*"

I watched as the doctors and nurses cared for the babies. It was the happiest moment of my life. But the moment was short-lived.

I noticed that the nurses attending to the older infant were scurrying around. I caught bits of the frantic whispers. *"Heart rate spiking . . . oxygen . . . Hurry!"* Anna heard the whispers, too.

"It's nothing," I said. "I'm sure they're just taking precautions."

But they weren't just taking precautions. The baby's lungs were not as developed as everyone had hoped. The lead pediatric doctor directed his team to wheel the baby to another room. He glanced at me, and I could see in his eyes that the situation was grim.

"Ethan, tell me what's the matter!"

I still didn't know for sure what was wrong. I only knew that it wasn't good. "It's fine, sweetie," I lied. But it wouldn't be fine.

The baby spent the next twenty-four hours enclosed in a plastic bubble under constant supervision in the pediatric ICU.

The day after that, she passed away.

All I heard were the doctor's parting words. "You know, even with all of our advances, sometimes these things just happen."

I could've punched him. We knew perfectly well that things "just happen." What we couldn't comprehend, and what no doctor could tell us, was why they kept happening to us.

THE NAME WE CHOSE for our older daughter was Faith, since her death was, if nothing else, another major test of ours. Anna was adamant that we name the younger one Hope, because that's what she felt when she looked into the infant's bright blue eyes.

Octavius and Lance Burke drove down from Idaho for the funeral. Stuart, Heather, and their kids came, too. Grandpa Bright and Aunt Jo flew in from Oregon.

Before we left for the funeral home, Grandpa suggested I bring his old guitar along and play a song during the service as a way to say good-bye to Faith. Not only did I decline, but I told him that I'd had the instrument in my possession for too long and that he should take it home with him when he went back to Oregon.

"Hogwash," he shot back. "I feel better knowing it's being played." He paused. "It is getting played, isn't it?"

"Sometimes," I said.

Anna overheard both the question and my response. She frowned and said, "Not for at least three months."

"Oh," Grandpa intoned slowly. "I'm sorry to hear that." He put a hand on my shoulder.

"Do you remember when you found me playing the guitar after your grandmother passed away?"

"How could I forget?"

"Then let me just say this: *It helped.* And I'm willing to bet it would help you, too." He turned and shuffled out to the car.

Forty minutes later I told the pastor we were ready to begin. Then I took a seat next to Anna in the funeral home's tiny chapel.

The pastor gave a song and dance about not fully understanding the mysteries of God and how we can be comforted in the fact that life carries on, even beyond the grave. I certainly wanted it to be true, but as I stared at Faith's tiny casket, it felt more like wishing and less like believing. Oh, God, I prayed, please let it be true.

Anna held Hope tightly in her arms during the entire graveside ceremony. We both willed ourselves not to cry.

It felt beyond our capacity to accept that where there had been two precious little girls, now there was only one.

LATER that night, Anna and I lay awake in bed. Near the bassinet, I spotted the dark, shadowy form of a guitar case. It reminded me of what Grandpa had said about playing the same guitar in the aftermath of losing his wife: *It helped.*

Even though I was only six at the time that she died, I remembered that day. I'd been living with Grandma and Grandpa Bright for a year and a half when the tumor in Grandma's abdomen was discovered. Doctors tried to help her, but the end result was a painful death in the middle of a warm summer night.

The funeral was a few days later. Grandpa went missing as soon as the family got home from the cemetery.

My grandparents' home in Garibaldi had plenty of room, even with a flood of guests. Unfortunately, it had only two bathrooms— the primary one on the main floor and a master bath upstairs. After an oversized helping of Aunt Ruth's cheesy potatoes, followed by three cans of root beer, my digestive system needed a time-out. To my chagrin the main bathroom was occupied.

I wasn't supposed to go in Grandma and Grandpa's bedroom, but this was an emergency. I tiptoed across the room to the bathroom door. I was reaching for the handle when I heard a sound from within that stopped me short.

Someone inside the bathroom was playing a guitar and humming an unfamiliar tune. It was beautiful and vibrant and sad. I knew it must be Grandpa. My stomach pains seemed to disappear.

Why is he playing in the bathroom? I squeezed the handle and opened the door enough to peek with one eye through the crack.

Herbert Raymond Bright, the great patriarch of the Bright clan and the only licensed psychologist in Garibaldi, lay sprawled out in the bathtub, still wearing his black shoes and charcoal suit from the funeral. I didn't see any water in the tub, just a man in his fifties and a guitar. With his eyes closed and his head tilted back against the cold porcelain tile, he seemed to be smiling as he hummed and plucked the nylon strings. The humming changed to words. It didn't take a genius to deduce that the song was about Grandma.

"They tell me that you're gone,
But I know it won't be long,
Until I hold you once more,
And we finish the story . . . of love."

Something about the way he sang held me captive. I'd watched Grandpa's expression earlier as they lowered Grandma into the ground. He looked tired and broken then. But now? There was an undeniable sense of peace about him.

The humming resumed. Soon the singing started up again, the words flowing effortlessly to the same, somber melody.

"Last I checked the door was closed,
But now I see a little nose,
Just poking through.
Ethan, is that you?"

By the time it registered that Grandpa had just embedded my name in the middle of the song, he sat straight up in the bathtub. With a giant grin he stared at me through the crack in the door. I gasped at being discovered, then spun on my heels and ran.

"Ethan!" he shouted. "It's okay. Don't go. Come back!"

I tiptoed carefully back to the bathroom door.

"Hi, there," Grandpa said. "Come on in. I won't bite." He smiled warmly. "I might pinch or tickle you, but I definitely won't bite."

I shoved my nose into the crack. "I needed to use the toilet."

"Oh, I see. I'm so sorry. Let me just crawl out of the tub, then." He stood, then walked toward me, guitar in hand, and gave me a little hug. "Go ahead, Ethan. I'll wait in the bedroom until you're done."

When I was finished, Grandpa was sitting on his bed.

"I like your new song," I said. "Is it about Grandma?"

"Yes. I'm trying to let music work its magic."

"Magic?"

"Music can do things that nothing else can. Take your grandmother. I miss her like crazy, and I always will. But somehow when I play and sing, the words and music speak right to my heart and I feel like maybe everything is going to be okay. Kind of like we're still connected." He exhaled. "I've learned that the right words with the right music at the right time can heal the soul like nothing else. Doesn't that sound like magic to you?"

I nodded eagerly. "I want to be a magician just like you, Grandpa."

SINCE I still couldn't sleep, I pulled back the covers and got out of bed. I made my way to the guitar case. It had been months since I'd bothered opening the thing. In the strings was a pink envelope. I slipped out into the hall, where I could turn on a light. The note was dated twelve weeks earlier, long before the birth of the twins.

Ethan,
   Thank you for playing a song for me tonight. This bed-rest stuff is no fun, but listening to you play made me forget the discomfort. I wish you played more!!
   Which reminds me, how's my song coming along? I know you're busy. And soon, when the twins are here, you'll be even busier! Yay!!
   Given the frequency of your guitar playing lately, I know it may be a while before you get this. When you do, come play me a quick song! No matter what I'm doing, I'm sure it will brighten my day.

I love you so much, Ethan Bright. I know we've had our trials, but together we can get through anything.
XOXOXO
Anna

I crept back into the room and took the guitar to the bed. Sitting up against the headboard, I played a soft, slow rendition of Pachelbel's "Canon in D." By the time I was done, tears were rolling down my face. Anna was crying, too. The floodgates of her emotions, which had been locked tight all day, were suddenly flowing without resistance.

Eventually she looked up at me and smiled. "Thank you."

THIRD VERSE:
Trio, Accelerando Staccato

Chapter 6

I WON'T say that the sting of losing Faith went away quickly, but it did subside sooner than Anna or I expected. Not that we weren't still sad; we were just so wrapped up in baby Hope that there wasn't much time to continue dwelling on the loss. We did our best to focus all of our love and attention on the baby we still had.

At Anna's urging I dutifully played the guitar more regularly, not only for her but for Hope. Having read that listening to Beethoven and Mozart can help stimulate brain development, I played classical selections when Hope was little, though occasionally I threw in a good country song to make sure she was well rounded. And her eyes lit up every time I sang "Puff the Magic Dragon."

On her third birthday Hope announced that she was now "a big person . . . like Mommy." We told her she was still our little girl. She looked at us both very sternly and held up three little fingers. "No, I'm big *now*. See, I'm dis many . . . one, two, free!"

Yes, Hope was "free"—free to do just about anything that her little mind could dream up.

Even though her three-year-old antics were sometimes exhausting, there wasn't a single moment that we didn't love having Hope around. In the evenings after work, we would walk to the park and push Hope on the swings or watch as she screamed with delight going down the slide. Then we'd go home and sing songs or read stories. On weekends we'd go downtown and ride the trolleys, window-shop at the stores, or just hang out at the house. None of us really cared what we were doing, as long as we were together.

All things considered, we had everything we needed in life back then, and enough time together as a family to enjoy it. But I still felt I was far short of the kind of success I'd always envisioned for myself. I couldn't help feeling inadequate every time I thought of Stuart. He was earning more per month in interest on his holdings than I earned annually as a salary. Somehow it didn't seem fair.

"We're doing fine," Anna once told me when I was griping about my salary on the ride home from her brother's. "We're happy, and money can't buy that."

"After hanging out at their McMansion, don't you think our place is feeling a little crowded? Plus, Hope will be starting school soon, and I think we could be in a better school district."

Anna thought about that for a moment. "A bigger house *would* be nice." She added, "And maybe a newer car. I feel like yours is in the shop more than not, and mine isn't much better."

I didn't say much for the rest of the ride home. Instead, I sat thinking about how hard it is to get ahead on a single income. Anna and I had decided that she should wait to reenter the workforce until Hope was in school. We didn't like the idea of a stranger raising our daughter for eight hours a day. Of course, that meant that all of our expenses rested squarely on my shoulders. It was a burden I gladly bore, but one that suddenly felt heavier.

The reality was that I saw no path to making more money. I'd tried over and over to shop my songs to agents and producers, but it just wasn't happening. And while my day job offered the word "manager" in its title, it came with a salary that paid the bills and put food on the table, but not much more.

We didn't bring up the topic of finances for several months after that. During those same few months, the economy hit some unexpected bumps in the road. It didn't take long for the rumor mill to conclude that a RIF—reduction in force—was in the works. I didn't want Anna to stress over it, so I never mentioned the rumors.

Six months after the rumors started, a company-wide memo was distributed from the board of directors, explaining that they had "regrettably released" several executives at our headquarters in New York City. In their place, a woman named Jessica Hocker had been brought in to serve as the new vice president of sales and operations.

Within a month the new VP began laying people off. She quickly earned the name the Hatchet. Soon she showed up unannounced in San Francisco. When I arrived just after seven in the morning, she was there, flanked by a rent-a-cop. When she was ready, Jessica had Miriam Scott, the human resources manager, gather all employees for a meeting.

The first ten words that came out of Jessica's mouth were, "Good morning, it's a pleasure to be here with you." It was so obvious that she despised being there that I almost laughed out loud. The Hatchet was a short, plumpish woman, maybe a year or two older than me. Her physical features weren't unattractive, but all I needed were those ten words to know that this woman was trouble. Her next ten words validated my assessment. "My objective today is to implement some much-needed changes."

We were informed that those who were being let go would be called in to her office individually to hear the terms of the separation and then be escorted out of the building by security.

After concluding her remarks, she walked to the GM's office and closed the door. The first victim's name was called.

"Dana," said Miriam. "Come with me, please."

Dana Abbot was a young gal from accounting who'd only been with the firm for about a year. I'd only spoken to Dana a few times, but I knew she was the mother of two young children.

When Dana was heading to the exit, Miriam found the next person on the chopping block. To everyone's surprise it was Frank Dane, the general manager. He'd been running the entire San Francisco office for fifteen years. A short while later Frank walked out of his old office, looking as mad as I'd ever seen him, and marched to the front door.

It became obvious that Jessica's list of cuts was itemized alphabetically. As a B, this was a huge relief. My own boss, Mark Lloyd, had to sweat it out until almost noon, when they finally moved on to the M's. By then I'd already stopped watching the parade. I sat in my office trying to get work done until it was over.

With the alphabet complete, those of us who remained breathed one more huge sigh of relief, though the moment was bittersweet. Several people who still had their jobs were crying. As a manager, I felt it my duty to give them some encouragement.

While I was busy talking to people, Miriam Scott came back out of Jessica's office and called for Mark Lloyd. It felt like he was in there forever, but the clock on the wall said only twenty minutes had passed when the door opened again and Mark came out.

I thought the smile on his face was a good sign, but it didn't explain why the security officer was walking along beside him. Together they marched back to Mark's office. A few minutes later, when they reappeared,

Mark was holding a small box of his things.

As he passed nearby, Mark—the man who'd been impressed enough by my talent to hire me in the first place—gave me a courteous smile and a nod, and then he was gone.

Thirty seconds later, with my heart still racing, Miriam made her way to where I was standing. My heart sank. "Mr. Bright," the woman said, "Ms. Hocker would like to speak with you."

"You're home early," Anna said when I walked into the kitchen that evening. "Everything okay, hon?"

"It was a tough day. A woman from corporate was there. They call her the Hatchet, because she's got a knack for carving up businesses. They—*she*—cut our workforce by nearly fifty percent."

"So you . . . were part of the fifty percent?"

"No. But my fate may actually be worse. They fired Frank Dane," I explained. "They were going to make Mark GM, but he decided to take severance instead. Apparently, he's been looking for a way to move back to where he grew up in Pennsylvania."

"Oh, my gosh," she said, stunned by the news that my mentor and friend had jumped ship. "So who's going to replace Frank?"

I took a deep breath. "Me."

She let out a muffled laugh. "You?"

"Crazy, right?"

"No. I'm sure you'll do great. It's just to me you're still that kid playing music on the street, not a business executive." She paused. "Will your schedule change much?"

"That's the big downside. It will mean quite a bit of travel. Many of our key clients are down in L.A. and San Diego. And of course, I'll have to go to New York now and then to meet with Jessica."

"Who is Jessica?"

"My new boss, the Hatchet. I now report straight to the VP."

"Wow." She sounded genuinely impressed. "Look at you."

"I promise there won't be any glamour in it. After losing all those people, we're going to be shorthanded. I'm going to have to work my tail off just to keep things afloat."

She gave me a long hug and whispered, "I know you can do it."

"Thanks for the vote of confidence," I

replied. Sadly, I knew that my new boss did not share the same confidence.

"Consider this a temp position, if you will," Jessica had said to me. "If you're successful at it, then it could become permanent. If not, well . . . I think you know what's at stake."

Yeah, my job. I didn't share that with Anna.

Anna gave me a playful little squeeze. "Dare I ask if your new job comes with a pay increase?"

Jessica didn't think I deserved more money, but Miriam advised that, legally, everyone must be compensated based on the documented pay band of their position. When they told me what the band was for a GM, I had nearly choked. I allowed myself to smile for the first time. "That, my dear, is the only good news in all of this. I think we'll be able to move into something a little bigger, in the neighborhood of your choice."

Her eyes lit up like I knew they would. "Really!"

"Yes. But remember, if I want to keep the inflated salary, it'll take a lot of sacrifice on everyone's part. I won't be around as much. Are you going to be okay with that?"

"How much more will you be making, exactly?"

I whispered it in her ear. "A little more than twice as much."

She let out a little shriek and hugged me as hard as she could. "Then that's a sacrifice I think I can live with!"

IN RETROSPECT, maybe Mark Lloyd was wise to take the money and run. Anna and I had acknowledged right from the beginning that the GM position would be a sacrifice, and it was. For starters, I traveled almost every other week. Anna found a house in an upscale neighborhood thirty minutes farther from the office. With a one-hour commute each way to work, long days of meetings, and a boss like Hitler, my entire existence became one large sacrifice.

The next couple of years passed by in an instant. Hope was suddenly almost five and attending preschool. And every day, she was looking more and more like her mother— tall, a natural beauty, with a disarming smile.

Shortly after Hope turned five, Jessica

took me out to lunch during one of my New York visits and surprised me with the first quasi-compliment I'd ever heard pass through her lips. "I'm seldom wrong about people. I had you pegged as a creative type who could never cut it in a senior-level position. But you proved me wrong."

"Thanks," I said. "I think."

"You're welcome, Ethan. I know I can count on you to do whatever it takes to get things done, which is why I'm making you my new vice president of operations, western states."

More layoffs were coming in several offices, including San Francisco, so they'd decided to make me manager for all of the markets west of the Mississippi. That allowed them to cut GMs at other locations and dump their work onto me.

As time wore on, Anna grew less and less supportive of the demands on my time, even though we both enjoyed the financial rewards of my work. "I don't understand why you have to be gone all the time," she would say. "Do they really expect this much out of you, or are you just happier when you're at work?" That last comment stung. I hated being tied to my work. The only reason I continued to do it was for her and Hope.

"It'll ease up soon," I would assure her.

The year that Hope was seven was the most stressful of all. Most of the companies we dealt with had drastically cut their marketing budgets as a way to trim expenses during the downturn, so we were having to fight for every single "win" with customers. That meant more planning, more meetings, more customer visits, and more calls from Jessica pressuring me to pick up the pace of my teams.

But it wasn't only work that was stressful. Being at home was hard at times, too. On multiple occasions that year, Anna and I got into heated arguments over the silliest things. The stupidest was a spat over redecorating.

She asked my opinion about what color to paint our master bedroom. "Paint it whatever color you want," I told her.

The next evening, however, she brought several paint chips into my study while I was working and asked, "Can I interrupt?"

I was in the middle of rank-ordering everyone who worked for me. There were going to be more layoffs, and I had the dirty job of deciding who would stay and who would go. "You just did," I said.

"It'll only take a minute." She handed me two paint samples. "For the walls, do you want sackcloth or burnt cherry?"

"The reddish one." I hoped that was the one she liked, too, so there wouldn't be a negotiation.

"Good," she chirped. "Now how about the ceiling?" She handed me two more paint chips. "Apple blossom or whimsical linen?"

My head was still wrapped up in the names of the people I was about to send to the unemployment line. And when I saw the colors she handed me, I lost my cool. "Are you serious? You're asking me to choose between white and white."

"No, the linen is richer and a little more warm."

"You really want my opinion? Go with either one."

"Oh, yeah? Well, do you want *my* opinion? My opinion is that your opinion is . . . is *completely lame*. Kind of like you lately."

"Is that right?" I tossed the paint chips on the ground at her feet. "I'm *lame?* White is white, dear, whether you like it or not."

"And how lame is it that you don't care about the things that I care about? You used to."

"I don't have time for this," I said, then spun back to my computer. "This is the dumbest argument ever. Oh, sorry, the *lamest*."

"How lame is it that we're even married?"

Her comment sent a chill down my spine. I spun back around. "What's that supposed to mean?"

She shrugged. "When your schedule frees up and you have time to give it some thought, I'm sure you'll figure it out."

That was the first time she'd ever suggested that there were holes in the armor of our marriage that had the potential of being breached. It wouldn't be the last.

THREE weeks before Hope's eighth birthday, Anna called me while I was having dinner with hotel executives in Las Vegas who'd seen their profits steadily decline and were looking for an overhaul. It was the type of deal that couldn't be interrupted by a spouse, so I let it go to voice mail. When I got back to my hotel, I returned the call.

"It's almost midnight," she said coolly.

"I know. Sorry. These guys really wanted to talk."

"You sure you're not . . . getting into trouble? It is Vegas."

"Anna, I hope you don't really think that. This is me."

"Lately I'm not sure I even know who you are." She paused, waiting to see if I would respond. When I didn't, she said, "You do know that our daughter's birthday is approaching, right?"

"Yes. I got your e-mail about the party."

"You need to make sure you have that afternoon free."

"I'll have my assistant take care of that in the morning."

"Please don't forget. You already missed her school play, a dance recital, and a dozen other things she wanted you to see."

"I know. I'll be there. I promise."

Anna let my words hang there. How many things had I promised to do over the years? And how many of those promises had I fulfilled? I tried not to think about it, but I was faithfully fulfilling a more important promise to take care of my family and provide for their needs. Didn't that balance everything out?

Two days later, once I was back in town, Anna and I were talking on the patio late at night, trying to catch up on our parallel lives. She filled me in on what Hope had been up to, and I offered bits and pieces of where I'd been and the deals I'd closed.

Eventually she asked if I'd booked the time on my calendar for Hope's birthday party. I hadn't, but lied and said I had.

"Thanks." She sounded relieved. "You also need to get her a present. Don't take this the wrong way, but I'm tired of picking things out and saying they're from you. I think she's catching on."

"You're right. What is she into these days? Dolls, bikes?"

"Ethan, I shouldn't have to tell you things like that."

I let her comment annoy me more than usual. "I would love to spend more time with Hope, but I'm working my tail off so you can enjoy this life that you've grown so accustomed to."

"What is that supposed to mean?"

"You heard me. While I'm killing myself

every day, you get to hang out at home, have lunch with your friends, take a nap, whatever you want—no responsibilities whatsoever."

Anna's face turned bright red. "Well *someone* has to raise our child! How is that not a responsibility?"

"What happened to you going back to work when Hope started kindergarten, Anna? She's in third grade! Don't complain about me not being around unless you're willing to help make that possible. Because I can guarantee, the first moment I start to let off the gas at work, the Hatchet will have someone there to fill my shoes. And I highly doubt unemployment will pay for all of *this*." I waved my hands at the house and yard. "Is that what you want?"

"Of course not! I just want . . ." She let the words drift. The anger in her countenance suddenly melted into sadness.

"You just want what, Anna? The house, the manicured lawn, the new cars, *and* me around all the time? It's just not possible."

The sadness evaporated. She got out of her chair. "I was going to say, 'I just want my husband back.' But now I'm not so sure." She turned and stormed into the house.

Thirty minutes later I figured I should go inside and try to sort things out. I had another business trip the next day, and I didn't want to go away on a sour note. I found Anna lying on our bed.

"I'm sorry," I said.

"Me, too," she replied. Her voice was still tense.

I lay down next to her and stared in the same general direction. "Anything interesting up there? On the ceiling."

"I just see chaotic white space. It reminds me of our marriage."

"Ah, but that's not white," I corrected. "It's whimsical linen. Nine months ago the artist in you assured me it was much more warm and rich than plain white."

Her voice softened unexpectedly. "I don't know if the artist is there anymore. It just looks white to me now."

"That's okay. The musician in me seems to have faded as well."

She finally turned to look at me. "That's *so* sad. What happened to our dreams, Ethan? We should be sharing those things with Hope, and instead we've just given up on them."

I didn't have a response.

"You asked what Hope is into these days. *Music*, Ethan. She loves music. It's her favorite part of school."

"So, what, you think I should buy her an iPod?"

With a little groan she replied, "I was thinking now might be a good time for you to get her a guitar. One that's just her size."

I loved the idea as soon as she said it. "Ah, it's perfect."

"But Ethan," she cautioned, "a guitar is just a thing. You also need to give her some lessons. Teach her. Share your talent."

With my current travel schedule, Hope would have to start stowing away in my luggage in order to have time for lessons, but I knew better than to say that then. "I will," I pledged. "Absolutely."

The only thing that came out of her mouth was, "Good." Without another word she rolled over and went to sleep.

THE following afternoon, I flew back to Vegas to spend three days pitching ideas to the hotel chain. Then I went to Portland for two nights, followed by a day in Seattle and a three-day strategy session in New York. When I finally got back to San Francisco, there were just four days remaining before Hope's birthday party.

The first of those was spent in long meetings with the local creative team. Anna called me to see if I'd found time to buy the guitar. "Tomorrow," I told her.

The next day, I received a similar phone call. And the day after.

When I came home that night, two days before the birthday party, Hope was already asleep. Anna was sitting on the sofa watching a show. Her face had the telltale signs of fresh tears.

"What's going on? Everything okay?" I took a seat next to her.

"No," she labored to say. "Everything is *not* okay. Ethan, I feel like I'm just barely holding on. I can't take it anymore."

"What can't you take anymore?"

"For starters, I feel like a single parent! You're never around. *Ever.* And Hope and I end up sitting here alone. You know what we'd give just to spend a little quality time with you?"

"Haven't we already had this conversation,

like a hundred times? The only thing I love about my job is that it provides for our family. So unless you're saying that you're ready to get a job again and help pay the bills, then I don't know what you're crying about."

She dropped a bomb. "I'm ready."

"What?"

"I'm ready to get a job, if that's what it takes. I'm glad you have a good job. And I'm thankful that you support us like you do. But when I married you, I married *you*, not your income." Anna paused to grab a familiar white vomit bag from the coffee table and tossed it on my lap. "You'd be surprised at how often I pull this out and read it, Ethan. For richer or for poorer, remember? If richer means that I have your money but I don't have you, then from here on out I choose poorer."

I wasn't sure what to say. We'd once agreed to trade time for money, and now she was ready to make the same trade in reverse.

"Ethan, do you understand what I'm saying?"

"That I need to cut back my hours at work a little bit?"

She faced me squarely. "No. I'm saying I need a husband. And Hope needs a father. Life is slipping away, and I can't just sit and wait for some magical time in the future when all of a sudden we'll be a happy family again. I need you, and I need you now." She pointed at the list of wedding vows I'd jotted down years before on the bag. "If you're not willing to live up to those things, well, then . . ."

"Then what?" I pressed. The hint at divorce was obvious; I wanted her to come right out and say it.

Anna stared at me. "Please don't let it come to that, Ethan. I want our marriage to last. I really do. But honestly, for that to happen I need you to be the man who wrote those wonderful things on the day we got married. I'm tired of broken promises."

I understood what she was saying, but the consequences of carrying it out were sobering. "I want what you want, Anna. But that's one heck of an ultimatum: Give up your job or lose your family. I kind of feel like giving up my job would sink our family, too."

"Didn't you hear me? I don't care about

the money. Maybe I did before, but not anymore. It's just not worth it."

I leaned back on the couch and let out a long, deep breath.

It felt like all of the successes I'd worked so hard for were being exhaled right along with the air. What Anna was asking of me equated to professional suicide, and I wasn't sure I could pull the trigger. There's got to be another way, I told myself.

"I'll figure something out," I told Anna.

HOPE and Anna were both still sound asleep the next morning when I left for the office. The only break I had between seven a.m. and seven p.m. was the ninety-minute gap I'd carved out during lunch so I could go buy a guitar for Hope.

At noon, as I was putting on a jacket to leave, Jessica called from New York. "Ethan," she said without saying hello, "I just e-mailed you a file. It's a mock-up for a movie house that's looking for a little pizzazz to promote a new film. The producer put it together to give your creative team an idea of what he's after. He wants to see you today to go over it. I double-checked with Lisa, and she said you're available only until one thirty, so he's on his way."

My mouth went dry. "I'll be ready when he arrives."

"Good," she said flatly, then clicked off.

Twenty seconds later I was on the phone with Anna. "Can you *please* bail me out on the birthday present? Maybe run out and pick up a guitar this afternoon? I simply don't have time. The guitar store closes at eight, and I'm not sure I can make it across town by then."

Her voice splintered with emotion when she finally spoke. "You can't even keep your promises for a single day."

"Anna, I have to do my job."

"I can't live like this anymore, Ethan. Something's got to change or our marriage isn't going to survive."

"Anna, it's going to be different. But can you just get the guitar for Hope this afternoon?"

"And what about tomorrow afternoon?"

"What do you mean?"

"It's Hope's party. Have you taken the time off?"

Dang it! I'd been meaning to schedule a half-day vacation for weeks, but I kept getting distracted. I didn't want to be dishonest with Anna, but I said, "Of course. I told you before, it's all taken care of. I had my assistant block it out."

Anna started crying openly into the phone. "I spoke with her earlier today . . . I could tell she doesn't know a thing about it. You're lying to me, Ethan! There are a lot of things I'll put up with, but that's not one of them." She paused to catch her breath. "I don't know if I can get the guitar for you. I need time to decide if my love for you is enough to keep trying to make this work. I'm not asking for anything more than this family deserves." She hung up.

She was right. I'd been so focused on financially providing for my family that I had lost sight of their other needs. And worse, I'd allowed myself to be bullied by Jessica. But I was ready to change—I had to.

Lisa, my assistant, popped her head into the office. "The producer is here. Can I send him in?"

"Yes, thank you. Oh . . . and Lisa, would you mind blocking out tomorrow on my calendar? I'm taking a little vacation time."

"Will do, Mr. Bright." She turned to leave.

"Wait! Scratch that. I want tomorrow and the next two weeks."

"And your travel reservations?"

"Cancel them, please. I'll send Jessica an e-mail advising her of my absence." I added, "I haven't taken time off in over a year."

Chapter 7

AT SIX o'clock in the evening, while sitting in my next-to-last meeting of the day, I received an unexpected text message from Anna.

"I will get Hope's guitar. Please come home and pay sitter. Put Hope to bed. Give her a kiss from me and tell her I love her."

It didn't surprise me there was no "XOXO" or "Love Ya!" at the end of the message. But at least she'd consented to get the guitar. For now, that was enough.

My final meeting of the day ran over, so I didn't get out of the office until nearly seven forty-five. By then the city traffic was light.

"Dad?" Hope said as I walked in at eight thirty. "You're home?"

Since when did she drop "Daddy" from her vocabulary? "Were you expecting someone else?"

"No," she replied. "But it seems like you're always at work."

"I know, and I'm sorry. But it's bedtime. You got to stay up a little later than normal tonight because Mom's out, but she gave me strict orders to put you to bed when I got home." The babysitter, a ponytailed teen who lived a few houses down, let herself out.

After tucking Hope into bed, I waited for Anna in the living room.

At nine o'clock I began to get worried. If the store closed at eight, she should have been home already. I left her a voice mail.

By nine thirty an uneasiness settled into my gut. *Where was she?* It wasn't like her to be out so late, especially without checking in. I tried her cell phone again, but it still went straight to voice mail.

In my mind I rehearsed all the things she'd said during our earlier conversation. *You never have time . . . Something's got to change or our marriage isn't going to survive.*

That's it, I said glumly to myself as I paced the floor. She's given up. I've let her down one too many times, and now—what?—she's teaching me a lesson? Or . . . she's actually leaving me.

Just then the phone rang, and I pounced on it. "Anna?"

"Hello?" The deep voice was definitely not my wife's. "Is this Mr. Ethan Bright?"

A telemarketer, I told myself. "Yes. Who is this?"

"This is Reggie Wilson, a social worker with San Francisco General Hospital." He paused. "Mr. Bright, there's been an accident."

As soon as he said it, all the blood rushed from my face.

"Your wife is in serious condition," he continued, "and we'd like you to come as quickly as you can."

God's metronome stopped abruptly; time stood still. I whispered numbly, "How serious?"

"I think it's best if you come to the hospital and we give you more details here. Are you able to drive?"

"Yes," I said hoarsely. "I can be there in fifteen minutes."

"Perfect. I'll wait for you in the ER lobby."

"I have a young daughter. Can she come, too? I can't leave her."

"Of course. See you in a little bit."

"I'M SURE EVERYTHING is fine," I kept telling Hope as we drove to San Francisco General. "It's just a little car accident."

She nodded every time I said it, but she didn't say much.

When we entered the ER lobby, it was packed with people. Off to the side I spotted a well-dressed African-American man with a hospital badge clipped to his shirt. Maybe it was the frantic look on my face or the fact that I was towing Hope along behind me, but he seemed to recognize me. He waved us over.

"Are you Reggie Wilson?" I asked as I approached.

"Call me Reg; all my friends do. You must be Ethan Bright."

I got right down to business. "Where is Anna?"

"In surgery. That's about all I know. By the time they gave me your number, she was in the operating room. I told the nurses you were on your way, but they warned it could still be a while."

It wasn't that I doubted the social worker, but my chief concern was seeing my wife and finding out how she was doing. I nodded politely. "Well, I should probably tell the nurses that I'm here anyway." I excused myself for a moment and approached the intake desk. "We're here to see Annaliese Bright," I told the first attendant who looked up. "Can you point us in the right direction?"

She smiled and typed into her computer. Then her smile faltered. "Are you family?"

"I'm her husband, Ethan Bright."

She typed some more. "Mr. Bright, your wife is still in surgery. Once they're done, she'll be sent to the intensive care unit. The ICU has its own waiting area. I suggest you go wait there."

I nodded impatiently. "Fine." With Hope in tow, I quickly returned to Reg on the far wall and told him about the ICU.

He nodded like he already knew. I took off down the hallway.

When I got to the ICU, I ran into another brick wall. "Until the surgery is over," explained a doctor, "there isn't really anything we can report."

"So we still can't see Mommy?" asked Hope.

"Sorry, pumpkin. It looks like we'll have to wait a little longer."

Thirty minutes later Reg popped into the

ICU waiting room carrying a small stuffed bear. Hope was already sound asleep. "Oh, looks like I'm too late. She's already out." He handed me the toy.

"She'll appreciate it when she wakes up." I added, "Nobody has told us *anything*. Can you at least explain what happened?"

A sympathetic tenderness settled onto Reg's face. This obviously wasn't his first go-round with a frazzled spouse, and his patience seemed equal to the task. "Of course, Ethan. I only know what's in the report, mind you, but I'm happy to share it with you." He flipped through some papers. "Let's see . . . at approximately eight thirty, at the corner of Market and Guerrero, your wife, Anna, was struck by another vehicle while making a left turn."

My stomach churned. "Is the other guy in the hospital, too?"

"The other driver was a female college student. She was driving her parents' Escalade, which is big and safe. Last I heard, they were checking her out for a possible concussion and whiplash, but otherwise she came out with bumps and bruises."

"Was she drunk?"

He grimaced. "Nope. Texting while driving. I'd rather hand these kids a beer than a cell phone when they get behind the wheel."

"Texting," I said numbly. "So you never got a chance to see Anna when she arrived in the ambulance?"

Reg shook his head. "No. But I did get a chance to speak briefly with one of the EMTs who'd treated her."

"And?"

It was clear he didn't like this part of his job. "Your wife was hit right on her door. Her little Saab was no match for the SUV. The EMT's exact words were that he was surprised she was still alive when they pulled up to the ER."

It was hard to breathe, let alone speak, but I needed more information. "Do you know much about her injuries?"

"I know she was alive but unconscious when they loaded her into the ambulance, but that's about all."

Reg answered a few more clarifying questions before his pager started beeping, at which point he excused himself to go work on another case. The only sound in the ICU waiting room was Jerry Springer, who was playing on low volume on a flat-screen directly opposite the door. I turned him off and sat in silence.

Hope was sleeping peacefully with her head on my lap. When I tried to get out from beneath her so she could stretch out more on the couch, she lifted her head briefly and said, "I'm not going to sleep, Dad. I'm staying awake to see Mommy."

Ten seconds later she was conked out again, this time with a small cushion to support her neck instead of my leg.

I couldn't help but marvel at how much she reminded me of her mother. The same beautiful hair. The same long eyelashes and large round blue eyes. And definitely the same mouth. I wondered if I would ever see Anna's mouth smiling at me again.

I felt like I should be making calls to let our families know what had happened, but I hoped to have some concrete details to share before doing so. At eleven thirty, I bit the bullet and dialed Anna's father.

"Hello?"

By the sound of the voice on the other end of the line, he'd been asleep. "Hi, Octavius. It's Ethan."

"Oh. Awfully late to be calling, isn't it? Is everything okay?"

"I know. I'm sorry. Octavius . . . there's been an accident."

Realizing that I was about to share bad news about *his little girl* tore me to pieces. I gave him the condensed version of what I knew. When I was done, he was full of questions.

"Where are you right now? Is she there? Can I talk to her?"

I quickly explained that Anna was still in surgery and that I hadn't talked to doctors yet. "But an EMT on the scene said she was unconscious. I'm so sorry, Octavius. I wanted you to know as soon as possible. I'll keep you posted as I learn more details."

"Do you think there's a chance that she might . . . Should I come down there? Would that help?"

"I think the best thing might be to wait until there's more news."

"I understand." He thanked me for letting him know, adding that he'd let the family know what was going on.

I made a quick call to Grandpa, asking him to keep Anna in his prayers and to spread the word among the rest of the family.

A gray-haired doctor entered the waiting room about half an hour later, tailed by two younger doctors and one of the ICU nurses. Each of them wore faded blue scrubs and a look of exhaustion.

"Mr. Bright?" asked the eldest of the bunch.

"Yes," I replied nervously.

"I'm Dr. Rasmussen, one of the neurosurgeons here. I've been with your wife for the last couple of hours. We all have." He glanced at Hope, asleep beside me. "Let's go to my office. We'll have one of the nurses keep an eye on your daughter."

He led me to his office. The younger doctors pulled chairs closer in while Dr. Rasmussen closed the door behind us, then sat across the desk from me. "Mr. Bright, this is Dr. Schafer, an orthopedist, and Dr. Gooding, from internal medicine."

"Good to meet you all," I said. "And thanks for what you've done. But I don't think you brought me here for introductions."

"No," said Dr. Rasmussen softly. "We know you're anxious to hear how your wife is doing." He took a long breath. "The good news is that she's alive. Given how she looked when she first arrived, the fact that she's still with us is a small miracle."

"But . . ."

"But there are very serious complications that we're trying to manage. For starters, one of your wife's lungs collapsed. We have her hooked up to a machine right now that's doing the breathing for her. Also, in the ambulance her heart stopped beating and—"

"Her *what?*" I gasped.

Dr. Gooding piped up for the first time. "Her heart stopped. Defib paddles got it going again, but it took some doing."

I ran a panicked hand through my hair. "Will she be okay?"

"In time," the younger doctor continued, "the lungs and heart should mend. Unfortunately, one of her kidneys received direct trauma in the accident. As a result, we had to remove it."

"But people can function with one kidney, right?"

Now Dr. Schafer joined in. "Yes, they can. But when your wife's heart stopped, the other kidney went without blood for a long enough period that it, too, was damaged.

We're guessing it will only have about half its normal function. Which means even if your wife recovers from everything else, she'll still require regular dialysis to clean out the toxins in her blood or they will kill her."

Dr. Rasmussen looked like he had more to say, and my intuition told me that the worst was yet to come. "What else?" I demanded.

"As I said before," he replied, "I'm a neurosurgeon. Your wife's head sustained very serious trauma from the force of the impact. We've already performed a craniotomy. Her brain has a significant amount of swelling. We opened up a hole in her skull—her cranium—to relieve the pressure. But . . ."

My emotions couldn't take any more bad news. "Just stop it! How can it be worse than what you've already said?"

He let me gather myself before saying, "I'm sorry, Mr. Bright. But you need to understand the reality of your wife's condition. The biggest concern is that she lacks all perceptivity and receptivity."

"Which means what, exactly?"

"Perceptivity is a response of the nervous system to learned stimuli. Think of it as the act of thinking, or consciously perceiving the world around you. Receptivity is more of an innate response of the brain—things like turning to find the source of a loud sound or recoiling from a sharp pain."

I repeated my question. "Which means *what* exactly?"

"Which means she's literally not responding to *anything*. She's in a coma, Mr. Bright, and even if the rest of her heals, there's a chance that she won't come out of it, no matter what we do."

"So Anna will never wake up . . ." The words dropped from my mouth like cold stones on a grave. I was defeated, and I knew it.

Dr. Rasmussen said, "She's not really asleep. It's more like her brain has gone into hibernation. There's no way of knowing if it will ever turn on again. There's a standard we use, called the Glasgow Coma Scale, to measure basic reactivity to a stimulus. On each of the measures—eye response, verbal response, and motor response—she scored a one for a total of three. That's the lowest possible score, meaning there was no detectable response."

"But . . . she could improve, right?"

"Yes. And we'll take frequent measurements to monitor her progress. But Mr. Bright, I've had patients with higher scores than hers who have remained in comas for a very long time."

My mouth was so dry I could hardly speak. "How long?"

"Years," he replied softly. "Until they finally passed away."

Another doctor chimed in. "We know how difficult this is for you. Unfortunately, sometimes these things just—"

"No!" I snapped. "Don't you dare say, 'These things just happen.' *Don't* say it. These things don't *just happen*. They just happen to happen to Anna and to me, and I'm tired of it!"

The doctors waited until I'd had a moment to cool down. Then Dr. Rasmussen addressed me by name. "Ethan, none of us would pretend to know what you're going through, but I can tell you there is a big difference between telling someone their loved one is gone versus the situation you find yourself in right now."

"Oh, really?" I snarled. "And what is that?"

He stood and paced around his desk, then placed a hand gently on my shoulder. "Even though the odds aren't good, at least you still have a little hope to hold on to." He paused. "Ethan, I suggest you go home. It won't be until tomorrow sometime that you can be with your wife in the ICU. You should go get some rest."

I nodded absently.

Even though they wouldn't let me be with Anna, I wanted to be as close to her as I could, so I sat in the waiting room all night. Hope slept comfortably with my jacket over her.

Even when things in our life weren't brilliant, I'd always assumed that eventually our future together would be full of light, but with Anna on life support, I could feel the darkness settling in.

Chapter 8

AT SEVEN in the morning, Stuart and Heather showed up at the hospital with their two kids, Devin and Jordan, ages ten and twelve. I glanced at Hope, still asleep beside me; then I stretched my neck from side to side to get the kinks out.

"Sorry to wake you," said Stuart.

"It's fine. I can't believe you made it here as early as you did. What time did you leave? Like, four o'clock?"

"Four thirty. There was zip-o traffic."

Heather asked how Anna was doing.

I glanced quickly at Hope again to make sure she was still sleeping. "I haven't seen her, but it doesn't sound good. They warned me late last night that she could very well . . ." I stared at the boys.

Stuart recognized my hesitation. He quickly pulled out his wallet and handed each of them a ten-dollar bill. "Boys, go find a snack machine or something."

"You were saying?" Stuart asked as they left.

"Honestly, I don't have a lot of details yet. She's in a coma, though. And even if the rest of her gets put back together," I added soberly, "it's possible that she won't come out of it."

Heather put a hand over her mouth. It covered up her gasp.

"Good Lord," said Stuart. "Do you know how it happened?"

I shared what I knew about the circumstances of the collision. Then I gave them all a thorough rundown of the previous night. Hope woke up near the end of the discourse and cuddled up next to me. With her awake, I was careful to avoid saying anything about the seriousness of her mother's condition.

Jordan and Devin returned a few minutes later, much to Hope's delight. The boys were trailed closely by a nurse who called my name as she entered the waiting area.

"I'm Ethan Bright," I replied, jumping to my feet.

"I know you've been waiting a long time. The attending doctor says that you can see your wife now. Would you follow me?"

"Is she awake?" I asked.

The woman gave a slow shake of the head. "I think for starters you should probably come alone. The room isn't very big, and there's a lot of equipment. And given the shape she's in—"

"I understand," I said, cutting her off. Then I gave my daughter a squeeze. "Sweetie, do you mind hanging out here with Uncle Stuart and Aunt Heather so I can check on Mommy?"

Hope nodded and smiled in a way that said, "I'll be fine, Dad."

I followed the nurse down a long hallway, through a set of double doors, past a group of ICU nurses who were huddled behind a desk, and then tiptoed into Anna's dimly lit room.

There were monitors of all shapes and sizes, each beeping and blinking sporadically. There were respirators, oxygen tubes, miscellaneous wires and cables, graphs, and more IVs than I'd ever seen.

At the center of it all was the body of a person I didn't recognize.

"That's not my wife," I whispered.

The nurse flipped a chart. "Anna-lies Bright?"

"Anna*liese*," I corrected. "But that's not her." The person lying on the bed didn't look anything like Anna. The face was engorged, especially the left side, where the eye was swollen completely shut. The head was wrapped in thick sterile bandages. The nose and lips were all black and blue and disfigured from swelling. A jagged line of sutures ran from just below the earlobe to the center of the cheek. One forearm was heavily wrapped, and the other arm had bright gashes just below the shoulder.

I was secretly praying that I was right and that this was all just some big hospital screwup. Maybe Anna was at home. "I don't see a ring on her finger."

"They had to cut it off," the nurse explained. "With all the swelling in her hand, it had to go. It's in a plastic bag on the dresser."

My heart sank when I spotted Anna's ring, just where she'd said. Inching closer to the bed, I could just make out the distinctive shape of my wife's mouth, hidden there beneath all of the cuts, scrapes, and swelling. "Oh, Anna," I whispered.

The nurse scooted a chair over next to the bed so I could sit down; then she left. When she returned thirty minutes later, she was followed by Reg, the social worker, and two men I didn't recognize. The taller of the two wore scrubs, the other a suit.

"Mr. Bright," the nurse began, "this is Dr. Knight, the attending physician in the ICU today, along with Nathan Birch from our legal department. You've already met Mr. Wilson. There are a few things they'd like to go over with you."

"How you holding up?" Reg asked.

"Fair . . . I guess, under the circumstances."

He looked around the room. "It's a little tight in here, but there's definitely enough room for a recliner. I'll make sure they bring one in so you can rest up."

"Thank you. But I bet that's not what everyone came to talk to me about."

"No," Reg said softly. "Unfortunately," he continued, "another aspect of my job is to help prepare individuals and families for the eventuality that their loved ones might not make it. I believe Dr. Rasmussen and the others filled you in last night on the extent of her injuries. Is that right?"

I nodded. "I really couldn't comprehend it . . . until I saw her."

Mr. Birch was rifling through papers attached to a clipboard. He pulled a yellow sheet from the stack and handed it to Reg. "Mr. Bright, I think what Mr. Wilson is getting at," the attorney said abruptly, "is that, given your wife's current state, some important decisions are going to need to be made on her behalf. I know you probably don't want to be thinking about this now, but we need to know if she has a living will."

I didn't respond. Not because I couldn't, but because I didn't want to. During our first year of marriage, after losing everything in the fire, Anna made it a goal to have every eventuality nailed down. She'd made me sit down with her and an attorney to fill out several legal documents, one of which was a living will. I knew what her wishes were.

"If something should ever happen to me," she'd said, "I don't want you to have to worry about what decision to make. And I don't want to live on life support forever. Pull the plug, Ethan, and let me go peacefully."

It sounded sensible at the time. Now that it was actually happening, the thought made me sick.

"Ethan?" Reg asked again.

"What? Oh, sorry. I'm not sure if she has a living will or not. I'll have to look around at home." Even to me it sounded like a bad lie, but I didn't dare tell them the truth, for fear they'd stand up right then and turn everything off. "What if she *doesn't* have one?"

The lawyer leaned closer. "Then, as her husband, you would be her legal proxy. Should she not show signs of improvement, you would need to make some very important decisions for her."

Reg handed me the yellow paper. "If she doesn't have a living will, you'll need to fill this out, attesting to that fact. You would then be solely responsible for how we proceed."

"But the accident just happened yesterday, so we're not talking about making major decisions *now*, right? Not *that* decision."

Dr. Knight scooted forward in his chair. "Mr. Bright, I reviewed your wife's case with Dr. Rasmussen and the other surgeons. Based on her general lack of responsiveness, we're all in agreement that the likelihood of your wife recovering from this is not good. It's still early yet, so things could improve. I just want you to be prepared for the possibility that at some point down the road, you may need to think about whether or not your wife would want to remain like this or whether she'd prefer that you . . . let her go."

I let my eyes crash-land on Anna's distorted face. "I understand."

AFTER another hour I went out to the waiting room. Heather was reading a book.

Everyone else was watching an old episode of *The Smurfs* on the television. They all looked up.

"Is it my turn to see Mommy now?" Hope asked excitedly.

"I'm sorry, sweetheart. The doctor says right now only Daddy can see her." I didn't like lying to her. But what's worse, telling an eight-year-old that a doctor won't allow her to see her mother or giving the child the memory of seeing a lump of broken flesh that looks nothing like Mommy? I turned to face Stuart and Heather. "Would you mind taking Hope back to our house? I'm not sure how long it'll be, but you'd be doing me a huge favor if you could just watch out for her for a little while."

"Of course," said Heather.

After they were gone, I grabbed a bite at the cafeteria, then went back to Anna's room, where I watched the rise and fall of her chest for five straight hours. Periodically I would say things to test her reaction, like, "Anna, I'm here" or "Can you hear me?" Once I even shouted, but through it all she just lay completely still.

At three o'clock the new shift supervisor

came to inform me that I had a visitor in the waiting room. "She didn't leave a name."

I walked to the waiting area. A woman in her early twenties looked up. She had a nick on her chin, a fat lip, and dark blue rings under both eyes, but still she had a pretty face.

She swallowed hard, then stood and said, "Oh . . . are you . . ."

"Ethan Bright."

"Please . . . *please* tell me you're not related to Hope Bright."

"I'm her father. How do you know Hope?"

"*Oh, noooo,*" the girl whimpered sadly. She collected herself enough to say, "I'm Ashley Moore. I was a student teacher in Hope's class. I'm the one who . . ."

I tried to remain calm. "Who crashed into my wife?"

The girl nodded remorsefully, after which a long, awkward silence ensued. I just stood staring, waiting for her to say something.

Finally I couldn't take it anymore. "I have to get back to my wife. Was there something you wanted?"

Tears pooled above her cheeks. When she nodded, they all rolled down. "I wanted to say I'm *really* sorry about what happened."

"Is that it?"

Hearing the young woman use the word "sorry" for the harm she'd caused seemed absurdly inadequate to me. No amount of sorrow was ever going to make up for what she'd done to our family, and I wanted her to know it. So in the calmest voice I could find, I said, "Honestly, I don't want to hear it." I reached for my wallet, then flipped it open to a picture of Anna and held it up. "Do you know who this is?" I could feel my temperature rising. "Did you ever talk to her when she picked up Hope from school? Do you remember her face? Well, if you were to go to her room right now, you wouldn't recognize her. *I* don't even recognize her."

Ashley's face was as white as a sheet.

"Tell me," I said, "what was so important that you couldn't wait to send that last text message? OMG, was it your BFF? Well, because of your stupidity, *my* BFF is in a coma at the end of the hall."

"It was my boyfriend," she stammered. "He sent me a note—"

"And you couldn't wait five minutes to send a reply?"

At that, Ashley gave up. She grabbed her purse and dashed out of the room in a flood of tears. But she didn't get two steps before she ran into someone who was coming in the opposite direction.

There was a thwap followed by "I'm so sorry" from Ashley.

"That's quite all right, young lady," came the reply.

I knew that voice and was embarrassed that he might have overheard my tirade. When I turned around, he was standing, hunched over from age and relying on a cane. He didn't say a word.

He didn't have to. I could read Grandpa Bright like I was reading a book. From the look of disappointment on his face, I guessed he'd heard the tail end of my conversation with Ashley Moore.

"You came," I ventured.

The disappointment in his eyes quickly gave way to gentle tenderness. "I caught the first flight out." He hobbled over and gave me a one-armed hug. The other arm held fast to his cane. "I expected to find you in a state of sadness, and instead I happen upon you in a fit of . . . What was that? Infuriation?"

"Yeah. I lost my temper. That was the gal that ran into Anna."

"Ah," he said knowingly. "You should be careful not to let your anger taint your heart. You have a kind heart. No matter what happens to Anna, it would be sad to see you lose that."

"That girl . . . she . . . If Anna dies, I swear I'll . . ."

"You'll what?"

"Well, for starters, I'll push as hard as I can for criminal charges."

He just shook his head.

I shook my head, too. "The doctors are pretty sure she's going to die," I continued as I took a seat. "It's just unthinkable. Part of me just wants to curl up in a ball and stop existing." I paused, searching his wise eyes. There was love there and deep compassion, but nothing to suggest he would accept it if I just gave up.

"You'll find a way to get through this," he replied. "In time."

FOR the next couple of hours Grandpa and I stayed at the hospital. By three o'clock in the afternoon, I'd made up my mind that I was going to stay overnight again at the hospital. "I need to run home to gather a few things," I told Grandpa.

He followed me home in his rental. I had to keep my foot on the brake most of the time to keep from losing him.

The first words I heard when I walked in the door were, "Is Mommy coming home tonight?"

"Oh, pumpkin. Mommy's accident was a little more serious than I first thought, and she's not up to it just yet."

Hope was crushed. "So no party?"

The birthday party! I'd completely forgotten. A handful of kids were scheduled to arrive in less than an hour, expecting to play games and eat cake. Not only did I not have the slightest inkling what Anna had planned for the kids to do, I also couldn't just throw a party while my wife was dying at the hospital. "Oh, honey," I said, squatting down. "I know how much you were looking forward to a party, but I'm afraid—"

"Ethan," interrupted Stuart. "I hope I didn't overstep my bounds, but I saw the RSVP cards, and since I wasn't sure when—

or if—you were coming home today, I sort of made some arrangements."

"We planned a party," said Heather. "Is that okay?"

"Nothing fancy," Stuart added. "It's tough to get stuff for day-of. All we could book was a bounce house and Presto the Magician."

"Stuart, that's . . ." I was about to say *way too much to spend on a child's party,* but Hope was standing right there, and I didn't want her to think she wasn't worth it. "That's . . . very kind of you. What do you think about that, Hope?"

"It's great, but . . . what about Mommy? Will she be sad that she missed the party? Maybe we shouldn't do it without her."

"Oh, no, honey. Mom will be happy that you and your friends are having fun. We'll have Stuart and Heather take lots of pictures. Then you can show Mom everything that happened at the party when she gets out of the hospital. How about that?"

"That's right," piped Stuart while pulling his cell phone from his pocket. "I've got my camera right here. What do you say we go get ready and make this the best birthday ever?"

Hope thought about Stu's question. Her response surprised me. "If I have a choice, I'd rather go see Mommy."

I gave her a big hug. "I know, sweetie. And you will. But right now I need to go be with your mom at the hospital, so I need to know that I can count on you to have a good time while I'm gone."

She looked up at me and smiled courageously. "Okay, Dad." Then she ran off to get ready for her friends' arrival.

"Thank you, Stuart," I said. "How much do I owe you for this?"

"Nah, forget about it. This one's on me. You go be with Anna."

He may have been a rich, quirky little guy, but at that moment, I was very glad to have him around. "Thanks, Stu."

I stuffed toiletries and several changes of clothes into a duffel bag. Grandpa didn't say a word to me until I was headed out the front door. "Ethan, aren't you forgetting something?"

"Oh. Uh, do you need help getting your suitcase and things situated? You're welcome to have the guest room at the end of the hall."

"I meant Karl."

I stared blankly at him. "Why would I need the guitar?"

"To play it for her, and to play it for *you*. Don't you think it will help?"

"No," I replied honestly, "I don't."

He studied my face just long enough to make me feel like I was being psychoanalyzed. "I miss that old guitar," he said. "Too bad I can't play it anymore. These old fingers just aren't up to it."

"Neither are mine. Grandpa, I haven't played in months. There just are more important things. And after this whole thing with Anna, I don't think I could pick up a guitar even if I wanted to."

In his best therapist's tone he asked, "Really? Why is that?"

I'd purposely evaded his inquiries about Anna's whereabouts when it all went down, but I no longer saw the value in keeping it a secret. "Well, Anna was on her way home from a guitar store when she was hit. She was picking one up for Hope's birthday."

"That's enough to give up on one of your greatest talents?"

"Not just that. When I was a kid and you told me music was magical—"

"Oh, right. You said you wanted to be a *magician.*"

"Yeah, well, I don't believe in that sort of magic anymore. I wound up dedicating my life to music, but what's come of it? I can play the guitar, but the career it led me to leaves no time for anything else. And though I dreamed of being a songwriter, I couldn't sell a song to save my life. Anna's accident is just another way the guitar has let me down. It's not worth it anymore. I'm done."

"Hmm," he responded, drawing it out thoughtfully.

"You know what? I think it's time Karl was back in your possession. I really am tired of having it around. I'll put it in your room, and you can take it with you when you leave."

"But I don't want it," he said calmly.

I stormed off toward my room. There was Grandpa's old guitar case. I picked it up and marched it to the guest room.

"It's all yours," I told him when I got back. "Enjoy."

Just then I noticed he had something on his lap. It was an old wooden box, not much wider than a laptop, though maybe twice as thick. It had a brass lock and two leather straps for hinges. "Sorry," I said. "It's your guitar, and I no longer have a use for it."

"Well, if you're adamant." He let out a disappointed sigh. "But would you consider a trade?"

Grandpa lifted the box. "Just a little history. Something for you to read while you're sitting there at the hospital."

"A history of . . ."

"Me," he chirped. "I was planning on bequeathing copies of this to everyone after I'm gone, but you're the one who deserves to read this the most, because it will mean the most to you."

"Why?"

"Because, having had my guitar in your possession since you went off to college, you deserve to know the truth."

"The truth?"

With a solemn nod he said, "Indeed. The truth about Karl."

I must admit, that last bit intrigued me, but it was long past time for me to leave. "Sorry, Grandpa. Another time."

He favored me with another look of extreme disappointment. "Yes . . . another time." Then he dismissed me with a quick wave.

I loaded the rest of my effects into the car, then remembered there was one more thing I needed to have with me at the hospital.

My briefcase was in the den. I made sure its contents were still there, then turned to go. As I walked toward the door, I noticed Anna's corkboard hanging on the wall. One picture on the board grabbed my attention. It was Hope's class picture from school. In the picture was a familiar-looking student teacher. The photo was paper-clipped to a sheet of paper. I yanked them both down together, staring first at Ashley Moore and then at the attached note. It was a letter from the teacher, encouraging the students to have a wonderful summer. But it was the post-script that really mattered: P.S.—Ms. Moore and I would love to hear from you over the summer! Please write to us at the following addresses. . . .

The address of the college student I'd met earlier in the day! All of my anger came flooding back. I took the address, plugged it into my GPS navigator, and paid the Moores an unexpected visit.

What happened next was, in a word, regrettable. I drove to the Moores' home, screamed until they came outside, and drilled into Ashley. I opened my briefcase and showed the young woman what *real* notes were. Then, realizing that I was pushing the boundaries of rational behavior, I drove back to the hospital.

When I got to Anna's room, I sat at her side and talked to her for hours, telling her how much I loved her and how sorry I was for everything. Then I began reading aloud some of the notes she'd written to me over the years. But nothing I said brought her back.

By ten o'clock I was feeling the effects of the past forty-eight hours. I told her good night, curled up with a blanket on the recliner that had been delivered while I was away, and turned out the light.

Just as I was nodding off, I heard an unfamiliar sound coming from the hallway. *Shuffle-shuffle-thump. Shuffle-shuffle-thump.*

The sound stopped right outside the room. The door opened, and the sound entered. *Shuffle-shuffle-thump. Shuffle-shuffle-thump.*

When the shuffling stopped right next to

me, I carefully pretended that I was still asleep, suspecting that I was being watched. When the shuffling and thumping started toward Anna, I squinted with one eye to see if I could make out who it was.

If I hadn't already been lying down, the surprise at seeing Grandpa standing in the room might have knocked me clean over.

The source of the rhythmic thump was his old cane. I couldn't begin to fathom how he'd gotten into the ICU after visiting hours, yet there he was. Under one arm was the old wooden box.

Part of me wanted to tell him where he could go, but this was Grandpa Bright. If he thought it was important to make a late-night visit to Anna's darkened hospital room, then I wanted to know why.

INTERLUDE

Chapter 9

GRANDPA crossed the room and sat down on the chair next to Anna, then bent over and set the wooden box at his feet.

"Hello, young lady," he said softly. "Bet you didn't expect to see me here tonight, did you? Looks like your husband is out cold."

He craned his neck in my direction. I quickly closed my eyes.

"Too bad," Grandpa continued. "I really wanted to talk to him." He turned around once more, and I again opened my eyes.

"Anna, did Ethan ever mention that I fought in the Second World War? When he was younger, he used to ask about it all the time. There were things I would have loved to share, but those things might have led to other questions that I didn't want to delve into. So I remained mum about the whole ordeal.

"The thing is, I'm getting old. I won't be around forever. Before I go, I want my family to know about me and the war. That's partly why I came here to California. Ethan and I are a lot alike, and I think right now he could benefit from my experiences. But you know your husband—he's as stubborn as a mule. He wouldn't accept it when I offered it to him." He tapped the wooden box lightly.

"I know the timing is bad, with you in the hospital and all, but I wish he'd have just taken the darned thing and read it. I came here tonight to see if he'd reconsider, but alas . . . he's out.

"But here's the thing," Grandpa continued. "I sort of need to get this story off my chest. I've kept it locked up—in the box, in my heart—for a long, long time. So since he's asleep and you're a captive audience, do you mind if I just tell it to you? I haven't shared most of this with anyone. You're the first, Anna. Ethan would have been, but his mind is on other things now."

He paused again. "Ethan said he'd take the box some other time. So when I'm done, I'll just leave the journals here."

Grandpa cleared his throat. "Now, let's see . . . where should I begin? I don't want to burden you with unnecessary history, but neither do I want to give you too little and not have it make sense."

He tapped his lips with a finger. "Okay, I know the spot."

"*Interpreter*," he began. "That's what they called me. That's what they told me to tell people if ever I was asked. Interpreting messages, translating intelligence, reading things on maps or in newspapers from the relative safety of a military base. And I did do a fair amount of that, but most of my time was spent trudging around the countryside in a German uniform, trying to blend in, hoping to not get killed.

"I was a rare breed in the U.S. Army. Born in Germany, raised in the States by parents who spoke German in the home, and willing to fight tooth and nail against the Nazi regime in my birthland. It also made my service exceptionally dangerous.

"When I enlisted, my slight German accent raised some eyebrows at the local recruiting office. But after a thorough background check, they decided that my language skills could be put to good use. Once I was trained and transported to Europe, it became clear that interpreting things was only a small part of what they needed me for. 'You have the potential,' one senior officer explained, 'to operate behind enemy lines. With you navigating hostile territory, our boys have a better shot of not getting dead.'

"Anna," Grandpa said softly, "I hope I'm not boring you. You've always been exceptionally good to my Ethan. I couldn't have asked for a better companion for him. He was blessed the day he met you. I am praying that you'll recover from this. But if you don't find my yammering of any interest, just stop me anytime." He waited momentarily in the darkness, then continued with his story.

"ON A Sunday morning in November of 1944, I was operating by myself in a small town in Austria called Windhaag bei Freistadt. It was within a few kilometers of the rest of my reconnaissance squad, who were camped just over the Czechoslovakian border. My objective was simple: Find out if there were any straggling Nazis from a caravan we'd spotted driving through town two days earlier. If the coast was clear, my team could advance more easily toward several work camps to the south, near Linz, that were receiving—and likely killing—trainloads of prisoners.

"I circled the entire town twice. Finding no signs of enemy soldiers in the area, I approached a secluded home off the main road. There was smoke curling from the stone chimney, a sure sign that someone was home. I hoped whoever was there could offer more concrete details about the troops who'd come through. I knocked. A few moments later a nervous-looking woman opened the door.

"I'd learned that the sterner I sounded, the more they believed I was who I claimed to be, so I put a scowl on my face and barked at her in German. 'State your name! I'm on official business.'

"She called herself Elizabeth Richter. There was fear in her eyes, which I knew would help me get the information I needed. Two children, maybe three or four years old, appeared from behind a door. They were twin girls, both with long dark hair and dark eyes. I noted how different they looked from their blond-haired, blue-eyed mother. She told me their names, Aloisa and Arla.

"'Where is the man of the house?' I demanded. 'I must speak with him immediately.' I didn't really need to speak with him; I didn't even know for sure she had a husband. But if she did, and if he was around, it was better to know now than to be surprised later by his unexpected arrival. Especially if he had a gun.

" *'Nicht zu Hause,'* she stammered. Not at home.

"I explained that I'd received word that several families of Jews were suspected of hiding out in the surrounding area. 'Do you know of such filth infesting this town?' I hated saying things like that, but I knew very well that a true SS man would speak in that manner.

"The woman pulled back her shoulders and assured me that there were no such people in Windhaag bei Freistadt. 'Now,' she said, 'will you kindly leave us? We have much work to do.'

"She tried closing the door, but I stuck my foot in the jamb. I told her I was hungry. 'Would you turn away a faithful servant of der Führer so quickly?' I asked.

" 'Oh,' she replied. 'Come in. I have soup and bread.'

"I'd not yet been seated for two minutes when I heard a sound, a deep, painful cough from the other room. I leaped from my chair with both hands on my gun. One of the girls squealed, 'Papa!' before her mother could stifle the sound.

"I moved quickly into the living room.

Then I heard a faint wheezing. I thought it came from the floor. Kneeling down, I discovered two loose boards. Elizabeth watched with horror as I lifted the boards to find a man in his forties lying on the earth below.

"I smiled at the man and told him not to worry. I extended a hand to him and pulled him up gently. He was very weak. By the sound of his cough, I guessed he had pneumonia. I explained who I was and what my true purpose was for visiting. They didn't believe me until I showed them my dog tags and spoke to them in English.

"Once everyone settled down, the father, Abel, wrapped a blanket around himself and we all sat again to eat. And that's when things went terribly wrong. There was the sound of a door cracking. Then the house was filled with soldiers.

"Somehow I'd been spotted by a German patrol. When they saw me sneaking around, they followed. One of them had been peering in through a window when I pulled Abel from the floor.

"'Explain yourself!' their leader yelled at gunpoint. 'Who are you, and why are you helping these *verdammt* Jews?'

"Abel and Elizabeth tried to say they weren't Jewish.

"Hoping to avoid complete catastrophe, I said something like, 'I'm on special assignment, scouring the area for Jews believed to be hiding in the area. I came to this house on a good tip, and since they were preparing food, I sat down to eat. I told them if they fed me, I might make arrangements to keep them out of the gas chamber.' I laughed. 'The fools—they actually believed me.'

"Then one of the girls blurted out, 'You said you're American.'

"The captain lifted his pistol to my face and asked if that was true. I swore up and down that the child was making it up. Then he turned the gun to Elizabeth, pressing the muzzle to her temple. He told me if I was lying, he'd kill her.

"I couldn't stand there and watch them murder Elizabeth, especially in front of the girls, just to maintain my lie. I told them in plain English that I was proud to be an American soldier.

"When they'd had their fill insulting me, they searched Herr Richter for identification. It took thirty minutes to sort through his papers and make calls to their superiors in Linz, but eventually they confirmed that the Richter family was not only Jewish, but that Abel was a former professor in Vienna who'd been on the run since the start of the war.

"Capturing someone of Abel's stature, along with an American posing as a Nazi officer, was a small coup for the German patrol unit. Elizabeth wasn't Jewish by birth, but she'd married Abel and bore his children, so it didn't matter—her fate would be the same as her husband's. After stripping me of my German uniform, they loaded all of us into a truck and started driving.

"We went southeast for an hour to what they jokingly said was our 'new vacation home'—Mauthausen, one of Europe's largest and most notorious death camps.

"Mauthausen was not an ordinary concentration camp. It was reserved primarily for the *intelligentsia*—those with high levels of education, the social elites, the political enemies of the Reich. In addition to the main camp where I was, there were a series of smaller satellite locations. All of the

Mauthausen-run camps had the same common goal—namely, to work prisoners until they died.

"With a life expectancy of only four to five months for new prisoners, the turnover rate at Mauthausen was high, the likelihood of survival low.

"The first part of my incarceration was spent in a windowless holding cell with the Richter family while camp directors decided what to do with us. When the cell door opened two hours later, a large uniformed man entered. He introduced himself as Oskar. He was maybe forty-five, with a thick mustache and bulky hands. Surprisingly, he was all smiles. Oskar introduced us to a much younger man, no older than twenty, named Karl.

"'Karl is not just a new officer here,' he said proudly in German. 'He is also my son. I'm trying to show him how best to deal with'—his jovial smile turned wicked as he finished his thought—'*special* guests.' He paused again and looked toward his son. 'Karl needs to become stronger, braver, and you're going to help him.' Oskar motioned to a few guards in the hallway, who escorted us out of the building to a large gravel courtyard.

"In the middle of the courtyard was a large barrel full of freezing cold water. Oskar explained that the children were dirty and needed a bath. One of the soldiers picked up Aloisa and plopped her in the makeshift tub, clothes and all. Then Oskar motioned for Karl to step forward. 'Karl,' he said, 'you *will* give the girls a bath.' His words were colder than the icy ground on which we stood.

"Aloisa was shaking from the cold, Elizabeth was whimpering, and Abel was mumbling a little prayer. I just cried, partly out of sorrow for whatever was about to happen, and partly out of a sense of guilt that I'd chosen to knock on the Richters' door.

"Karl was trembling as he placed a hand on Aloisa's shoulder. Then he averted his eyes and pushed her under the water. Elizabeth, Abel, and Arla all shrieked. Karl's trembling turned to fits of weeping. After fifteen seconds he vomited all over himself, releasing his grip on the struggling child, who shot up out of the water, gasping.

"Oskar, of course, was furious. He barked

obscenities at Karl, then marched forward to the barrel. He grabbed Aloisa by the hair and threw her back under the water until she stopped struggling. Then they dragged Arla to the barrel and did the same thing."

Grandpa's voice was wavering. My own stomach was churning.

Grandpa pressed on. "Most of the soldiers grinned as the last bubbles rose to the surface. Karl and I just watched in horror. Abel and Elizabeth were begging to be shot so they could join their children. Oskar told them they would have to wait to go to hell.

"In the next hour they shaved our heads and assigned us to barracks. Elizabeth went to a small contingent of women, Abel was put with a cadre of Austrian-born Jews, and I was assigned to a group composed of military and political dissidents from all over.

"As I said before, Mauthausen was designed as a slave camp. A few skilled prisoners were assigned tasks such as metal fabrication. Most of the women were rented out to neighboring communities to do chores. But the rest of us spent our time hauling hundred-pound rocks out of the massive on-site granite quarry.

"Within my first week there, I saw at least fifty people collapse and die from fatigue. One of them was Abel Richter.

"Two weeks before Christmas, we were assigned a new night guard over our barracks. It was Karl. In his new assignment, Karl was expected to roam among a group of five contiguous buildings, including mine, from lights out until dawn, exercising swift and severe punishment against anyone found out of their bunks.

"On his third night, something woke me. Music, coming from nearby. I tiptoed to the closed barracks door. On the other side of the door was the main entryway. My curiosity pulled my eyes to a small crack between the poorly hinged door and its jamb. Much to my astonishment, Karl was there, sitting on a stool in the light of a single candle, quietly playing a beautiful acoustic guitar.

"After several minutes I decided I should return to my bunk. Unfortunately, the floor board upon which I was standing squeaked loudly. I froze, but the music stopped and the door swung inward. Karl had a cocked pistol pointed at my chest, but it wobbled in his trembling hand. He waved me into the entryway and quickly shut the door behind us.

"Finally, in English, Karl said, 'You are the American spy, yes?'

"I assured him I was no spy. When he asked what I was doing out of my bed, I told him the truth—listening to beautiful music and remembering what it was like to hold a guitar in my hands.

"He raised an eyebrow. 'You play?'

"I nodded, then asked him why he was playing in our barracks rather than at the guardhouse or the officers' complex.

"'The acoustics here are *wunderbar*,' he whispered. Then he told me he should shoot me for being out of bed past curfew and that his father would honor him for making an example of an American.

"In response, I told him he would be doing me a great favor by putting me out of my misery. At length he lowered the gun and said he wouldn't kill me, on condition that I not tell anyone that he'd allowed me to be out of bed.

"'Thank you,' I whispered. 'I won't tell a living soul.'

"The next night, at about the same time, I again heard the soft strumming of guitar strings. I decided to press my luck once more with Karl. I tiptoed to the door and knocked as quietly as I could.

" *'Was machts du? Bist du blöd!'* he whispered sharply. *'What are you doing? Are you stupid?'*

"I told him I couldn't help it; the sound of the music was too tempting to stay away. I cautiously sat down on the floor. He kept his gun trained on me while debating what to do. Finally he holstered the weapon and went back to playing the guitar.

"For the next thirty minutes I sat quietly watching as his fingers plucked and strummed the instrument in the most amazing ways. I loved playing guitar, but I was a novice compared to Karl."

Grandpa hesitated. "He was sort of like your Ethan in that respect, Miss Anna. Too bad he's given all that up. Anyway, watching Karl's quiet practice sessions became a ritual.

"After a couple of weeks, Karl started opening up, telling me about himself. It was strange for me to think of him as anything other than a Nazi soldier. But it soon became apparent that he was no different than I; he was just a young soldier fighting for his country. He hinted that he was not a supporter of Hitler.

"In addition to the guitar, Karl said he also played the piano, cello, and harp and aspired to play in an orchestra. His dad hated the idea, but his mother had always been supportive.

"It didn't take long for others in the barracks to notice the nightly serenades and that I kept sneaking out of bed to listen. Everyone thought I was insane for trusting the young Nazi.

"A Hungarian man was the official calendar of our barracks. The Hungarian informed us each morning which day of the week it was and what date. When he announced it was December twenty-fourth, hardly anyone cared. It wasn't until Karl's visit that I was reminded. The first song he played was an Austrian original, *'Stille Nacht'*—'Silent Night.' I don't think a song has ever warmed me more.

"Karl continued to play a string of well-known Christmas songs. After thirty minutes I thanked him with a smile and a nod, then got up to return to my bunk. Before I got to the door, he told me to stop. As I watched him, he reached into his guitar case and withdrew a large loaf of fresh bread. 'From my mother,' he said. 'Merry Christmas.' I asked if she knew who it was for, and he nodded.

"I thanked him for the kindness, then slipped back into the bunkroom and quietly divided the bread among the men.

"As I lay in bed that night, I thought about the gift I'd received from the 'enemy' guard. It wasn't just a loaf of bread I'd been given. He knew that the penalty for giving extra food to 'the slaves' was a quick trip to the firing squad. Yet he'd done so anyway.

"The night after Christmas he was back just before midnight, practicing the guitar. 'You're losing too much weight,' he said.

"I'd only been in Mauthausen for about five weeks, but I'd already shed at least thirty pounds.

"Karl produced a piece of cake, wrapped in paper. I felt guilty eating it all by myself, but he stipulated it was meant for me alone. 'I can't help everyone,' he explained. 'But I can help you. Don't deny me this opportunity.' From then on, snacks came each night.

"At the start of February 1945, nearly three months into my imprisonment, whispers spread that the Germans were losing the war. In response to the rumors, the SS guards and kapos at Mauthausen began killing inmates with increased frequency.

"On February eighth Karl was a nervous wreck when he showed up for guard duty. He came straight to my bunk and pulled me out into the entry, where he explained that our barracks had been wagered as part of a sick poker bet among the SS, and as a result, we were going to be gunned down at dawn. I think I probably shrugged. It was bound to happen sooner or later.

" 'I haven't been your friend just to see you get killed!' he snapped. Karl had a plan. Inside his instrument case, stowed beneath the neck of the guitar, was a compass, a map, and some food. These, he explained, would help me reach the nearest U.S. Army platoon, which had recently made camp about thirty kilometers to the north. He showed me on the map where they'd last been seen.

"'What am I supposed to do?' I asked. 'Walk out the front door?'

"He smiled and said, 'Something like that.' He told me he'd be back right before his shift ended at five in the morning to give me the rest of the details.

"At a quarter to five, I heard the front door open again, followed by a soft *'Pssst . . . Herb . . . Come.'*

"In the entryway, Karl was sitting on the floor taking off his boots. He indeed intended for me to walk right out the front door of the camp. 'I do not live on site, because my father has high rank and our home is nearby. Every morning, I carry my guitar through the west gate. There is a guard on the wall near the gate, but it is too dark right now to see faces. He frequently waves at me, but nothing more. Take my clothes, my coat, my guitar, and my key for the gate, and everything will be fine.'

"I couldn't let him do it. 'It puts you in too much danger.'

"Karl smiled and said he would claim that I'd attacked him and taken his things. Then he added, 'And even if nobody believes it,

I'm sure my father won't let anything happen to me.'"

Grandpa let out a sigh. "So I put on the clothes. Five minutes later, bundled in Karl's thick overcoat and with a cap pulled low to hide my face, I walked out of the barracks. Before I closed the door, he handed me his gun. 'Just in case,' he said.

"I thanked him, and that was that. Carrying the guitar case, I trudged toward the west gate, waved casually to the guard on the wall, then walked out of Mauthausen and never looked back.

"A day and a half later, having traversed the countryside with the aid of the map and compass, I allowed myself to be captured by a small group of Americans who were on patrol. They threw me in a makeshift holding cell at their camp until they were able to verify that I was who I said I was.

"The next morning, I was given a choice: I could be discharged and return to the States, or I could join their battalion and continue fighting. I chose the latter. Once I put on fifteen pounds, I was deemed fit enough to drive a vehicle.

"I was assigned to drive a transport truck.

Karl's guitar stayed with me. It made for a perfect stress relief following skirmishes with the increasingly disorganized German army. We all got the sense that the end of the war was close at hand.

"Early in May we crossed into Germany and pressed on to a town called Berchtesgaden. The next morning, we plowed our way up a steep single-lane road to Hitler's mountaintop hideout, the Eagle's Nest. It was largely a symbolic effort, but for us, capturing Hitler's private lair was cause for celebration.

"My truck was near the rear of the convoy, so I was one of the last to enter the premises. Once I made it inside, I took myself on a self-guided tour. On the ground floor, at the end of one hallway, I found a bathroom. I decided I wanted a souvenir. And so I whipped out my pocketknife and removed the bathroom door handle. I tucked it into my pants pocket.

"We stayed at the Eagle's Nest for the better part of a week. Near the end of that week, we got word that Nazi strongholds were falling all across Germany and Austria. Mauthausen was on the list.

"My very first thoughts were of Karl. Though I hated the idea of returning to the place where I'd been held prisoner, I had to know what became of my friend. With the permission of a sympathetic lieutenant colonel, I was allowed to take a jeep and two other infantrymen for a quick jaunt back to Linz.

"When we finally arrived at Mauthausen, I was thrilled to see the American flag flying overhead. I recognized a few of the former prisoners, but I didn't see anyone from my old barracks.

"Most of the Nazi SS had fled before the U.S. troops arrived. Those who didn't were being detained in one of the barracks under constant watch. Among them was Karl's father, Oskar.

"'Ah, the American spy who escaped,' he said when he saw me. 'I never forget a face.'

"I wanted to punch him. 'Where is your son, Karl?' I demanded.

"His face turned bright red. 'I have *no* son!' he hissed defiantly.

"Later that evening, I stumbled across Elizabeth Richter. She had been assigned to do housekeeping for a family in the town of

Mauthausen, where she was able to help herself to scraps of food.

"When she saw me, she gave a little smile. 'You made it,' she whispered. 'Thank God, you made it!'

"It had been nearly four months since I'd last seen Elizabeth at camp, but the guilt over what had befallen her and her family on account of my actions was as fresh and real as the day I watched Oskar drown Arla and Aloisa.

"I burst into tears. I said, 'I'm so sorry, Elizabeth! If not for me, things would have been so different for you. I'm sorry.'

"'Shhh,' she said softly. 'You mustn't apologize for things beyond your control.'

"'But I led them straight to you. It was my fault!'

"She smiled sympathetically. 'If you insist on feeling guilty, then I see only one course of action. This.' Elizabeth stood tall, and in the softest voice possible she said, 'I forgive you.'"

Grandpa was weeping unabashedly now. "'*I forgive you,*'" he repeated more forcefully. "To this day," he said, articulating with precision, as though commanding me to pay attention, "those remain the absolute sweetest words I've ever heard. I think they saved my life just as much as Karl did.

"The following morning," Grandpa continued, "the officer in charge informed me that Oskar wanted to speak to me again.

"'Ah, the spy returns,' he said when I entered his room. 'As I was lying in bed last night, I realized I should have been more forthcoming yesterday. You deserve to know what became of Karl. One morning we found Karl hiding in his underwear. I think you know what morning that was, don't you? He had helped you escape. He didn't even deny it. As punishment for treason, we took him and everyone else in the barracks to the edge of the quarry.

"'I told him,'" Grandpa said gruffly, taking on the tone of his former captor, "'if he shot the other prisoners, I would spare his life, but if he jumped off the cliff of his own accord, then the others would live. I knew he was too weak to hurt the prisoners. There was no hesitation. He jumped.'" Grandpa's words were drowning in his own emotions. He lowered his head and cried until the tears stopped flowing.

Now I was wiping my own face. Karl had been a hero. I'd been playing a hero's guitar for as long as I could remember, and I never knew it.

"'And what about the other prisoners?' I asked Oskar.

"He let out a laugh. 'I shot them myself . . . one by one.' Then his face narrowed. I felt like he was staring right into my soul. 'But I wanted you to know Karl's fate,' he declared, 'because I want you to always remember that his death is on your head.'"

With that, Grandpa got up slowly and stood beside Anna. "Thanks for listening to the ramblings of an old man," he said. He checked his watch. "I promised the nurse out front that I wouldn't be more than an hour. I guess I better get on my way. Rest well, Anna. We're all praying for you. And for your family."

He reached out and touched Anna's scarred arm, bowed his head solemnly, and then picked up his cane and turned to go.

Shuffle-shuffle-thump. Shuffle-shuffle-thump.

I squeezed my eyes as tight as they would go. He passed by without saying a word. He'd already said more than enough.

FOURTH VERSE:
Solo, Lento Grave

Chapter 10

WHEN the morning nurse came in to check Anna's vitals at quarter to nine, I was still curled up on the recliner in the darkest corner of the room and was pretty sure she didn't see me. She began tending to my wife.

"Good morning, sunshine," she said. "Feeling any better today?"

Is that nurse humor? I wondered. *Talking to the dying about getting better?* "She can't hear you," I blurted out.

"Oh! Mr. Bright. I'm so sorry. I didn't realize you were there." Her voice dropped to a whisper. "Sorry. I'll shut up so you can get some rest. I just need to take her blood pressure and temp."

I thanked her for the quiet and closed my eyes.

The rest of that day I was in and out of sleep. Nurses came and went. A few doctors, too. I didn't try keeping track of who they were. When I was awake, I just sat there staring at Anna in the dimly lit room. Watching her breathe. Watching her do . . . nothing.

Grandpa and Octavius both called in the afternoon to see how things were going. Aunt Jo called once, too, wanting to know if I'd gotten the flowers she sent. I had.

Later that evening, Stuart called and put Hope on the line. "You doing okay, honey?"

"Yes. How is Mommy?"

"She's . . . doing better."

There was a long pause. "Can I talk to her?"

"Hope, your mom . . . well, she can't really talk right now. But she sends her love. Okay?"

More silence, then a quiet "Okay, Dad. Tell her I love her, too."

"I will. Are you having a good time with your cousins?"

She was. She went on to tell me all about her birthday party and how Uncle Stuart surprised her with a brand-new bicycle. "Can I show it to you tomorrow?"

"Maybe. It depends on how your mom is doing."

"Dad? Mommy is going to get better, isn't she?"

I glanced over at the tubes protruding

from Anna's nose and mouth and watched as the ventilator compressed air with a soft wheeze.

"Of course. Don't you worry. Everything is going to be fine."

THE next few days were about as lonely as anyone could ever imagine. I stayed holed up at the hospital, hoping for any sign that Anna was getting better, but every time a doctor came in to check on her, it was more of the same bad news.

At the end of the week, Reg brought a familiar yellow form with him. "Ethan, I know you've been pretty much camped out here, but have you had a chance to check if Anna has a living will? Because if she doesn't, we'd like you to sign this so we've got the right paperwork in place before we begin thinking about next steps."

"I haven't really been home to look," I said.

"Have you thought about how you might like to proceed in the event that she doesn't have one?"

"Not really." Sadly, I was getting very good at lying. The truth, however, was that "how to proceed" was what I spent most of my time thinking about. "But is there anything wrong with how we're proceeding right now?"

"Not at all. Watching and waiting is the right thing to be doing. From past experience I know that most comas last from a couple of days to a few weeks. The odds of recovery drop off fairly quickly after that, but we're only one week into this. In the meantime, though, please look around at home. If there's any chance she has a living will, we really need to know. I want to make sure everything we do is in accordance with her wishes."

"I'll poke around in our files," I mumbled.

"Hope? Hello?" It was early in the afternoon when I walked into my house. Grandpa's rental car was parked beside Stuart's Jaguar, but when I stepped into the entryway, it was like everyone had disappeared. "Hello?" I called again, louder. "Is anyone home?"

Finally I poked my head out the patio door and yelled into the backyard. "Stuart! Hope! *Anybody?*"

"Dad?"

I heard Hope's voice, but I couldn't place her. "Hope?"

"Up here!"

Our backyard was fairly spacious. Most of it was filled up by manicured lawn. At the far corner of the lot was a stand of three tall pine trees. It was there, in the middle of the pines, that I located Hope's face about ten feet up, leaning out an open window—a window that hadn't been there when I was last at home.

"Hi, Ethan." Stuart's head popped into view above Hope's. "I thought the kids needed a fun place to play."

"You built a . . ." *A tree house.* Hope had been begging me to build one since she was old enough to say the words, but it never seemed to fit into my schedule.

"Hired it out, actually. I'm all thumbs with a hammer. The crew just left about thirty minutes ago, so this is our first time testing it out. You want to come up?"

The tree house was big, complete with a shake roof and cedar siding. "Where is everyone else? There's no one in the house."

"Up here, Dad," said Hope.

"What about Grandpa Bright?" I asked as

I started walking across the yard toward the trees.

"Relaxing up here on one of the chairs," piped Stuart.

"Welcome home, Ethan," Grandpa called from inside the abode.

Stuart recognized my consternation over how an old man with a cane made it ten feet up a tree. "He was the ultimate test of our elevator system," he said, beaming. "It's pretty simple, really. A few well-placed pulleys and a winch from a Jeep Wrangler, and *voila!*"

"Fine. But please, no more big surprises like this. Between the tree house and the party, I'm going to have a hard time competing."

"Understood," he said. "So what's the latest on Anna?"

"There's been no change whatsoever."

Stuart disappeared briefly, then poked his head outside again. "Hope wants to give you the grand tour. You ready to come up?"

I nodded and went around to the "elevator." It was an elongated crate with open sides, supported by thick cables and pulleys attached to the tree above. I stepped into it, pushed a button on the winch, and ascended to the front door.

Hope led me all of fifteen feet to the designated sitting area, where Grandpa Bright was in a soft chair that Heather found at a garage sale. Then she showed me where her kitchen set would eventually reside, and her doll collection, and her refrigerator—

"Whoa, hold on," I said. "This is a play house, not an apartment."

She folded her arms. "Fine. I can put a bookshelf there."

"Excellent idea."

We all stayed in the tree house for another half hour. But I started getting antsy about Anna. "I need to get back to the hospital."

"I'm going with you," said Hope.

"No, sweetie. Not yet. I'll tell you when it's okay."

Grandpa banged his cane on the tree house floor and said, "Oh, c'mon, Ethan. Let the poor girl see her mom."

"Excuse me?"

"You heard me. Let the girl go see her mom. She deserves it."

I turned quickly to Hope. "Honey, why don't you run inside."

"Yeah," said Heather. "Kids, how about we all head into the house for a while?"

I waited until everyone was halfway across the yard before I lit into Grandpa. "How dare you undermine my authority like that?"

He gripped the top of his cane. "Needed to be said."

"Why? What gives you the right to say that in front of Hope?"

He met my stare. "What gives you the right to keep her away?"

"Because I'm her father and I know what's best for her!"

"Then when will she get to see her mom?"

"When Anna wakes up."

In a subdued voice he asked, "And what if she suddenly slips away? Hope already knows something is wrong, more than what you've told her. Don't you think she deserves to know the truth and a chance to see her mom again while she's still alive?"

I wasn't ready to concede just yet. "If it means saving her from a lifetime of nightmares that would come from seeing the patchwork quilt of her mom's body? *Absolutely!*"

"Very well." He sighed. "You're her father.

If that's how you feel, then I'm sorry I spoke up the way I did."

I left Grandpa alone in the tree house and went inside to gather some things. One item I knew I needed to find was in the den, filed under "Legal Documents" in our metal cabinet: Anna's living will.

I scanned through the legalese to confirm what I already knew. Anna had gone to great lengths to develop her position on dying. After studying all sorts of facts dealing with recovery rates for patients on life support, she'd settled on one month as the magical number for aborting life-support measures.

"I wouldn't want you holding out longer than that," she'd told me, "if there isn't a strong indication that I'll recover." My own living will said the same exact thing. Both of us had signed that, in the event of certain medical conditions, we would allow life-support machines to be removed after four weeks. With a quarter of that time already gone, it felt infinitely too short.

As much as I would have liked to run it through the nearest paper shredder, I stuffed the documents into my duffel bag, along with a few fresh clothes. Then I went searching for Stuart and Heather.

"I need to ask a favor," I told them. "I know you guys can't stay here indefinitely. But it may be a few more weeks before I'm really able to get away from the hospital. Would you mind watching Hope at your place for a while?"

"You mean, take her back to Fresno?" Heather asked.

"Yes. Maybe it will help take her mind off of visiting Anna."

Stuart looked very concerned. "You sure it's wise taking her so far from home?"

"I'm not sure about anything anymore, Stu, except that I need to be with Anna. Will you help?"

"Of course."

Hope was playing in her room with Devin. Before I left for the hospital, I stopped in to tell her what was going on.

"Why can't I stay with you?" she asked.

"Sweetie, Mommy needs me right now. And I need to make sure you're safe while I'm with her. Now give me a hug before I go."

"When will I see you again?"

"Soon," I said. "You'll hardly even miss me."

"You promise?"

"I promise," I said warily. "You, me, Mommy—we'll all be together again before you know it. Maybe a week." *Maybe more.*

She relented. "Okay, a week. And then I get to see Mommy."

LATER that night, as I was reading True Love Notes aloud to Anna, I was interrupted by a familiar sound approaching.

Shuffle-shuffle-thump. "May I come in?"

I'd already turned to face the door. "What brings you here?"

Grandpa was holding the old guitar case in one hand and his cane in the other. "I'm reneging. I don't want Karl back."

"Neither do I."

"Tough luck. It's all yours now, free and clear. I'm too old to play it anyway, and it'd be too much work taking it back with me on the airplane." He sat down in the chair near the foot of the bed.

"You're flying back to Oregon?"

"I thought I could be of help here, but maybe I was wrong."

"Well, I'm glad you came down. And I'm sorry you're going back so soon. But I really don't want the guitar."

"It's staying." He leaned it up against the table near his chair. His old wooden box was on the same table. Grandpa caught me stealing a glance at it. "Oh, I was wondering where this went to."

"Very funny."

The smile on his face softened my mood. "It's true?" I asked. "What you told Anna?"

His smile grew. "I thought you might be listening."

"How could anyone sleep through all that yammering?"

With a solemn nod he said, "It was all true. Every last word."

"You really took Hitler's bathroom door handle?"

"Sure did."

"Do you still have it?"

His smiled dimmed. "No. I got rid of it a long time ago."

"Why?"

"I was tired of clinging to the past. What I saw during the war didn't magically go away after I came back home. It hung around in my head, in my heart. At times I felt consumed with anger and guilt. Eventually I decided I needed to let those feelings go."

Grandpa's eyes wandered to Anna's face. My gaze followed. "Traumatic events can cripple you, Ethan, if you don't deal with them properly. I've learned that through a lifetime of encounters with heartache. I've also learned that no matter how bad things seem in the moment, it's only a moment. This too shall pass, as the saying goes. What I went through was awful, but I survived."

"Oh, I get it. *You* survived your ordeal, so I should be able to get through mine, is that it? That's why you decided to finally share your story with me. This is probably just some sort of therapeutic experiment to you. 'Hmm . . . Let's see if the old shrink still has it in him, eh?' Does that about sum it up?"

He pounded his cane on the floor defiantly. "Stop it right there, young man! That was *not* my intent. You're not my patient; you're my grandson. And yes, I did share the story because I thought it might help with what you're going through right now, but not in the way you think. I thought, perhaps, when you read or if you heard how simple it can be to just . . ."

"To what?" I pressed.

Grandpa shook his head. "No, I don't want to spoon-feed you, Ethan. If you *really* want to know how I thought my story could help, then just give some more thought to what I told Anna. Or better yet, read the journals. I know I'm not a particularly good writer, but I promise, the answer is sitting right there, plain as day. Don't dig too deep, though. Look for the low-hanging fruit, because the sweetest things in life are usually right there for us to grab."

"You're seriously not going to tell me?"

"Of course not. What good would that do you?"

"It would save me reading your depressing tale, for one thing."

Grandpa's smile returned. "Nobody's forcing you, Ethan. But it's there if you want it." He looked at his watch. "Wow, I've got a plane to catch. Oh, and Ethan? Play the guitar, won't you?"

"I'll think about it," I lied.

I WAS SOUND ASLEEP the next morning when my cell phone rang.

"Ethan, it's nice to know you're still among the living. How's your vacation?" Jessica's voice sent chills down my spine.

"Not great."

"Sorry to hear that." I knew she couldn't care less. "Anyway, what are the chances of you coming in for a few days—just to help with a couple big new accounts we're trying to land out west, near you?"

I'd completely forgotten about work. I hadn't even called in to tell them what had happened to Anna.

"Jessica, that's not going to be possible."

"Well, if you can't come into the office, how about a teleconference? Just a few hours tomorrow and then three or four the following day. Oh, and if you have a laptop, we could—"

I ended the call. The phone rang again ten seconds later.

"Ethan? I guess we got disconnected."

"No," I stated matter-of-factly. "I hung up on you."

"I hope you're joking, or we have a serious problem."

"Yeah," I said, staring at Anna. "We have a serious problem."

I braced myself for the ax that was no doubt about to fall. But her response surprised me. "Oh, jeez. . . . Let me guess. You're not on vacation at all. This is some sort of interviewing excursion."

I was too shocked to speak. She became desperate. "Just tell me what they offered you and I'll beat it by five percent."

"Jessica . . . I didn't. It's Annaliese."

"Is that a marketing firm?"

"My wife."

"She offered you a job?"

"Stop it!" I snapped. "Just listen for two seconds. My wife was in an accident seven days ago when I came home from work."

She let out a huge sigh of relief. "Thank heavens, because you're already paid top dollar. How's your wife doing, by the way?"

I was as furious as I've ever been. In a few short minutes she'd managed to wake me up, ask me to cut my vacation short, bribe me to stay with the company, and then, to top it all off, act like my wife's health was a minor afterthought.

"She's *dying*. And I quit."

I hung up for the second time and turned off my phone. Then I moved from the recliner to the hard chair next to Anna's bed.

"Good morning. Did you hear that, Anna?" I asked. It was like I was talking to a door, and I desperately wanted access to the person on the other side. "I'm officially unemployed. Heck of a way to start the day, huh?" I waited, doubting that she would reply. "Still tight-lipped, I see. Of course, now that I quit my job, we can spend as much time together as you want. Do you hear that, Anna? It'll just be you and me and Hope, doing whatever you want." I reached out and took her hand in mine. "How does that sound? Anna? Please, sweetie, just give me any indication that you can hear me. Lift a finger or blink an eye. Wiggle a toe. Or smile. If you're just holding out because you're mad at me . . . please don't. I'm serious, Anna. I need to know that you're there. I *need* you."

I'm a sane person . . . I think. But I felt precariously close to losing it. She didn't hear a thing I was saying. Not only was I talking to a door, but I guessed the room on the other side was empty.

MIDMORNING I CAUGHT sight of Grandpa's wooden box sitting on the table and decided to open it up, partly out of curiosity and partly out of a sense of guilt for how I'd treated my grandfather during his visit. For the rest of the day, I sat reading his journals to Anna, seeking whatever nugget of wisdom Grandpa had been hinting at. Yes, I found his exploits moving. But if his point wasn't to show me that everyone has trials, then I was still missing something.

To help focus my mind on something other than the questions that I didn't want to face, I opened up my briefcase and retrieved a few of Anna's True Love Notes that I hadn't yet read to her.

I opened the topmost envelope. It was from the day of Faith's funeral. The first line sent a chill through me. "Ethan, part of me died yesterday. I'm sure that part will never heal, never return." I glanced at my wife on the bed. "Is this a coincidence, Anna, or are you trying to tell me something?" She remained silent.

I started over from the beginning, trying hard to keep my tears at bay. "'Ethan, part of me died yesterday. I'm sure that part will never heal, never return. Why is life so cruel? God takes some and leaves others with no apparent rhyme or reason.

" 'And yet . . . we have Hope. Maybe that's how God compensates for the bad times, by making sure there is always a little hope to hold on to. Ethan, you have been my rock through all of this. I depend on you. I need you. I love you fiercely.

" 'Last night, as I was lying in bed, mourning the loss of our daughter, I was beginning to question whether all of the pain we have endured is worth it. And then you brought your guitar to bed and played me a song. Thank you for that. It reminded me of all the wonderful things we've shared together. It made me feel loved. That's exactly what I needed.

" 'I know together we can endure all things, come what may.

" 'Forever yours, Annaliese.

" 'P.S. Please play for me more often. We both need more beautiful music in our lives.' "

Karl's guitar case was still leaning against the little table.

"I'm done with guitars," I said to Anna,

but partly to Karl as well. "Where has play-ing the guitar gotten us? If I didn't play, we'd have never wanted to teach Hope how to play, I'd have never asked you to pick one up for her birthday, and you wouldn't be lying there not hearing me talking to you like a lunatic. Besides, didn't you hear Grandpa's story about his guitar? That thing's a magnet for misery, and I've had enough of that. I'm *not* playing it. I'm just not."

Chapter 11

EVEN though I was young, I recall quite viv-idly how my father imploded after my mother "left." At first he tried to put on a coura-geous face, but that façade didn't last more than a few weeks. One day I came home from first grade and found him passed out on the couch when he should have been at work.

After that I found Dad passed out fre-quently when I came home. I learned to fend for myself. We lived like that for only a few months before Dad decided he lacked the emotional fortitude to be a widower–father. I didn't disagree, and neither did Grandma and Grandpa, who kindly offered to take me in.

As a kid, I couldn't fathom how a father could just give up on life like my dad had. At least not until my experience waiting for Anna to breathe her last breath.

I'd been trying so hard to stay optimistic as I sat there next to her bed day after day. Either a miracle would happen and Anna would pull through, or Hope and I would rise above the loss and carry on without her. But no matter what, I would not end up like my dad.

However, on day ten at the hospital, while I was reading another stack of Anna's notes, something inside me changed. It felt like the tiny shreds of hope that I'd been clinging to just evaporated.

I began to give up, and I soon understood how my father had fallen to such a state of wallowing. I never went over the edge like him, but I dangled my feet far enough over the precipice that I could see what was waiting at the bottom, and it wasn't pretty.

I continued on in that state for days, still hiding Anna's living will from the hospital staff. The days blurred together.

I occasionally checked the date on my cell phone to see how close we were coming to the magical four-week mark of Anna's coma. I wasn't ready to let go.

Twenty-two days after the accident, Dr. Knight brought a larger-than-normal entourage with him when he made his daily visit, including Dr. Gooding and Reg Wilson. "Good news," he announced. "Dr. Gooding says your wife's internal injuries have healed nicely. Her lungs, especially, have come a long way, so it's time to see how they do without the ventilator."

"But the dialysis machine stays?"

"That's right," said Dr. Gooding. "It's sort of a permanent fixture. But assuming she doesn't need all the breathing apparatus, we should be able to get her out of the ICU and into a regular room."

"Ah," I commented.

The process of turning off equipment took about thirty minutes. When they were done, the only things still attached to Anna were the feeding tube, an IV for fluids, and the dialysis machine.

The interns and nurses wheeled Anna out to her new room. I stayed behind to gather my things. Reg stayed behind, too.

"You're not looking so good lately," he said candidly.

"Can't a guy grow a beard if he wants to?"

"Ethan, it's not just the beard. You look *defeated*."

I picked up my duffel bag and briefcase.

"I know this has been horrible for you, and I'm not sure I wouldn't feel the same way in your position. But from where I sit, I have to believe that you hanging around here twenty-four seven is not doing you or your wife any favors. What about your daughter?"

"She's in good hands," I snapped. "I talk with her every day. I wish you'd show less concern for me and more for my wife."

"Ethan, with Anna we've reached a point where there's little left for the doctors to do. She's shown no progress responding to stimuli, and it's been more than three weeks. Usually by now, if a patient is going to recover, we would have seen some significant improvement."

"What are you saying?"

"I'm saying it's time to start thinking about how long we're going to carry on like this. How long do you plan to leave your wife living on a feeding tube? You really need to start thinking about letting go so that you and your daughter can move on."

Through clenched teeth I said, "What you're hinting at amounts to murder, and I won't murder my wife."

"No," he said calmly. "What I'm suggesting is that maybe she's *already gone*. Now that her brain has had a chance to recuperate, and given her lack of progress, we need to think about what the most humane thing is for her. How long do we sustain her body in a vegetative state?"

I thought of the living will hiding in my briefcase. My mind rehearsed the legal language that defined Anna's wishes for just such a scenario. *One month.*

"As long as it takes," I replied, then spun to go.

"Ethan," Reg called. "You forgot your guitar."

I didn't even turn around. "You can have it."

ANNA'S new room was in the corner of the building, which meant it had windows on two walls, providing twice as much natural light during the day.

On the morning after leaving the ICU, I awoke to find Karl's guitar case propped up in the corner of the room between the windows. I hated seeing it there. It reminded me of all of my failings: never became the songwriter I'd dreamed of becoming; never wrote Anna the song I promised to write; stopped playing for my wife and daughter because I was too busy; didn't take the time to pick out a guitar for Hope's birthday, which led Anna to her state of semi-life. . . .

I might have walked Karl down to a Dumpster behind the hospital and been done with it. But somehow I knew I'd regret it later. After all, Grandpa had gone through hell to get it.

The days leading up to the magical one-month anniversary of Anna's accident were some of the lowest of my life.

On day twenty-seven one of the nurses poked Anna's heel with a pin, causing a small flinch in her toe. It wasn't much, but it took her Glasgow score from a three to a six. I thought this was the turning point, where the injustices of the world would be corrected and I would have my Anna back. But when Dr. Rasmussen came in, he put a heavy damper on the situation.

"I'm sorry," he explained, "but this doesn't mean much. The movements we're seeing are more likely indicative of muscular contraction than a response of the nervous system."

"But you're not one hundred percent certain?"

"Ethan, in medicine nothing is ever certain. We don't know everything. But what we know is that even if your wife has some minimal brain activity, her likelihood of recovering is very small."

"How small? I want numbers! There's got to be data on this that will support some other outcome."

"Okay," he replied calmly. "Let's look at where your wife was twenty-four hours after the accident, which is the best predictor of outcome. She had the lowest score possible. Of those that recover, most start to show marked improvement within the first week. It has been almost four weeks for Anna, and this is the first bump we've seen in her score."

"What is the prognosis for a person with a score of six?"

"I don't have hard data on that, but as far as I'm concerned, the most likely outcome is still that she will not recover."

Then came day twenty-eight . . . and twenty-nine. Anna was still ingesting food through a tube, and her toe still flinched when prodded, but that was the extent of her existence.

Mentally and emotionally I was bankrupt. Life as I'd known it was officially over. Anna would never recover. And worst of all, I could no longer see myself functioning as a parent.

"I'm sorry, Anna," I cried.

I was interrupted by a phone call. It was Stuart's number on the screen, which meant Hope would be on the other end of the line. I didn't feel much like talking, but I couldn't just ignore her.

I tried to sound happy when I picked up and said hello.

"Dad? Please, please, please, *please* let me see Mommy now."

"You know I can't do that." I waited for an objection. "Are you still doing okay at the Burkes?"

"I'm fine. I'm getting to be a really good swimmer. And Aunt Heather bought me two new swimsuits today and some really nice clothes. When can I show them to you?"

"Hope, I'm sorry," I said. "I have to go."

I clicked off. What kind of a parent intentionally hangs up on their own kid? I asked myself. *The kind who shouldn't be a parent.*

I went to the spare bed on the other side of the curtain. Three hours later, at eleven thirty, I was still wide awake. I got up and went back to Anna's bed. Standing beside her in the darkness, I took her hand in mine. "Why won't you just wake up?" I asked. "I just want you here. I've been trying to keep it together, but I can't."

My pining was cut off by my cell phone. When I saw the number on the caller ID, I hesitated answering—Hope should have long since been asleep, and I wasn't in the mood to talk to my brother-in-law. After five rings I answered. "Hello?"

"Ethan, it's Stuart. You need to come down here—*right now.* Hope is gone."

MAYBE it's just me, because I've experienced it so many times, but I swear there's nothing like a good calamity to pull your head out of the last calamity.

As soon as Stu said, "Hope is gone," it was as if somebody flipped a switch on inside me. No longer was I the moping, wallowing, unshaven, victim of poor choices who was waiting for the death of his wife to put the final nail in the coffin of his life. Okay, maybe I was still unshaven, but I definitely wasn't a zombie, and that was an excellent start. I was *alive*. I was *me* again.

"What do you mean she's gone? Gone where?"

"If we knew, I wouldn't have called. She said she was going to her room after she got off the phone with you." The panic in his voice was growing. "It was her bedtime, so we figured she was going to sleep. Heather and I watched a movie. We went to check on her about thirty minutes ago, just to make sure she was okay before we went to bed, but she wasn't there."

"You sure she's not just hiding?"

"She's not here, Ethan. The window in her room is wide open, and the screen is popped out."

I felt sick. "Have you checked everywhere outside?"

"Ethan, we've checked everywhere! We called the police, and they're already issuing an Amber Alert. You need to be here."

"Of course." My head was spinning. "Stu, she didn't have any money, right?"

"Well . . . she might have had some cash."

"How did she get money?"

"Allowance. I couldn't not give her an allowance, since the boys were getting one."

I calmly asked, "How much?"

"The boys get fifty dollars a week, and I didn't want her to feel slighted, so maybe a hundred and fifty or so."

"Are you *insane?* She's eight! You know what, never mind."

I was grabbing my keys, throwing on shoes, and heading for the door. "Stuart, the Amber Alert was the right thing to do. But I have a feeling I know where Hope is. You're not far from the Fresno Amtrak station, right? Isn't there a station near you?"

"It's a couple of miles, yes. But we can see the trains just half a mile away when they pass by."

"Go there!" I said as I reached the hospital's lobby. "And if she's not there, check the bus station. Check all the public transportation in town. Call the cab companies, too. See if anyone picked up a little girl asking for a ride to San Francisco."

"You think—"

"Yes. I think she's got a wad of cash and she's going to spend it to get exactly what she wants. *To see her mother.*"

Twenty minutes later, shortly after midnight, as I was speeding through Oakland along Interstate 580, my cell phone rang.

"We got her!" Stu screamed. "And she's okay. You were right; she went straight for the tracks and followed them to the station."

Sitting there in my car, I cried the first tears of joy in as long as I could remember— maybe the first ones ever. "Thank you, Stuart."

"It was you who knew where to look."

"I'm just glad she's safe. Are you taking her back to your place?"

"Well . . ." he drawled. "Not exactly. She says she bought a train ticket to San Fran, and she's waiting for the train to pick her up."

"Stubborn little . . ."

"Just like Anna," he quipped.

"Yeah." I sighed reverently. "Just like Anna. Do you mind hanging out at the train station for a while? I can be there in two hours."

"Take your time. Her train comes at five in the morning."

"Can I talk to her?"

He chuckled. "She says she's not speaking to you."

"Understood. Well, at least tell her I'm coming and that I love her. And give her a big hug for me. I'll be there as quick as I can."

At a quarter past two in the morning, I stepped inside the Amtrak station. Heather and Stu were sitting on a small wooden bench with Hope sprawled out between them, sound asleep.

"Hope," I said, nudging her just a little. "Hope, Dad's here."

"I'm going on the train," she mumbled half-consciously.

"How about we go in my car?"

She lifted her head. "No. I'm going to see my mom."

The drive from San Francisco had given me time to think, and my number one thought was how close I'd come to losing Hope. It scared me to death. No, it scared me much worse than death. She was all I had left, yet in my selfish stupor, I'd nearly convinced myself that she'd be better off without me. That was about to change.

"I know," I told her. "I'll take you there myself."

She smiled—the big, beautiful smile she'd inherited from her mother. "Promise?" she asked.

"I promise."

HOPE stayed asleep the entire ride home. Dawn was breaking when we pulled into our garage. I carried Hope to her bed; then I crashed on the sofa. My own bed looked plenty inviting, but I wasn't ready yet to sleep in it alone.

Later Hope woke me up. "Dad, you look like a gorilla."

I opened one eye. "I thought you liked gorillas."

"I do. *At the zoo.* But you don't want to look like that when we go visit Mommy."

"Oh, right. That."

"We *are* going. You promised."

"You're right. I did. And we will. But Hope, there's something I need to talk to you about before we go. Why don't you sit down?"

"Is it about Mom?"

"Yes. Hope, I haven't been completely honest with you about your mom's accident . . . because I didn't want you to worry. But since we're going to see her, I want you to know what to expect. Honey, Mommy's car accident was very serious."

She tried to put on a brave face. "I know, Dad," she said softly. "That's why you've been staying with her at the hospital and why I haven't been able to talk to her."

"That's right. The accident hurt her brain, sweetheart, and it caused her to *sleep* for a long time. It's called a coma. She hasn't been awake since her accident."

Hope stared at me. "Like Sleeping Beauty?"

"Just like that. I was hoping she would pull out of it and then I could take you to see her. But now we're not sure that's even a possibility."

"You mean, she might not wake up?"

I knew the time for lying was long past. "Yes."

Finally she asked, "Have you kissed her? Like Sleeping Beauty."

"Hope, this is . . . It's not a fairy tale, sweetie. This is real. And as much as it hurts, we need to understand that Mommy is probably never going to wake up. She isn't going to be *Mommy* again."

Hope's tears started to fall. Then she asked a question that I didn't want to answer. "But Dad, if Mommy is asleep and isn't going to wake up, what should I tell her when we go to the hospital?"

I pulled her close. "I think maybe the thing to say is good-bye."

"THE gorilla is gone," I announced as I exited the bathroom.

"There's nothing to eat," replied Hope.

I told her she could pick any restaurant on the way to the hospital. She chose McDonald's. Then she asked, "Isn't today Friday?"

"I believe so."

"Don't you usually work on Fridays?"

"Well . . ." I said slowly. I felt like she

needed to know exactly what I'd done, and why I'd done it. "I decided I needed to be around here more for you. So I quit. I'll have to find another job, but I promise it won't be one that keeps me away so much."

She wrapped her arms around my neck. "I love you, Dad."

An hour later we arrived at the hospital, fully fed on hotcakes and Egg McMuffins. Before we reached Anna's room, I warned Hope that her mother had some scars on her face and that her hair had been cut short, so she might look a little different.

"I don't care how she looks," she replied. "She's still my mom."

I gave Hope a little squeeze of assurance before opening the door. "No matter what," I told her, "we're going to be okay."

Hope hurried straight to the bed. Thankfully, the worst of the visual trauma from the accident had gone way down. Most of the bandages around Anna's head had been removed. A pink scar across her cheek marked the site of a once-deep gash, but now even that didn't look so bad.

"Mommy?" she said softly, testing the waters. "It's Hope."

When no reply came, she called a little louder. When that didn't work, she stood high on her tiptoes and gave Anna a kiss, then waited a few moments to see if Sleeping Beauty's spell was broken. She turned around and looked at me sadly when nothing happened.

"It was worth a try," I said.

For the next hour I had Hope sit next to her mother and just talk to her. She explained how she was feeling about the accident, how much she missed talking to her—whatever came to mind. Hope shed a few tears, but there were some happy moments, too. Like when she talked a lot about all of the things she got to do with her cousins.

We hung around the hospital for the rest of the day, just taking it easy. It was good for Hope to feel close to her mother.

After dinner Dr. Rasmussen made a late visit to check on Anna at the same time that Reg came to check on me. They both remembered Hope from the night of Anna's accident. She didn't recognize either of them, but she shook their hands.

"You're looking better today," Reg told me while Dr. Rasmussen was examining Anna.

"And for good reason. Last night I was reminded of something Dr. Rasmussen told me right after the accident."

The doctor turned around. "Me? Refresh my memory," he said.

"You said I'm not without hope. Last night, for a little while, Hope was gone. Literally, disappeared—*lost*. But now that she's found, I'm seeing things a little more clearly."

My briefcase was lying flat on top of Anna's dresser. "Reg, before either of you go, there's something I need to give you." My hands started trembling, but I fetched the briefcase, opened it up, pulled out the envelope, and handed him Anna's living will.

He read the document, with Dr. Rasmussen looking over his shoulder. When he was through, he let out a small sigh and handed it to the doctor. "It can't be easy for you to give this to me."

"No. It's the hardest thing I've ever done."

Dr. Rasmussen said, "The fine print says one month."

"I'm late. Are there legal penalties for withholding this?"

"Late?" replied Reg. "The intent isn't that

we measure this sort of thing to the very second; it's that we do our best to respect her wishes. Besides, there are thirty days this month, so in that sense you're right on time."

"You hear that, Anna? For once I'm right on time."

"Ethan, I assume the fact that you're giving this to me means that you're prepared to carry it through."

Hope had rejoined the group. I pulled her close, painfully swallowing the lump in my throat. "Yes. It's time to let her go."

He nodded. "Well, I think it's good that your daughter has a chance to spend some time with her. I suggest we wait four or five more days. It'll take that long for legal to get all of the paperwork in place. And that will give you time to notify other family members and friends. How does that sound?"

Hope and I looked at each other, and then we both nodded.

"Dr. Rasmussen," Reg continued, "does it sound like a plan the medical team will agree to?"

"Given Anna's current status, I don't see

why not. Ethan, you take the time you need to have folks say good-bye, and after that we'll turn off the dialysis. It should be very gentle. Okay?"

"Okay," I mumbled. "Five more days."

HOPE was adamant that we spend the night at the hospital. That meant Hope got the room's second bed and I was relegated to the recliner. I couldn't sleep. I got up and paced around the room. In the shadows I spotted the dark form of Grandpa's guitar case.

I'd been avoiding the thing. But I grabbed the case by the handle and walked it back to the recliner. I turned on the reading light on the wall above my head and pulled the case onto my lap. The last time I'd opened it was several months before the accident, late one night before a business trip that would have me away from home for weeks. Anna had begged me to play for her before I left, so I favored her with one quick song before we both went to sleep.

For the past month I'd known exactly what was waiting in there, sealed in a pink envelope. For the first time in our marriage,

I wasn't sure I wanted to read what she'd written.

I lifted the lid. My reluctant eyes scrolled up the neck of the guitar to where I knew the note would be waiting, woven carefully between the strings. I froze. There was no note.

I didn't know whether to be relieved that I didn't have to face her final message or disappointed that for once she'd dropped the ball. I slid the case onto the floor while lifting Karl out. But as I tilted the guitar up, there was a muffled thump from within. When I flipped it over and twisted it just right, with the strings facing the floor, *two* pink envelopes dropped onto my lap.

"What did you do, Anna?" I whispered aloud. "One note—that was the deal." Eventually, I put down the guitar and held the envelopes up to the light. Each one said "True Love Note" on the front in Anna's artsy hand, centered between musical eighth notes.

I broke the seal on the lighter of the two envelopes. The paper inside was dated four and a half months earlier. It was very short, and bittersweet.

Ethan,

Sometimes I feel like writing these notes is the only chance I get to tell you that I love you. That's so sad! I miss you. I wish you didn't have to go on your trip tomorrow. Hope misses you, too. We both need you. Thanks for playing for me tonight, but I need to hear you play more often—because if you're home to play, it means you're home!

Love, Anna

Glancing once more at the bed, I whispered, "I'm home."

I tore into the second envelope. I couldn't shake the feeling that something wasn't right. Why would there be two notes?

I gently slid the papers from the envelope. My heart nearly leapt out of my chest when I read the date in the upper corner of the top page. It was the worst day of my life, and what could have been the last day of Anna's, exactly thirty days ago. *The day of the accident.*

Good evening, Mr. Bright.

I can only assume it is evening that you are reading this—probably very late at night, since that's the only time I see you lately. Today was a bad day. I'm sure we both agree on that. I don't think I've ever been more upset with you or more disappointed. Today I was so mad that I honestly was ready to walk, to take Hope and go. I thought maybe that would teach you a lesson.

But guess what? I couldn't do it. And do you know why? BECAUSE I LOVE YOU! Which is why I needed to write this note now and get these feelings off my chest. We'll talk about this, but for now this is an outlet for me so the rest of my day isn't ruined by pent-up emotions.

For now, though, it's settled: I love you. And no matter how little I see you or how often I have to pick up the pieces for your absence, I'm going to keep on loving you. That's what I agreed to do when we got married. For better or worse, right? But that doesn't mean you're off the hook. Ethan, what will it take to convince you that this family needs YOU, not your inflated salary? I know it's me and Hope that you're working so hard for, but we were doing just fine back when you were writing jingles. We did things together as a family. Can't we get that back? Think about it.

I want you to know that I'm sorry for the way we spoke to each other today. I'm sorry for the feelings I had in my heart, and I promise those feelings are gone now. And just in case you're feeling a little guilty about today, too, I want you to know that I forgive you.

Rest easy, my love. My heart is yours, forever and always.

Annaliese

I read and reread her final note until my eyes were blurry. Three words remained fixed on my brain for the rest of the night.

I forgive you.

How does one man tell another man—*another father*—that you're ending the life of his daughter?

"Octavius? This is Ethan."

"Good morning. How is Anna doing?"

"She's . . . about the same."

"Oh. And Hope? How is she faring? Last time I talked to Stu, he said she's really itching to visit the hospital."

"I brought her here yesterday. She sort of forced my hand."

"I know you said from the get-go that there wouldn't be much value in me visiting until there was a change in her status, but I think it's time I came down to see her, too. What do you say?"

I knew that was the perfect lead-in for the message I had to deliver, but I couldn't get the words out yet. "I think it's time."

There was nothing but static on the line for several seconds. "You sound like something's on your mind, Ethan. Care to share?"

That was it. "Yes . . . you should come. Actually, I'd like as many members of the family to come as you think should."

He hesitated again. "This doesn't sound good."

"No, it's not. Years ago Anna and I created living wills which stipulate that in such a situation as Anna's right now, we not prolong her life. The time frame she felt appropriate was one month. Which is . . ."

"Now," he added soberly.

"Yes. Based on the recommendation of the doctor, we've decided that the odds of recovery are slim, and given the language of the will, we've agreed to move forward with Anna's wishes."

"I see. When?"

"They'll turn off dialysis in five days. She'll maybe make it a few days beyond that."

He quietly said, "I'll be there to say good-bye."

The next call was to Grandpa Bright. The conversation went about like I expected. He let me do most of the talking.

Once I explained about the living will and invited him and the family to come down to say good-bye, I told him everything that had transpired since he went back to Oregon—how I'd slipped into what I described as a "three-week despair" and how Hope's disappearance had pulled me back from that very dark place.

"How is that young lady doing?"

"Hope? She's handling the whole thing much better than me. Sometimes I feel like she's the adult and I'm the child."

"I meant . . . the *other* young lady. Abbey?"

"Ashley?"

"That's the one."

I wasn't surprised that he wanted to swing the conversation in that direction. In the middle of the night, after reading Anna's final note, my mind pieced together what it was that Grandpa wanted me to learn from his concentration camp experience.

The sweetest things in life are usually right there for us to grab. That was the key. When he'd told the story in Anna's hospital room, he'd described one phrase as being the sweetest words he'd ever heard. Anna had written that exact phrase in her final note—three simple words that weren't simple at all. *I forgive you.*

The thought of forgiving Ashley Moore seemed to be absurd, and yet I knew that's what Grandpa thought I should do. "I don't know," I admitted. "The last time I saw her, she was standing on her front porch listening to me rip her to shreds."

"Everyone makes mistakes. Did you finally figure out why I wanted you to read my journal about Mauthausen?"

"Yes. I don't know if I can do it. I don't know that I want to."

"It isn't easy, that's for sure. But having

been on both sides of seemingly unforgivable deeds, I can assure you that the only way for everyone to heal is to forgive."

I'm sure he was hoping he'd shown me the light. He hadn't. I still felt the same animosity toward Ashley. I slipped out of the conversation as quickly as I could. "I'll give that some thought, but I've got some more people to call. Will you please talk to the family and tell them what's going on?"

"Of course. I'll be down there with whoever is able to join me."

"Good morning, Dad," said a bright-eyed Hope as soon as I clicked off. I hoped she hadn't heard too much of what I said.

"Good morning. All rested?"

"Yes. Was that Great-Grandpa?" She slid off the bed. "Who is Ashley?" she asked casually as she walked to Anna's side.

"Oh . . . just someone who did a very bad thing."

She stood beside my recliner. "Did she say sorry? Mommy says when someone says sorry, we should forgive them."

"I wish it were that simple. I really do."

"It is," she replied without pulling away. "Mom says."

Chapter 12

ON THE third day before *the* day, Hope and I left the hospital around noon. We took care of a few things, like shopping for groceries, sorting the mail, and paying bills. But Hope insisted that we go back to Anna's room at night because "Mommy only has a few nights left and she shouldn't have to sleep alone."

Who could argue with that?

Later that evening, while I was tucking Hope into her hospital bed, she caught me off guard. "Do you say prayers at night?"

The honest truth was that I gave up praying on the day we lost Hope's twin sister, Faith. "Not exactly," I ventured. "Do you?"

"Sometimes."

"Are you asking because you'd like me to pray with you?"

"No. I was just thinking maybe if *you* prayed for Mommy, it would help. I've been praying for her every night since her accident, but I guess it's not working."

"Yes, Hope. Tonight I'll say a prayer for Mom."

"Thank you, Dad." She rolled over and closed her eyes.

When I was sure Hope was asleep, I went to Anna's bed. "Hey there. I suppose you know what's going on, right? Dr. Rasmussen has set a date to unhook your . . . I can't even say it without getting choked up. Did you hear Hope tonight? She wants me to pray. Do you mind if I kneel down beside you?"

I grabbed a pillow for my knees and tossed it on the ground. I knelt down and tried my best to say something intelligent.

"Um . . . God? Let's be honest, if you're as mighty and all-knowing as some people think, then you already know that I'm only doing this because I told my daughter I would. I really don't have any grand expectations. So let me say what's on my mind and then I'll leave you alone.

"Now then, about Anna. You and I both know that she got a raw deal. The fact that it should have been me at the guitar store instead of her will haunt me until I die." I paused. "Which reminds me," I continued, "the way I see it, you got this whole thing wrong. If you think it's so important that Hope only have one parent, you should have left Anna, not me. I'm the guy who screwed things up. Listen, when I married Anna, I found everything I wanted out of life. Have you seen her smile? It's like a piece of heaven. And then you added Hope to our family, and I found another piece of heaven. I don't need anything else. I know Anna's chances right now are not good. But you're God, right? So let's make a deal. . . . Tak*e me*."

As soon as I said those words, I started bawling. I was overwhelmed by the possibility that maybe, if God was really merciful and just, there was a solution to all of this mess that didn't involve Anna dying.

I opened my eyes again. Keeping my focus on Anna's eyes, I sat perfectly still, hoping—*praying*—that they would miraculously open. From the corner of my vision, I also watched her fingers. Just a twitch would do—any indication that God was willing to strike a bargain. After five minutes of nothing, I bowed my head again.

"Fine," I muttered. "I'll stay, if that's want you want. I've got Hope, and she needs *somebody.* So thanks and good night. I mean, Amen."

I COULDN'T sleep. Three little words were giving me fits.

I forgive you.

Anna wrote that to me in her letter, but that was before she knew my actions would wind up killing her. Would she forgive me now? And even if she would, could I ever really forgive myself?

And then there was the matter of Ashley Moore. That had my stomach in knots, too. Was Grandpa right? Did I really need to forgive her, and was that for her benefit or mine? Or both?

Would Anna want me to forgive?

By the time the morning light drew Hope out of sleep, I was more confused than when I'd laid down eight hours earlier.

"Dad?" Hope asked. "Are you okay?"

"I've been better," I admitted, "but I'll get over it. What do you say we run downstairs for some breakfast, then go for a walk? It looks like a nice day outside."

When we were ready, we said good-bye to Anna, then caught the elevator down. While we were walking, my cell phone rang. It was a number I didn't recognize, but the area code was very familiar: 503. *Oregon.*

"Hello?" I asked.

"I hope I'm not calling too early." It was a voice I recognized immediately but one I hadn't heard in several years. "Dad?"

"Hi, Ethan. Is this a bad time? I'll call back. . . ."

"No, it's fine."

"There's a bench," Hope whispered. "Let's sit down."

"So . . . what's up?"

There was a pause; then he said, "Tomorrow's the big day, right?"

I leaned back. "Are you coming?"

"I'd just be in the way. But I'm sure Dad will fill me in. He's been keeping me posted. I wish you'd called when this happened."

"I'm sorry I didn't call you, but when challenges arise, it's typical to turn first to the people you can rely on." My dad has a habit of saying things that don't sit quite right with me, and I have a habit of responding with snarky remarks.

Oddly, my father didn't seem affected by my comment.

"You know," he said, "what you're going through is like déjà vu for me, and I don't want you to make the same mistakes I made when your mother died."

Ah, that. "Dad, I know how hard it was for you, and I don't blame you for how depressed you got."

"My heart broke in a million pieces, like I'm sure yours is broken right now. But a person can get over being sad. It wasn't sadness that sank me, Ethan. It was the anger. Anger at God, at the doctors, at anyone I could think to blame. The heart doesn't heal from that. It just festers, like an infection."

My mind flashed to an image of Ashley Moore weeping in response to my vitriol.

"Do you remember the day you got married?"

The apparent shift in subject caught me off guard. "Of course."

"I hadn't spoken to you in almost two years when I decided to drive to Idaho to see your wedding. When I finally got my minute alone to speak with you, do you remember what I said?"

An image of the white vomit bag flashed

across my mind. "Yes," I said. "You made me promise to learn to forgive Anna."

"Close, but no. I didn't limit what I said to Anna. You promised me you'd learn to be forgiving . . . even when it's hard."

I didn't say anything.

"Ethan," he continued, speaking gently. "If you're harboring anger, drop it. Don't waste a single day being angry. It won't help you. And it won't help Hope."

I looked at my daughter. She was staring back at me, smiling. There was a spark of something in her eyes. The only way to describe what I saw was *love*.

And suddenly I understood. There were more important things than how I felt or thought about the woman who'd crashed into Anna. There was happiness. There was family. There was Hope.

I took a deep breath. Maybe one day the feelings in my heart would magically subside. Or maybe they would fester until they erupted. But I decided it wasn't worth waiting around to find out. I couldn't risk carrying around feelings that might ambush my happiness with Hope. And if there was a chance that it really was as simple as forgiving another, I was willing to give it a try.

"Thanks, Dad. I'm glad you called."

"Really? I mean, you're welcome. It was good talking to you."

"You, too." I hung up.

"What's wrong?" Hope asked. "You look . . . nervous."

"I am. I need to visit the woman who hit Mom."

"Can I come?"

I thought about it, then nodded. "Having you there might help me say what needs to be said."

AN HOUR later we pulled up to the Moores' house. A full month had passed since my last visit. Hope held my hand as we walked up the porch steps. I took a long breath, then rang the doorbell. Nobody answered.

I rang again. Still no answer.

Hope rang a third time. The door swung inward. Ashley had been crying. She kept one hand on the door frame and the other hidden behind her back.

Hope gasped. "Miss Moore? What are you doing here?"

Ashley didn't smile. She hardly looked at Hope when she answered. "Surviving."

"So you're the one who . . ."

"Crashed into your mom? Yes, that would be me."

Hope looked appalled. This was not the bright-eyed, bushy-tailed young college student who'd spent a semester in her classroom. This was a woman who was suffering, just like I'd wanted her to.

"So . . . is she gone yet?" Ashley asked.

I stood there, taking it all in—the blood-shot eyes, the tangled hair, the wrinkled flannel pajamas, and the way she turned her body to keep me from seeing whatever she was holding. That was actually a little un-nerving. Maybe she armed herself, I thought. I moved slightly in front of Hope, just in case. "You mean Anna?"

She said, "I'm probably not supposed to know what's going on, but I have a friend at the hospital who's been giving me updates."

"No, she's not 'gone.' That process will start tomorrow."

"Is that why you came? To tell me I'll of-ficially be a murderer? Say whatever you want. I don't care anymore."

Hope squeezed my hand, nudging me on.

"It's not like that. Actually, I came here to apologize."

"You *what?*"

"He means he's sorry," Hope blurted out.

"Thank you, Hope, but I've got this. Ashley, the way I reacted, it was wrong. There's no excuse for it, and I'm sorry."

Ashley's lip was quivering, but she managed a "Thank you."

"There's more. I can hardly believe I'm saying this, but I don't want to be angry at you anymore. I certainly don't condone what you were doing while you were driving that night, but I know . . . I know you didn't intentionally cause the accident. We all make mistakes from time to time. Sometimes big ones."

"What he's trying to say is—"

"Hope. Really, I got this." I cleared my throat. "What I'm trying to say is that this whole ordeal has been very hard on me, but only recently did I begin thinking that it is probably equally hard on you. I've never liked the phrase 'Forgive and forget,' because I don't think we ever forget. But I like to believe that with forgiveness maybe we can remember with peace. So I want you to know that I forgive you." As soon as the words left my mouth, I felt like a giant weight had been lifted. I pulled Hope closer to me. "*We* forgive you."

Ashley crumpled, falling to her knees on the floor in a heap. As she fell, her previously hidden hand came forward to catch herself. When her hand hit the hardwood, the thing she'd been holding came free. The entryway was covered in little yellow pills.

Hope gasped, and so did I. Then Ashley began sobbing—giant gut-wrenching sobs that hurt just hearing them. "I'm . . . so . . . sorry!" she wailed. "So . . . sorry!"

It took several minutes to get her calmed down and moved to a couch in the living room. While I picked up the pills, Hope kept an eye on Ashley. When I dropped the first few pills back in their container, I discovered something else in there—a tightly rolled piece of paper, like a miniature scroll, with a handwritten message that will remain forever seared on my brain.

After reading it once, I immediately asked Ashley for her parents' phone numbers at work. The first one I reached was Mrs. Moore.

I quickly recited what had happened, and she told me she'd be home as fast as she could.

Then I read the note over and over until my eyes hurt.

Dear Mom and Dad,

Please give this note to Mr. Bright. I'm sure you'll want him to know . . .

Mr. Bright,

You were right. I was stupid for texting in the car. My boyfriend is a marine in Afghanistan, and he'd just sent me a note telling me he was safe. I hadn't heard from him in more than a week. I was so excited that I couldn't wait to respond. But it was stupid and irresponsible.

This past month has been unbearable. I keep having nightmares about the accident, about Anna, and especially about the things you said to me.

Every day I feel like I want to die. It should have been me, not your wife. It was my fault. What I did to your family is unforgiveable! I can no longer live with the guilt.

It's only fair. If Anna must die, then I should, too.

Ashley Moore

P.S. Mom and Dad, I love you—and I'm sorry.

"I DID it. I visited Ashley today." Even if Anna couldn't hear me, I couldn't wait to tell her about everything. "I'm glad I didn't wait any longer. She was going to end her life. She had the pills in hand, ready to swallow, when I rang the bell. Can you believe that? Had I showed up a minute later . . .

"Mrs. Moore wasn't too happy to see me again," I continued, "but she was grateful that I showed up when I did. The Moores admitted Ashley to the psych ward upstairs. The doctors want to evaluate her for a few days; I'm sure they'll get her the help she needs. Ashley asked to talk to me before they admitted her. She wanted to make sure she hadn't misunderstood me at the house when I told her I forgave her. Then you know what she did? She hugged me like her life depended on it. Then again, I guess it did."

I sat down and leaned back in the recliner.

It had been a very tiring day. Hope was so exhausted that she fell asleep on the other bed almost as soon as her head hit the pillow.

No family members had come by the hospital yet, but they'd called to let me know they were in town. The Brights that were able to come—Grandpa, Aunt Jo, Aunt Beth, and my cousin Seth—checked into a hotel. I told them they could stay at my house, but they didn't want to impose. Anna's dad and brother Lance were staying with Stuart. The plan was for everyone to meet at the hospital in the morning to say good-bye, after which the doctors would cease dialysis.

I accepted the harsh reality, but I hated it. I wanted so badly to show Anna that I could be the man she thought I was. And there were still a million things I wanted to say to her and do for her, new promises I wanted to keep, and old promises yet to fulfill.

Old promises, I thought. *Like a special song, just for her.*

I sat up. Grandpa's guitar was staring at me again from the corner. How many years had passed since I was supposed to have written Anna a song? It was a promise I'd made on the first day of our marriage, and now, as the last day of our marriage loomed, there was still no song.

I sat up farther, my gaze drifting from the guitar to Anna's face. "What do you say, sweetheart? Is it too late to make good on my promise?"

It wasn't long before my fingers were strumming gently.

While I played, I imagined Anna could hear every note and that she was humming along like she used to do. For thirty minutes I went through all of the songs that had ever spoken to her heart—the ones she loved dancing to, the ones she sang in the shower, and the ones she said reminded her of me. I ended with *our* song—Pachelbel's "Canon in D."

I thought of how happy she'd be to hear that song again. That's when I decided what *her song* should sound like.

I started over from the beginning of the canon.

Sometimes writing songs is work. But once in a while, when you feel something with your whole heart, the song just sort of *happens*, like it was there all along just waiting to be discovered.

Maybe there's a reason I never made it as

a professional songwriter, and maybe that reason is because I wasn't very good at it—or at least not as good as I needed to be. Nobody ever bought one of my songs. Nobody ever heard one of my rock hits on the radio or downloaded one of my country songs on iTunes. But when you write a song for the love of your life, none of those things matter. There is no good or bad; there is only the guitar in your hands, the notes in your head, the words that you sing, and the love you feel.

I started the canon slowly at first, then a little faster. But I wasn't really playing Pachelbel's music anymore. This was Anna's song. It was only for her—her lyrics, her melody, her story, all tied together with my pain. What had been a classical piece only moments before was now a moody country ballad, built on the same chord pattern. My mind pieced together words to describe everything I felt. Then the lyrics and tears started flowing in time with the tune's Nashville rhythm.

The first memory that came to mind was the very *first* worst day of my life: listening to the doctors explain that our oldest daughter had "expired." Then the image in my head jumped to a much more recent worst day. There I was in my mind's eye, crying uncontrollably beside Anna's bed a month earlier.

I cleared my throat and sang the first verse.

> *Have you ever sat and cried yourself to sleep?*
> *Have you ever dreamed of things you'd never want to see?*
> *And have you ever questioned what you don't understand?*
> *Well I have. . . .*

Next my thoughts turned to what was about to happen, starting tomorrow morning. Where would Anna *be* after she was officially "gone"? With God in heaven, I hoped. I glanced up at Hope, who was still sleeping. She was the greatest gift Anna and I ever received. Seeing her reminded me of all the good things in my life. I reflected on how she'd twisted my arm to get me to pray for Anna, thinking that it would magically reverse the irreversible. More lyrics began pouring out.

The music shifted key for a brief refrain. I

pictured myself kneeling next to Anna's bed with a pillow beneath my knees.

Then the words of that prayer came spilling out of my mouth in the shape of a chorus, but the only thing on my mind was Anna's beautiful face. Even with the scars, it was perfection to me.

The melody morphed once more back to the classical version of the work that had been our wedding march. As my fingers plucked out Pachelbel's famous notes, I sifted through more memories.

I remembered the early years of our marriage. The struggles and how we got through them together. I remembered miscarriages. I remembered spending too much time away from my family.

The country ballad consumed the original melody once more. The second verse began as my mind rewound back to when I'd first met Anna in Austria and how she'd asked how far I would go to be with her.

In the back of my mind, I remembered what my grandfather had told me shortly after his own wife died. "The right words and the right music at the right time can heal the soul."

Like magic, I could already feel it healing mine.

As the final note sounded, I wiped away the residue of water from my eyes, and I thanked God with all my heart that I did. With blurred vision I might not have seen the miracle. . . .

It was small and weak—almost imperceptible, but I swear it was there. A movement. A miracle. *A smile.*

Postlude

THE walnut casket was up on a stand, not ten feet away. I wished I didn't have to sit so close. From my seat in the front row, I could make out my own reflection in the shiny lacquer finish, which only reinforced the fact that a very big part of my life was being laid to rest.

A pastor was at the pulpit giving pretty standard remarks. "Losing a loved one is never easy. . . ." Blah, blah, blah.

Hope was sitting beside me. This was her first funeral, and she seemed to be taking it all in.

"You doing okay?" I whispered.

She nodded. "The flowers are nice. Mommy would love them."

"I think you're right. I bet we can take some with us at the end."

After the service, we followed the hearse to the cemetery, listened to another short sermon, and then watched as the casket was lowered into the ground. Afterward family members came up and gave Hope and me hugs and words of encouragement. Some of them wanted to keep talking, asking how we were getting along and wondering if there was anything they could do for us. I appreciated the offers, but I really just wanted to go home.

At length we were able to head to the car.

"I need to make a quick call before we go," I told Hope as I turned the key in the ignition. "So I need you to keep quiet for a few minutes. Then you and I can talk. Okay?"

I turned on the Bluetooth device in my ear and gave the voice command to dial my old boss. "Hello, Jessica? It's Ethan Bright."

"Ethan? How is everything?" The sweet tone in her voice actually surprised me; I didn't know she had it in her.

"Fine, thanks. Listen, is it too late to apologize for how I spoke to you last time?"

"No need. It's me who should be apologizing. I had no idea what you were going through. By the way, I never accepted your resignation. I've been waiting to see if there's a way of getting you back."

"That's sort of why I'm calling."

"Oh, thank heavens! When can you start?"

"Wait. I wanted to talk to you about *a* job, just not that one."

"But you're my number one guy, remember?"

"I do. I also remember that I wasn't very happy doing it. What I was actually wondering is whether there's a chance I can have my *old* job back. The one I started at."

"Didn't you start as a jingle writer?"

"Yes."

"But that job makes half of what you're earning under me."

I shot a quick glance at Hope. "I know, but there are benefits of that job that you just can't put a price on."

With a dramatic sigh she said, "Well, then consider yourself a jingle writer. You can start whenever you like."

"Thanks."

I tapped a button on my earpiece, and the phone turned off. Hope and I chatted for a while, mostly about the funeral and how she was feeling. She was sad, of course, but she seemed okay.

I suggested that Hope take a nap. We had a long drive ahead of us. She fell asleep against the door, leaving me with my thoughts.

Most of my thoughts were about Anna. I also pondered something Grandpa had said recently. After returning his wooden box so he could share its contents with the rest of the family, I told him I was gearing up to document the story of me and Anna in a journal, just as he'd done. There were details I didn't want to forget, and things I wanted Hope to know and remember as she got older. When I asked if he had any pointers, the advice he offered was perfect. "Writing your story is just like writing a song, only with more words and less rhythm. Start with the first verse, and take it one note at a time."

I can do that, I thought. Heaven knows, I've got lots of notes. . . .

WE PULLED INTO our driveway early the following morning, after driving most of the night. Hope grabbed the flowers we'd been given from the funeral and rushed inside.

I left our bags in the trunk and followed her in. She was already in the master bedroom by the time I caught up with her.

"These are for you!" I heard Hope say.

"Oh, they're so pretty. Thank you!"

Anna was just waking up. The dialysis machine next to the bed was still finishing up its nightly cycle. My heart leapt at seeing her, as it had done a million times since she came out of the coma three months earlier. She still needed lots of physical therapy, and she didn't care much for the scars on her face, and we were finding small holes here and there in her memory, but none of those things mattered—we were together, and we were happy.

"Are these from Grandpa's funeral?" she asked.

"Yes," Hope replied. "I told Dad you would like them, and he said we could bring a few home. Smell them!"

She took a whiff, then looked at me. "How are you holding up?"

"I'm fine," I said. "It was sad seeing him go, but it was his time."

"I wish I could have been there. I missed you guys. The nurse came by every day, and Stu and the kids came by once, but it's much better being with you two."

"We missed you, too, Mom." Hope paused; then her eyes lit up. "Oh, guess what Dad bought me in Oregon?"

"Umm . . . an Oregon coast T-shirt?"

"No, a guitar! He's going to teach me how to play!"

A broad smile swept across Anna's face—the one that reminded me of heaven. "Oh, how wonderful. Now I can have two people play songs for me." She tilted her head and winked at me. "Speaking of which, I missed your serenades the last few nights. How about a little concert in bed?"

"I'll never say no to that." I smiled.

Karl was leaning against the wall on the other side of the room. I opened up the case to find what I knew would be there: a pink envelope woven in the strings, with a couple of handwritten quarter notes on the front. I placed it on my pillow so I could enjoy it later.

Then I kissed Anna gently on the forehead and played her song.

Have you ever sat and cried yourself to
sleep?
Have you ever dreamed of things you'd
never want to see?
And have you ever questioned what you
don't understand?
Well I have. . . .

Did you ever hear that heaven's love is very
far?
Did you ever look for heaven deep within
your heart?
And do you ever thank the Lord for all he's
given you?
Well I do. . . .

And just last night,
Before I went to bed,
I knelt to pray to Him,
And this is what I said . . .
Take my life if you'd like,
Because I found what I came to find.
Or leave me here for a while,
'Cuz I found heaven . . . in her smile.

Did you really search the world to find true
*   love?*
Did you ever ask the girl if that would be
*   enough?*
And do you ever thank the Lord for all he's
*   given you?*
Well I do. . . .

And just last night,
Before I went to bed,
I knelt to pray to Him,
And this is what I said . . .
Take my life if you'd like,
Because I found what I came to find.
Or leave me here for a while,
'Cuz I found heaven . . . in her smile.

THE
ORCHARD

THERESA WEIR

A troubled young woman falls for a man about whom she knows almost nothing. Will their hasty marriage make—or ruin—her life?

The Legend of Lily

LILY'S father sold herbicide and pesticide to farmers. She sometimes came into contact with the world of farming but never the actual soil and crops. Never the tractors or plows. No, only with the mysterious liquid her father sold in giant drums and big plastic jugs.

The child knew her dad sold important stuff that people needed to farm, but beyond that, she really didn't care.

"If I sell enough this summer, I could win us a free trip to Disney World," the father told his daughter.

Lily sat in the passenger seat of the Monte Carlo as they headed for their third stop of the day. She hardly ever got a chance to sit in front, and it made her feel important and grown-up.

The windows were down, and Lily's hair stung her face. Every so often, she would glance at her dad as he smoked and talked. He wore a new plaid shirt with short sleeves, and he smelled nice because of the aftershave he'd put on before they'd left the house.

"What kind of rides do they have at Disney World?" she asked.

"Everything," her dad said. "Everything you can think of. Boats that go through jungles and caves with pirates. But my sales have to be good. You'll help me with that today, won't you?"

Lily nodded and bounced her legs in a sudden burst of enthusiasm. She was seven, and her feet didn't quite touch the floor. "I'll help you, Daddy."

He reached across the seat and squeezed her arm. "Of course you will. You're my girl." They were a team.

Soon Lily's father drove around to the back door of the VFW, and Lily helped him unload. Dusty pickups filled the lot. The VFW buildings they visited all looked the same. The ceilings were low, and the lights were fluorescent. Long, narrow rooms with paneling on the walls. Flags on metal stands. Pictures of men in uniform.

Lily's father moved to the front of the room and began talking to the crowd of mostly men. Lily watched, amazed, because he suddenly seemed like somebody from television, like somebody who was on the news. Somebody she would believe and trust. Not that she didn't trust him. She did, but this was different. He seemed so smart as he told them about *his product.* One of the things he talked about was how safe it was. The safest on the market.

Lily had brought her crayons, and her father had given her a sheet of paper that advertised the herbicide. Even though she'd turned it over, she could still see the design through the paper. She tried to pretend it wasn't there, concentrating on drawing a house and family.

Beyond the world of crayons and paper, she heard her dad talking to the men about broad-spectrum herbicides and incentives. "I've got a ten-minute presentation I hope you'll watch," he finally said. "That will be followed by a demonstration I guarantee will sell you on our product if the film doesn't do it for you."

The lights were shut off, and Lily had to stop coloring.

She understood very little of the film, but a man's voice used words she'd often heard her father use. Words like *carryover* and *drift*. It made her feel special to know these words.

The heat, the dark room, the hum of the projector. Lily fell asleep and stayed asleep until she felt someone shaking her arm. She lifted her head from the table and blinked, trying to focus.

The film was over, and the lights were on. Lily's dad gave her a smile, then turned back to the crowd.

"At our company, we're concerned about the safety of the farmer and the consumer," he told them. "We care about the environment, and our products are safe. In fact, our new herbicide is as safe as drinking water. Safer than some drinking water, when you consider the number of wells contaminated with parasites and bacteria."

That got a laugh from the men.

He popped the top on a gallon herbicide container and poured clear liquid into a clear glass. He brought the glass to his lips, swallowed the contents, then held the empty glass high. "Safe enough to drink." Then he poured again and offered the glass to Lily.

"I'm not thirsty," she said.

People laughed, but it was a nervous laugh.

"Come on." Now she heard the command in his voice.

The contents of the glass looked like water, but it smelled like the trunk of her dad's car. It was an odor she associated with him.

"Drink it." He smiled, but the smile didn't reach his eyes.

Lily took the glass. It wasn't full. It wasn't even half full.

Lily became aware of the silence in the room. She looked around, and it seemed like every person in the building was staring at her.

"Tastes like soda," her dad whispered.

He was lying. Lily knew he was lying.

She lifted the glass to her mouth and drank. Fast.

It burned all the way down. Lily's stomach clenched and she struggled to keep the chemicals from coming up. It was like drinking fire. But they were a team, and she wanted to go to Disney World. She wiped her mouth with the back of her hand and smiled.

"Good?" her father asked.

She bobbed her head. Then, with her belly burning, she gathered up her picture and crayons while the men placed their orders.

The Courtship

Chapter One

Burlington, Iowa, 1963

THEY say that as soon as we're born we begin to die. I hadn't spent much time thinking about death until I was eight and a neighbor lady brought over a bunch of mushrooms. They looked like white toadstools. Some were freshly picked, with dirt clinging to their roots. Others were fried. No adults were around as she crouched and lowered the plate to my level. "Have one, Theresa. I'm sure your mother won't mind."

She smelled like soap and clothes that had just been ironed. She wore pink lipstick, yellow beachcombers, and white sandals. She was so unlike the moody women in my family.

I ate a mushroom.

Later my mother and aunt put their dark

heads together and whispered their concerns about the food.

They could be poisonous.

Oh yes, they look poisonous.

A book on mushrooms materialized, and soon the neighbor's gift was declared lethal. An innocent but serious mistake.

It seemed that the simple act of placing your hand to your mouth after touching one could bring about violent death within hours.

I didn't tell anyone that my life was over. Instead I went to my room, lay down on the bed, and waited to die.

I mentally went through the list of symptoms.

Rapid heartbeat. Yes.

Sweating. Yes.

Dizziness. Yes.

I expected to hear an ambulance come roaring up the hill to collect the neighbor and her family. But if everybody in their house had eaten the poison mushrooms, no one would be able to call for help. Maybe they were all unconscious. Or dead.

That night I didn't sleep, and when I got up the next day, I opened the mushroom book, which had been left on the table, and I revisited the symptoms. Fear made me weak.

"Are you feeling okay?" my mother asked, more with annoyance than maternal concern. If I told her I was dying, she would get mad, because almost everything I did made her angry. Two years had passed since my father had left us. Once he was gone, he was gone. No phone calls. No letters. No visits. He just walked out the door and never looked back. "He didn't want kids," my mother later explained. I was relieved to discover he disliked kids in general and that his disappearance wasn't caused by anything I'd done.

"I'm okay," I said, and hurried from the house. Outside, I spotted the neighbor woman in her straw sun hat and blond loveliness. She gave me a wave, looking very much alive.

Death will occur within hours.

I gave her a wave back, much happier to see her than she was to see me.

What if time wasn't linear? If you were to draw a line on a piece of paper, then fold that paper, the day I ate the mushroom would touch the future. Maybe the future was what I'd really felt.

I would live. But the mushroom incident set up a theme that would continue for the rest of my life, an acute awareness of human fragility and the knowledge that, consciously or subconsciously, we are all at the mercy of our fears, and we are all waiting to die.

Henderson County, Illinois, 1975

A FARMER dressed in denim overalls took a seat at the bar. "Bottle of Blue."

We served two kinds of beer, Blue Ribbon and Budweiser. All in bottles, nothing on tap. I opened the bottle and put down a cardboard coaster with a glass.

The bar was located on the ridge of what locals called the bottoms, where, before dams, the river had been miles wide and the fertile soil left behind was rich, almost too dense to cut with a plow blade. On a winter day, when the sun hit that shiny black gumbo, you could smell the river that used to be there.

Outside, the wind raged across ground that had been deliberately stripped bare of trees. Through the glass double doors, the air was a yellow haze, and I could smell the chemicals from the fields. The man in front of me gave off a hint of something like garlic.

The scent recalled the story farmers told about a girl named Lily whose father made her drink herbicide. Like all tales passed from person to person, no one knew if the girl and the salesman really existed. While working in the bar, I'd heard various versions, and I always asked if the storyteller had ever seen the child or the father.

The answer tended to be variations of the same. "No, but my brother did." "No, but my uncle did." I'd never spoken to an actual eyewitness and had finally come to the conclusion that the story was an urban legend that was rural, perhaps started by a rival herbicide salesman or possibly an environmental group.

The exhausted farmer lit a cigarette. He came here a lot because only a truck stop and a gravel road separated his land and the bar. He could park his tractor and walk straight from the field. He was shy and polite, but I was an outsider. If I lived here fifty more years, I would still be an outsider.

Business was slow for a Saturday, and he hoped more farmers would show up so he had someone else to talk to. He made an attempt at polite conversation. "Windy."

I looked through the doors and lifted my eyebrows in surprise, as if I hadn't noticed. "Wow."

He wouldn't complain. He wouldn't tell me that he'd just spent the last twelve hours on an old tractor with no cab. He poured beer into the short glass and took a swallow. "Nice and cool in here."

His words reminded me that it was spring outside. And hot.

The farmer slid some coins across the top of the bar. His square-tipped fingers were cracked and dry. "Get yourself a beer."

I glanced at the clock. A little past six.

Eight o'clock. That was my target. But I rarely lasted that long. When I unlocked the front door and flipped on the OPEN sign, I always swore I wouldn't drink that day. But somebody usually ended up buying me a beer. And another.

My drinking was justified, because if I got drunk enough, I would perch at the end of the bar and entertain customers with my acoustic guitar and halfway-decent voice, my repertoire consisting of Neil Young, Cat Stevens, and a few songs I'd written myself.

"Thanks." I put the money in the register and served myself a beer, wondering if it was possible to be an alcoholic at twenty-one.

I came from a long line of people who embraced suffering and angst and their own dark nature while trying to drown it with anything that could numb the mind. Forget my mother, who'd been known to rant and wail: "Oh, I wish I were dead!" My uncle was the master. My mother had been way too melodramatic and heavy-handed. My uncle's technique was subtle, and he wore his cloak of despair in silence. I liked that.

There was something reassuring in knowing things couldn't get any worse. There was a comfort in not waiting to fall and not waiting to get knocked down. This might explain how, at the ripe age of twenty, I'd joined my uncle in his cornfield bar along a sad, lonely stretch of highway not far from the Mississippi River.

I was in training.

The bell above the door jingled. This

customer was a regular named Larry. He had his family with him. His bleach-blond pregnant wife and three dirty, barefoot kids.

Larry hefted the kids onto bar stools and ordered a round of Stewart's sandwiches— little prepackaged hamburgers heated in a small oven. They were good the way fake food was good.

The kids were already crying and fighting. I felt sorry for them and disgusted by them at the same time.

"I'm thirsty," one of them whined.

"Can they have some water?" Larry asked.

My uncle and I looked at the sign on the wall, put in place by the health department. The drinking water was unfit for children because of high nitrate levels. And if nitrates were in the water, no telling what other toxins were in there.

Which was why I stuck with beer.

My uncle opened the upright cooler and pulled a gallon of milk from the shelf. He lined up three short beer glasses, filled them, and nudged the glasses toward the kids. "On the house."

The pregnant wife was putting balls on the pool table. "Let's play a game, Larry."

"Not now, babe."

Larry had his elbows on the bar. The kids finished off their milk, gummed up the sandwiches, and jumped to the floor, where they slapped hands in front of the wooden rack that held the pool cues.

The door jangled again.

I looked up, expecting a different version of Larry. But this was someone new. Someone I'd never seen in the bar before.

I could hear the kids yammering away. Peripherally I saw one of them peek over the edge of the pool table and reach for the cue ball with one gooey hand.

The jukebox was playing, and Larry leaned across the bar. "You know who that is, don't you?" His voice was a harsh whisper, and his eyes had that gossip glint. "Adrian Curtis. His grandfather died of cancer a few months ago. Some people say his farm is cursed."

Adrian Curtis took a seat at a table on the opposite side of the bar, in front of the window.

I shrugged. "A lot of people die of cancer."

"Yeah, but the grandfather also lost three kids to a freak accident. And then there's the worker who had the tractor roll over on him. Crushed to death."

Larry's wife leaned close. "And what about the guy who hung himself?"

"He didn't do that on the farm," Larry said. "That was later. After he moved away." He glanced over his shoulder. There was no way the man could hear him—the music was too loud. "You know that missing woman from Oquawka? The one they're still looking for? Police called in a psychic from the cities." Larry laughed quietly. "You believe that? Psychic kept saying she saw a woman's body in a grove of trees. Kept talking about straight rows of trees. Police looked all over the Curtis Orchard but never found nothin'."

"You really think the farm is cursed?" I asked.

"I don't know." Larry looked at his wife, who had returned to the pool table and was lining up a shot. "It's just weird. That's all. A lot of people connected to the place have died. That's all I'm sayin'."

My uncle picked up Larry's empty bottle and placed it in the plastic tub under the counter. "I'll wait on him."

"That's okay." I grabbed the round plastic tray. "I'll do it."

At the table, I braced the tray against my stomach, setting an ashtray and coaster in front of the man named Adrian Curtis. He was the most handsome farmer I'd ever seen in my life, with light curls, square jaw, eyes as blue as a Billie Holiday song. I planned to treat him the same as any other customer, but it would be hard.

He hadn't come from the field. Instead of denim and dust, he wore black pants and a crisp white shirt. "Wedding or funeral?" I asked.

He blinked, as if noticing me for the first time.

People say I remind them of Audrey Hepburn. I've never seen the resemblance other than my short dark hair. I know my features can be a bit startling, with big eyes in a small face, but some guys occasionally find me attractive. I'd never really cared before, but my heart was suddenly beating a little faster, and the air was spiked.

"Wedding."

"You don't sound happy. Weddings are supposed to be happy."

He seemed caught off guard; then a reluctant smile touched his lips. "It brought back some memories, that's all."

His voice was what I thought it would be. Smooth and mellow.

"I hope you at least got some cake," I said. "So, what can I get you?"

He tapped a cigarette from a new pack. "Whatever's on draught."

"We only serve bottle beer." I rattled off our two selections.

He patted his shirt, his hands searching for a pocket that didn't exist. I grabbed a book of matches from my tray and held them out to him. Our fingers brushed. "Thanks." He lit his cigarette, and I noticed his lips were full and sensual.

"What?" He'd caught me staring.

"Nothing." I felt heat rise in my face and wondered if I'd ever reach a point in my life when I no longer blushed. I shook my head. "Nothing. It's just been a strange day."

He smiled. "Oh, yeah. Tell me about it."

A song finished playing, and the bottom dropped out of the room. Behind me, the kids were arguing. Outside, through the window, I saw my uncle standing under the big road sign. He flipped the switch. The lights came on. PILOT HOUSE.

I hadn't been crazy about the name, but it was a fitting nod to the barges that carried grain and coal up and down the Mississippi River that flowed on the other side of the levee. Before it was the Pilot House it had been the Coach and Four Lounge. Before that it had been my maternal grandmother's home until her death. Adrian Curtis now sat in the living room where years earlier on Christmas Eve I'd opened a little china tea set decorated with pink roses.

Right now I prayed there was still a song left on the jukebox, something that would fill the empty spots in the room. I heard a series of mechanical clicks as one record was replaced by another. Music filled the space once more, making everything better.

"Get yourself a beer too. If you drink."

Did I ever. "Thanks." I hurried behind the bar to fill his order.

Larry and his wife were now in a huddle. "Wasn't he supposed to marry somebody and they broke it off at the last minute?" she whispered.

Larry nodded. "I heard she dumped him."

I pulled a beer from the cooler, then hooked the bottle under the metal opener, popped the top, turned a glass upside down on the neck, and carried the cold drink to Adrian.

He didn't look up. "I should be used to it by now," he said.

"Used to what?"

Elbow on the table, he removed the glass and lifted the beer bottle to his mouth, then placed it on the coaster. "People talking about me."

"Nobody . . ." I stopped my obvious lie before I embarrassed myself more. "I didn't think you could hear us."

"I couldn't. It's the body language that always gives it away."

"Sorry."

"Did you get yourself a beer?"

"You still want to buy me one?"

"Sure. Why not? But you have to sit here and drink it with me."

Sometimes people got the wrong idea about me. "I can't." I pulled back on the friendly demeanor. "I'm working."

"I didn't mean to imply anything. It's just been a long time since I talked to someone about anything other than apples, weather, and crops. It seems I only leave the farm for weddings and funerals."

"How do you know I won't talk about crops and rain?"

"Because you aren't from around here. I can tell. And I'd really like to talk to somebody who isn't from around here." He smiled, and I smiled in return.

"Someone with news of the outside?" I pulled out a chair and sat down. "I can tell you that people are zipping around in flying cars. And that three-pill meal? It's now a reality. So if you have vertigo and you like to eat, you haven't missed anything."

"What's your name?"

I told him.

"That's one of my favorites."

I didn't believe him. "My brothers and I were all named after saints."

The bell above the door sounded, and my uncle stepped back inside. I could feel his disapproval even though he was clear across the room. I got to my feet, chair scraping. "I have to go."

"What time do you get off work?"

I was already walking away. His words

stopped me. I knew I wasn't his type. "Never," I said. "I never get off."

He laughed as if my answer was the most entertaining thing he'd heard in years. And maybe it was.

"I can't believe you were so friendly to him," my uncle said two hours later, once all of the customers had left, including Adrian Curtis. "You don't want to get mixed up with a guy like that."

"How am I getting mixed up with him? I served him a couple beers."

"I saw the way he was looking at you. He'll be back."

"He's a farmer." Not that I had anything against farmers, but I couldn't see myself hanging out with one. "He won't be back."

"Wait and see," my uncle said.

A FEW hours later, we closed up for the night. I turned off the lights inside and out while my uncle removed the cash register drawer and left for his trailer behind the bar. I opened the sofa bed in the lounge and was ready to slip out of my jeans when I heard a faint tapping. I peeked around the corner.

Someone stood in front of the glass double

doors. I couldn't make out any features, but I knew it was Adrian Curtis.

After a brief hesitation, I crossed the room and unlocked the door.

"Do you like horses?" he asked.

Was he drunk? He'd only had two beers at our bar, but maybe he'd stopped somewhere else. "I'm still waiting for that birthday pony," I said, "so I'll say yes."

"Want to go for a ride?"

"On a horse? Now?"

It was after two. Not that I adhered to any conventional or unconventional bedtime, but you just didn't ride horses at two a.m.

"The moon is bright. I thought it might be a nice night for it."

This moment was important, and if I rejected him, I might never see him again. I thought about closing the door. Then I thought about going to bed in the lounge just a few feet from the men's restroom. "Sure. I'll come." What did I have to lose?

I found my keys, locked up behind us, and went with him.

"Where are these horses?" I asked once we were in his truck, heading down the highway.

"Horse. One horse. And he's on my farm."

One horse. Would we take turns? I was familiar with the way guys liked to teach women to play pool, leaning over, wrapping their arms around the girl, who would laugh and pretend she didn't know what was going on. Was this like that? Would we ride double?

Was there really a horse at all?

I noticed Adrian was still wearing his dress clothes. Not exactly riding attire. Had he been sitting outside waiting for the bar to close? The idea was unsettling. Going with a stranger—*any* stranger—to the middle of nowhere was a stupid thing to do.

I block out bad memories. I pretend bad things never happened to me. That's how I cope. But sometimes old memories surface when I least expect them. Sometimes a situation or a smell or a melody brings them back. Brings them crashing down.

Now, a ride in the middle of the night with a potentially dangerous stranger reminded me of another night I hadn't thought about in years. "You know, I didn't realize how late it was." I struggled to keep the panic from my voice. "I have to get up early tomorrow."

That was a bad lie coming from someone who worked in a bar. "Don't *you* have to get up early?"

"I don't need much sleep."

Rapid heartbeat. Yes.

Sweating. Yes.

Dizziness. Yes.

"Take me home. I want to go home." I cringed at how pathetic I sounded.

"We're almost there." He turned off the highway. We dipped down a narrow lane, tree branches above us blocking the moon.

He stopped the truck at a metal gate. I'd expected a barn or corral, but the headlight beams illuminated just pasture and timber. Beyond the beams, I filled in the blanks with my imagination.

"Have you ever been around horses?" he asked.

My heart was hammering, and my mouth had gone dry. "Some." Enough to know you didn't ride in the dark.

Adrian shut off the headlights, cut the engine, and got out. I stayed in the truck. Through the windshield, I watched Adrian climb the gate, hook his heels on a crossbar, and whistle.

Moments later, through the open passenger window, I heard the soft thud of hooves beating against the ground. Suddenly a horse burst from the darkness, blowing air out its nostrils.

The horse was real. I got out of the truck.

It was like finding that birthday pony tethered in my front yard against all odds and all expectations.

I didn't trust men. I wanted to trust them because I knew there must be some good men in the world, but the ones I'd known had lied to my face while plotting acts of violence.

The smell of the horse's hair, the soft nicker, and the heat of its body when I leaned over the gate and put out my hand to pat a chest of rounded muscle all brought me reassurance.

The horse was real. Adrian had told me the truth.

I suppose it was a testament to how messed up I was, but in those few minutes, by not trying to trick me, by not having an ulterior motive or evil, hidden agenda, he'd gained a little of my trust.

Adrian coaxed the horse close, swung his

leg over, and mounted. No bridle, no saddle. Dressed in black pants and a white shirt.

"What's his name?" I asked.

Adrian was quiet a moment. "Mr. Red."

I laughed. "A horse is a horse, of course, of course."

Mr. Red shifted and snorted. "Stand on the gate," Adrian told me. "Put your left foot on top of mine and swing your right leg over."

I stood on the gate, and he helped me up behind him.

I'd always shunned dates with flowers and dinner and movies. That kind of thing had never been a part of my life. It was something other people did, so I was surprised to find that such a romantic gesture as a moonlit ride on a horse appealed to me.

The animal moved slowly and surely through the dark. I trusted it. More than I trusted the man in front of me, the man I was now clinging to.

THE next day, Adrian showed up at the trailer behind the bar where my uncle and I were peeling boiled eggs for pickling.

I answered the knock to find Adrian at the bottom of the steps while I stood above him in the open door. He was dressed in faded jeans and a flannel shirt with the sleeves rolled a couple of turns.

"Would you like to go do something?" he asked. "Maybe a hike through the woods?"

I looked over at my uncle. He'd stopped peeling and was staring at me. He mouthed the words *bad idea*.

"I'll be back by four." I slammed the door and hurried down the steps.

A HALF hour later, we were back on Adrian's farm.

We parked the truck inside a gate and hiked through a rolling pasture to finally stop on a hillside cloaked in dense trees and lush spring grass. We explored land that was too wild and steep to tame with a plow. Dark, secret places where moss and mushrooms grew near streams, where beautiful wildflowers bloomed on hillsides that never saw the sun. It seemed like his world, and only his world.

Adrian stopped in front of a flat stone. "It's a pioneer grave."

It looked like a rock to me. We both crouched and touched it.

"When I was little, you could still read the name and date." Adrian ran his hand across the surface. "The grave belongs to a teenage girl."

"I wonder how she died."

"Diphtheria." He straightened. "That's what somebody said anyway. I've heard if you dig up the body, the disease will still be there. You can catch it."

I moved my hand away, and I imagined the surface of the ground like the soft leathery covering that protected a walnut, hiding a secret world just under our feet. I imagined the pioneer girl with plump flesh and healthy skin, and I had to remind myself that if she was under there, she would be a skeleton.

"So the guy who owns the bar is your uncle?" Adrian asked. "What about the rest of your family?"

I got to my feet and moved away from the grave. "My uncle and grandmother are the people I'm closest to. My parents divorced when I was little. My mother remarried and has a new life with her husband. She cut off ties with her older children, and we never hear from her." The words came quickly. "She associates us with him. She can't look at us without being reminded of her first husband."

I didn't like to talk about my mother or father. It was embarrassing. I tried to tell myself that I had nothing to be ashamed of, but when you're abandoned by both parents, it's hard not to feel that you did something wrong.

I suppose my mother's bitterness toward life was understandable. How could a beautiful young woman not crack after being left for a wealthy divorcée old enough to be a grandmother? "My older brother is married and dealing with issues of his own," I said. "My younger brother is part of my mother's new family. I rarely hear from either of them." I could see Adrian found my history and lack of family ties a curiosity. "What about you?" I asked.

He'd fallen into step beside me. "I have a sister and brother, but they don't have anything to do with the farm. It's just me, my father, and my mother."

"Your family has farmed the same ground for a long time, right?"

"I'm the fifth generation."

"It would be nice to have such deep roots." An alien concept for me, someone who'd never stayed in one place very long. Someone who never even thought about the future.

"So you want kids?" he asked.

The thought of me as a mom was absurd. But why not? Creating my own family. "Yeah." And anyway, that kind of thing lurked in the future, and the future didn't exist for me.

"How many?"

"How many?" I laughed. "I don't know. Two? Three?" What did it matter? Not when today was one of those gorgeous spring days that came before the oppressive heat of summer. Brilliant blue sky, and air so dry the shadows were almost black.

For me our hike was random, but it had to be different for Adrian since he knew what lay beyond each twist and turn.

At one point, I caught a glimpse of what looked like a small structure through the trees. I picked up my pace.

Adrian hurried after me and grabbed my

hand, trying to tug me in the opposite direction. "This way."

"I think I saw a building."

"There are a few old settler cabins around. Nothing interesting."

"I want to see." I slipped away from him and ran through the woods.

Yes, a cabin. The windows and doors were covered with plywood. Vines crept across the porch and roof, vanishing into cracks. "You should fix this up."

"The shed was built for my great-grand-mother when she had tuberculosis." The words came out like a confession. "They thought the fresh air would do her good, but they also wanted to keep her away from her kids so they wouldn't catch it. She died when she was really young. In her twenties, I think."

"Oh. I'm sorry."

"It happened before I was born, but I don't like the place." He hung back, as if he couldn't make himself step any closer. "Some people say the farm is cursed."

"Don't tell me you believe in that kind of thing," I said.

He shrugged, lit a cigarette, and leaned against the trunk of a tree, arms and ankles crossed. "A lot of people have died on this farm."

I rubbed my arms even though I wasn't cold. "Farming is a dangerous occupation."

"Some of the deaths had nothing to do with farming. Like the kids my grandparents lost. Carbon monoxide poisoning. A freak accident. And the guy who hung himself . . ." He shook his head.

"So you think there's a curse?"

"Not an actual spell, but some kind of bad mojo. If we're talking about that kind of thing, then yeah, I think the place is cursed." He was smoking like mad now, and I could tell the topic was making him nervous. "I could tell you stories about this place, but I won't."

I didn't know what to make of him. Someone who came across as tough and incredibly masculine, now displaying an irrational side. But who was I to trivialize his emotions? Fear was real, even when the trigger was nothing more than superstitious nonsense.

"So, do you believe in ghosts?"

"I've seen things," he said. "When I'm plowing the fields late at night. Things I can't explain."

"Darkness can play tricks on you."

Adrian gave himself a shake, as if throwing off something invisible. He laughed in an attempt to make me think he'd been kidding about ghosts and curses. "We shouldn't talk about sad things. Let's keep walking. I want to show you the apple trees."

Chapter Two

FIFTEEN minutes later, Adrian and I came upon a grove of apple trees.

"They're straight from every angle," I said, amazed.

"It's called checking. The trees are lined up with string. It's kind of a lost art since most people don't plant trees by hand anymore." He picked a tiny green apple no bigger than a grape and bounced it in his palm. "Do you know you could plant every single seed from every apple on this tree and you wouldn't get the same variety? In fact, no two seeds would grow the same tree."

"Why's that?"

"Apple seeds don't contain genetic DNA."

"Would you get something better?"

"One in a million chance. Most likely all the seedlings would be inferior to the original."

I imagined an orchard where no two trees were alike.

He tossed the tiny apple into the orchard grass. "These trees were all grafted. It's the only way to end up with marketable apples."

I could see the misshapen bump on the trunk where two varieties had been forced into something they weren't meant to be. So strange to think the rootstock was a completely different creature than the rest of the tree. Cutting and binding two living things together until they became one.

"This whole area of the orchard, all of the young trees, are a new variety. One day I was trimming and noticed that a single branch on one of the heirloom trees was different from the rest of the tree. A mutation called a bud sport. I flagged it, and when fall came, I discovered that the apples on that single branch were some of the best I'd ever eaten. The original tree was destroyed by lightning, but luckily I'd grafted scions from the branch, and this is the result. We should have the first real crop in about seven years."

"Do the new trees have a name?" I asked.

"Sweet Melinda."

"Melinda . . . That's lovely." I wondered who he'd known named Melinda. The girl he'd almost married?

Jealousy was a foreign emotion, and I had to look away, focusing on a row of small trees. I thought about what Larry had said. What the psychic had told the police. A body hidden in a grove of trees. "I've heard that apple seeds are poisonous. Is that true?"

"Apple seeds contain a small amount of cyanide." Was that annoyance in his voice?

"I wonder how many seeds it would take to kill a person."

"A lot."

"Hundreds? Thousands?"

"I don't know. A cup, maybe. I've eaten a lot of apple seeds in my life and have never gotten sick."

Adrian approached a tree that had a small

red box hanging from a branch. He tipped the container and looked inside. Then he reached into the pocket of his flannel shirt and pulled out a small pad of paper. "We're monitoring for codling moths." He uncapped a pen and jotted something down. "The traps contain pheromones that attract the moth. We check them every three days and make a record of how many codling moths we find. That determines what and when to spray." He returned the tablet and pen to his pocket.

We sat down in the shade of one of the older, larger apple trees.

He looked me in the eye and said, "I like to draw." It was a bold declaration, or possibly a confession. Farmers didn't draw. "Usually with pencil," he said, "but also with pen and ink."

"I draw too," I told him. "Also in pen and ink." I had tablets full of my drawings, and I dreamed of going to art school.

Adrian was looking at me as if he couldn't believe it. "I've never known anyone else who uses pen and ink," he said with excitement.

"What kinds of things do you draw?" I asked.

"Animals. Plants. People." He pulled out the pen again. And he drew on me in black ink. I watched him sketch a morning glory, then a thistle. Even on skin, his drawings were accurate.

"They're all weeds." I turned my arm, admiring his skill. "Bane of a farmer's existence. Draw something you don't need to eradicate."

His brows met as he gave it some thought; then he began drawing again. He smelled like hay and apple cider. And if beneath that he also smelled like pulpy roots and the garlic odor of the farmers who visited the bar, I chose to ignore it.

"An apple?" That was kind of obvious.

"Not any apple. This apple is a Red Delicious. It's tall and narrow and has bumps on the bottom."

"Is it sour? I like sour apples."

"It's sweet. An eating apple. Almost too sweet."

"So it's something else you don't like?"

The edge of his mouth curled in amusement. "I don't like Red Delicious apples. But they have nice, flawless skin. They can actually look purple if temperatures drop the right number of degrees at just the right time. They're beautiful."

"Well, I'm glad you didn't draw an apple with a hole in it."

"Do you know what makes that hole? The codling moth worm. Once the codling moth takes over an orchard, you're screwed. It takes a lot of pesticide to create a beautiful, perfect apple."

"What does a codling moth look like?"

"Like this."

He drew it on my inner arm. There was something mysterious about the lines of the moth. Something that felt old and timeless. The moth also looked sinister, and now it was on my skin. It made me feel the way reading the mushroom book had made me feel, filling me with an inexplicable dread. As if the image were somehow leaching poison into my skin. *Death will occur within hours.*

"What's wrong? Don't you like my moth?"

"It's something else you work to eradicate."

"You asked me about it."

"I know, but . . ." I looked at it again. Why, it was beautiful, with dark patterns on delicately fringed wings. What had I been thinking? But it had seemed sinister a moment earlier. Sometimes sensations come over me that have nothing to do with reality.

The wind kicked up, stirring the wildflowers. From far away came the noise of a farmer driving a tractor across a field.

"Give me the pen," I said. "I want to write you a note." He made me feel more feminine than I'd ever felt in my life. If I didn't watch out, I'd soon be polishing my nails and wearing perfume.

I pulled his arm to my lap and pushed up his sleeve. I could see the blond hair on his tan arms. I could feel the sinewy muscles and veins beneath the skin. Farming had made him hard and strong.

"What are you going to write?"

"You'll see."

Dear Adrian.

He twisted for a better view.

"Don't look." I shielded his arm so he couldn't see.

I was certain that years later I would recall the texture and taste of the day, the sun on my face, the smell of grass, the distilled bril-

liance of the sky. It was as if the day had
been built just for me.

Be mine, I wrote on his arm. A harmless,
Valentine-candy sentiment. But he had to be
mine. He could belong to no one else.

He touched the faint red mark on my
wrist. "How did this happen?"

I shrugged. "Kids do stupid things," I
said.

"How old were you?"

"Fourteen."

"I'm glad you're still here." He traced a
finger over the red line, then lifted my wrist
to his lips. Then he slipped the pen from my
fingers and proceeded to draw a bracelet on
my arm. A beautiful thing of vines and
leaves. Making it all better.

I never wanted to leave. I didn't want the
day to end.

Later, when we finally headed to the bar,
I came upon a pad tucked behind a toolbox
on the passenger floor of Adrian's truck. I
opened it and discovered several pencil
sketches of a girl who looked familiar. Some
were faces, and some were full bodies.

"Is this me?" I asked, even though I knew
it was.

He glanced away from the road and snatched the sketchbook from my hand. "Don't look at that." He slowed the truck long enough to tuck the drawings behind the seat. His face was red.

The few drawings I'd seen represented hours of work. I suppose infatuation and crushes start in a flash. Two days ago, he didn't know I existed. Now he was spending hours drawing pictures of me, and I was dreading the hours we would be apart. This was hard for me to grasp because I'd never understood how girls got wrapped up in guys. I prided myself in remaining true to who I was. I prided myself in needing no one. I'd watched women fade to become more like their boyfriends, taking on their likes and dislikes. Giving up who they were. I was suddenly one of those girls. Lovesick. Helpless. Weak. Overpowered by something beyond my control.

He was just a man. Nothing special about him. And yet there was. Something very special. Something that spoke only to me.

I couldn't imagine never seeing him again or never experiencing another afternoon like the afternoon we'd just shared.

I MAY HAVE BEEN infatuated with Adrian, but he seemed to be equally infatuated with me. He began stopping in at closing time, and he would casually invite me to join him. In the dark, in the middle of the night, he and I would sit by the river, or sit by the pond, or sit in the pasture in front of a bonfire. Early evenings, when it was still light, we took sketch pads to the orchard. Adrian admired my work, but he was a much better artist than I was. He had a distinctive style, something I hadn't yet found.

Sometimes on our outings I packed a picnic, and sometimes we ended up in a canoe on the pond. It was always spontaneous, and it was romantic in all the ways I would expect something to be romantic, designed just for us. Some might say it wasn't healthy for two people to spend every moment together, but if others had been around, we would have ignored them. We wouldn't have given them a thought.

"How about a game of pool?" my uncle asked.

The bar was empty, and we often shot pool to pass the time.

I racked up the balls and he broke, dropping a solid green seven.

"I'm worried about you," he said.

I knew he was talking about the amount of time I was spending with Adrian. "He's a good guy," I told him.

"You haven't known him long enough to know who he is. He's not like us. He's not like you."

"Is hanging out with him any worse than what I'm doing now?"

I had stripes. I chalked my stick and took aim at the nine ball.

The game was a choreographed dance. Left hand reaches for the blue square, chalking the tip while eyeing the table. Look ahead to predict where the upcoming play will end and the next begin.

"Living in a bar?" I dropped three balls, then missed a bank.

"You never seemed to mind when you needed a place to crash."

He moved methodically, without pause. He had a wonderful brain for this kind of thing. Being an engineer, angles came naturally to him. He was one of the few people I knew who'd gone to college, and that alone made him seem bigger than life to me.

My uncle missed an easy shot. Not only missed, but scratched.

This hadn't always been my uncle's life. At one time he'd lived in Chicago, where he'd worn suits and white collars. Where he'd lived in a penthouse overlooking the Magnificent Mile.

But things happen. He'd given a friend a ride across the country only to discover that the friend had murdered someone the night before. The next thing you know, my uncle was a felon who no longer had a need for suits and white collars. He was here because he had nowhere else to go.

"You can't get mixed up with him," Uncle Jim said. Faded blue eyes looked at me from across green felt. "I don't want to see you hurt." A nice way of saying Adrian would dump me when he got bored. Maybe he was right. I'd seen it happen all my life, so it was something I'd considered, and the thought made my stomach twist until it felt like I was bleeding inside.

My uncle's disapproval made me want Adrian more.

"Eight ball in the side pocket." I took aim. Low, snap, click, recoil. The black eight dropped neatly and solidly.

"You don't know anything about him." And then my uncle, who had never in his life given me a direct order, said, "I think you should stay away from him. You should stop seeing Adrian Curtis."

"I'M GOING to have to move." I passed the bottle of wine to Adrian. We were lying on a quilt a few feet from the edge of a pond, stars overhead, clouds, a half moon. Crickets and frogs and fireflies. Another beautiful night together.

Of course, *move* for me simply meant pack my car. I could have it loaded in fifteen minutes.

"Move?" He took a swallow of wine. "Why?"

"My uncle and I aren't getting along."

"What's wrong?"

Why had I started this? It would ruin our time together. I lit a cigarette. "He doesn't think we should see each other. It's nothing personal. He just . . ." My words trailed off. Saying my uncle didn't want me to get hurt implied that Adrian and I had a relationship.

"You wouldn't move far, would you?"

Did I detect a hint of panic in his voice? "I don't know."

There were no towns between my uncle's bar and Adrian's farm. I'd have to go the other direction, across the river into Iowa. Maybe I could find a cheap apartment there and a job tending bar, a job that actually paid money. Right now I was making room and board. A sofa bed and all the Stewart's sandwiches and pickled eggs I could eat. How could a gal leave that behind?

"All I know is that I can't deal with him any longer." I'd endured one hostile adult for too many years. I didn't need another.

"Come live with me."

Had I heard right? I had a buzz going, and maybe the roar in my head had distorted his words.

"My house isn't much." He took a drag from his cigarette. The tip glowed, and I could briefly see his face, his eyes squinted against the smoke. "It's tiny. Originally built for apple pickers."

Everything shifted. What I had known as my life changed in a matter of seconds. Like finding out you'd put a puzzle together all wrong. I dumped the pieces and began reconstructing, creating a completely new picture. Did he mean what he was saying, or was it something he wouldn't give any thought to come morning?

I didn't want him to think this is what I'd been angling for, because it wasn't. "Move in together . . . Wow. I don't know . . ."

"Not move in together. Get married. We'd have to get married."

Married. We'd just met. "You're drunk." I held my breath.

"Not *that* drunk."

"Married . . ." Moving in together, yes. But marriage . . . a legal commitment. I had serious doubts. "We hardly know each other."

"Some people are together for years, and they never really know each other. We know each other as well as a lot of people do."

True.

"I'm going about this all wrong. It should have been dinner and a ring."

"I don't like rings."

"Well, dinner."

"I'm a nonconformist. I wouldn't have liked that either."

He laughed, but quickly became serious again. "Say yes."

I took one drag followed by another. "When? How?"

"As soon as possible."

This was crazy. I'd been wondering how I would ever live without him once he quit coming around, and now he was asking me to marry him. It would never happen. That's what I told myself.

I was old enough to know that life was full of disappointments and the things you want most are usually unattainable. But for right now, for tonight, I would savor the thought of our spending the rest of our lives together, even if it didn't happen.

A sound penetrated the buzz in my head. "What's that?" I asked.

"I don't hear anything."

"A motor or something."

"Oh, *that*. The orchard sprayer. I didn't even notice. Guess I'm used to it."

"Now?" It had to be two or three o'clock in the morning.

"My father likes to spray the apples at night. Less drift, and the sun doesn't evaporate the pesticide. Gives it more of a chance to work."

The sound of the sprayer faded, then returned. I imagined tractor and sprayer moving between the rows of trees, a cloud of chemicals coating leaves and small, developing apples. The sound of the sprayer blended oddly with the sounds of the frogs and crickets, reminding me of the story of Lily.

"Have you ever drunk farm chemicals?" I asked.

"I saw a salesman drink herbicide." Adrian was uncomfortable, and I could tell he wondered if he should have admitted to such a thing. His voice held unease, the same unease I'd heard that day in the woods, by the old cabin.

"Did the salesman have a little girl with him? A girl named Lily?"

"I've heard that story too."

"Is it true?"

"It's just a legend," Adrian said.

"But you saw a man drink herbicide?"

"It was common practice at one time. I saw several men drink it."

"Did you ever drink herbicide?"

"God, no."

His denial of ever having participated in something so foolish should have reassured me, but it didn't. And now I finally had proof that the story about the girl named Lily was at least half true.

ADRIAN didn't forget. The next day, he was more insistent than ever. Through a haze of bewilderment and disbelief, I went with him to get a marriage license. Maybe it would really happen.

That night as we closed up the bar, I told my uncle about the upcoming nuptials. I thought he'd see that he'd been wrong, that I was more to Adrian than someone he would eventually toss away.

"You barely know him."

Adrian draws flowers on my arms. He wants me to marry him. "Can't you believe he cares about me?"

"That's not what concerns me. Give it a few more months. If you really care for each other, a few months won't make a difference."

But everything had already been set in motion. Now that the idea of marriage had been planted in my brain, I couldn't go back.

It was so close; I could almost see myself wearing an apron, taking a roast out of the oven. And my uncle had unwittingly played a role. He'd driven me away. I felt a certain satisfaction in that. *See what you did?* I wanted to point this out to him, but surely he knew.

"When everybody said you knowingly gave a murderer a ride across the country, I didn't believe them," I said. "I defended you. I told people you were innocent."

"That's different. He's practically a stranger to you. You know nothing about him."

I thought about the day-to-day of what marrying Adrian meant. About moving out. No more sofa bed, sleeping with my head just feet from the men's urinal. No more Stewart's sandwiches.

I looked up at the bar and felt a brief twinge. My uncle would be alone. He would peel pickled eggs by himself.

The sorrow I felt floated away as quickly as it had come. Adrian. Twenty-four hours a day.

"Are you sure you understood him correctly?"

Maybe Uncle Jim and my mother were more alike than I'd thought. "You're mean."

"It's just . . . I'm not saying he can't love you, but . . ."

Why couldn't he just be happy for me?

"You've been on a path of self-destruction your whole life," my uncle said. "Adrian is just another mistake. A big one."

He was wrong. "I'm breaking a pattern. Can't you see that?" Oh, what was the point? He would never understand. It was over. I could kiss this dark life good-bye. A new, perfect life was ahead of me. My uncle was jealous. Who else would work for him? Nobody.

"You don't want me to leave. You don't want to lose your free labor." I was getting mad.

"Go ahead, then. Marry your farmer. And when you come to your senses, don't come back. Don't knock on my door in the middle of the night begging me to give you a job and a place to sleep."

THE next morning, I loaded my battered white Mustang with all of my belongings. Boxes of books, sketch pads, ink and pens, journals, two acoustic guitars, three boxes of albums, and an old Remington typewriter in a black case. The few clothes I owned, mostly purchased from thrift shops, fit in a mint-green suitcase.

Once I had the car packed, I locked the front door, removed the key from my key ring, and slipped it through the mail slot.

I didn't tell my uncle good-bye. I might feel bad about that later, but not now. Now it felt right.

I drove to Adrian's farm, turning off the highway onto a blacktop road. Three miles and the farmhouse roof appeared. Behind the house was a circular drive that opened to a white barn and sheds.

It felt strange to come here without Adrian, like a different place.

I cut the engine and stepped from the car, remaining in the V of the open door, one foot inside. The house had two porches with ornate trim, hanging pink petunias, windows of stained glass.

A curtain dropped, a door slammed, and a middle-aged woman came down the walk toward me. She was gingham, dark curly hair, rosy cheeks, Keds. A magazine-ad mom, alien yet familiar. I knew it was Adrian's mother. I even knew that her name was Ruth. I'd bought cider from her in the salesroom, but I doubted she'd remember me—just one of hundreds of customers stopping on a busy fall day.

"Are you here for apples?" Her voice was a friendly singsong. "Apple season won't start for another three months."

"I'm looking for Adrian."

She frowned and dropped the friendly face. "He's working."

I told her my name, hoping to clarify things.

She glanced at my car, packed and loaded with boxes and clothes. "Looks like you're moving."

"Is Adrian around?"

"Adrian works all day. He's in the field right now and won't be done until after dark."

Her open hostility took me by surprise. "If you tell me where he is, I'll find him myself."

"I said he's busy. You have to leave. Go on." She waved a hand at me, shooing me away like a stray cat.

I stared at her in disbelief. "Adrian hasn't mentioned me?"

"Oh, he's mentioned you."

What did that mean? "Did he tell you we were getting married?"

"Adrian is too young to get married. I told him that before."

I was beginning to feel a familiar dread. Had Adrian changed his mind? Had he even meant to marry me in the first place?

"He's only twenty-three," she said. "How old are you? You don't look a day over sixteen."

"I'm twenty-one." No need to mention that I hadn't been twenty-one very long. Funny that she thought twenty-three was young. It seemed old to me.

She straightened, making herself taller. "You'd just get bored. Get bored and leave, so you may as well stay away from my son." She crossed her arms, waiting for me to get back in the car.

Instead of leaving the farm, I drove down a back road, past the orchard, where I spotted a red tractor pulling a yellow sprayer through a cornfield. I parked, got out, and waited for the driver to complete his journey across the field. He saw me, drove the tractor to the gate, shut it down, and jumped to the ground.

Adrian. Dressed in jeans, a leather belt, boots, and a dark T-shirt. His arms were covered with a fine layer of dirt. Even his eyelashes were dusted. "I thought I was picking you up at the bar later."

I told him about my uncle and about the encounter with his mother. This was where he'd confess that he'd changed his mind.

"I ignore her as much as possible." He shrugged. "She goes her way and I go mine. Don't worry. She'll eventually come around."

I had doubts about that, but I wasn't sure I even cared. I was marrying Adrian, not her.

I created a space for him in the car. He wedged himself into the passenger seat, a crate of my junk on his lap.

I turned the wheel, made a three-point turn, and headed back the way I'd come, toward the farmhouse. Following Adrian's directions, I drove past a grove of apple trees and a pond to finally turn on a grass and gravel lane that ended at a small, white dwelling, set back from the road but still close to the main house.

"It was originally built by settlers, then updated over the years for pickers," Adrian explained. "Has some of the original hand-hewn logs and floor. Very rustic, I'm warning you."

The cramped, two-bedroom structure smelled stale, like a building that no one had lived in for a long time; obviously Adrian came here only occasionally. It was furnished with a double bed and sofa. A wood-burning stove stood in one corner. For someone who'd been living in a bar, it seemed pretty nice. My own space. Our space.

"It needs a little work," Adrian admitted.

I could already imagine some of the things I would do. Fresh paint. A small table in the kitchen with flowers in the center.

He reached for me, pulling me close. I caught the heavy, pungent scent of chemicals. "Haven't you been spraying?"

"I've been around pesticides and herbicides my whole life and I'm healthy."

He *was* the picture of health. I couldn't deny that.

His skin felt hot from the sun. Sweat

dripped from his hair, fell on my face. It ran into my mouth, tasting like salt and the spray from the field—already a taste and smell I associated with him.

THE next day, my paternal grandmother and I stood side by side in the tiny kitchen of her Burlington, Iowa, home, both of us wrapped in floral-print aprons as we crushed strawberries. Canning jars and lids had been sterilized and were lined up on the red Formica table. With stained wooden spoons, my grandmother and I poured and scooped the strawberries into a deep pan on the stove.

While she stirred, I added lemon juice and pectin to the fruit.

I nervously rubbed one bare foot over the other. "I've met somebody," I told her.

She adjusted the flour-sack towel on her shoulder. "I figured something was going on. Hadn't seen you around much."

"We're going to get married soon."

She didn't even look up, and there was no hesitation in the hand that stirred the strawberries. "Hmm."

Maybe it was a German thing, but my

grandmother never hugged or kissed me. I didn't care. I wasn't a hugger either, and I knew she loved me deeply. Through her, I kept up on my father's life, and sometimes he and I even crossed paths, usually by accident.

"What about your art?" she asked. "What about school?"

She'd been a clerk in the men's department of JCPenney most of her married life, but her first paying job had been guitar accompaniment to silent movies, and I'd grown up listening to her play and sing. She understood the heart of an artist.

"I'll keep drawing," I said. But I had to wonder if I'd ever make it to art school. "Adrian is an artist too. Pen and ink just like me."

"Does he like strawberry jam?" she asked. "This beau of yours?"

"I don't know."

"What kind of food *does* he like?"

He liked beer. He liked wine. "I have no idea."

Both of her eyebrows shot up. Her thoughts needed no words. "Bring him over and I'll fix him some of my potato pancakes."

I suppose it was a bad sign, but it was impossible to imagine Adrian in her house, sitting at her table, eating her pancakes.

When I told her who he was, I could see her struggling to put her own emotions and concerns in the proper place. On one hand, you don't marry someone you hardly know; on the other, Adrian came from good stock. Solid stock. To her mind, he was someone who could take care of me, give me a home, a stable life.

"If you live on a farm, he's going to expect you to cook for him. Three hot meals a day. Is that what you want? Cooking for a man? Cleaning up after a man?"

"I can do it."

She looked skeptical. "I suppose I could teach you how to cook a few things. Find out what he likes, and I'll put some recipes together."

"That would be great," I said, while imagining my grandmother's goulash and creamed corn. Or worse, her sauerkraut and hot dogs. Somehow I didn't think those kinds of meals would appeal to Adrian. But I could make tacos. I could make pizza.

"Does he treat you right?"

I was relieved to see that she'd already accepted the inevitable. Unlike my uncle, she wouldn't get mad and wouldn't reject me.

"That's the main thing," she said. "Because if he doesn't, you don't have any business marrying him. I don't care how pretty he is, or how blue his eyes are, or how good he is in the sack."

"Grandma!"

"It's true. Strawberries are boiling. You can add the sugar now."

The Marriage

Chapter Three

I WOULD have preferred that our marriage take place at the county courthouse, but Adrian couldn't turn his back on tradition and had insisted upon getting married in a church. It was supposed to be just the two of us. Inviting no one solved many problems considering the odd relationship I had with my mother, my absent father, and the fight I'd had with my uncle. But at the last minute, Ruth had insisted she and Adrian's father be present.

Her insistence upon coming was odd, especially after the way she'd treated me. "Couldn't you just tell her no?" I'd asked.

"Nobody tells my mother no," Adrian had said. "She'd just come anyway."

My grandmother would have been hurt if she'd discovered she hadn't been invited, so she was present too. A few bodies in the front pew. I knew they were there, but it almost seemed they belonged to another dimension. My heart was beating too fast, and anything beyond me, Adrian, and the minister was a blur.

Standing at the altar, Adrian looked handsome in the black suit he'd worn the first time I'd seen him. I wore a cream-colored sweater and a long brown skirt with brown boots. I felt a sweaty, heightened euphoria because of what we were about to do. The kind of thing you get when a roller coaster is approaching the peak.

The interior of the church smelled like furniture polish and old wood. In the subdued light, Adrian looked deathly pale, his face covered with perspiration. Something of his terror transmitted to me. But I didn't want to examine the situation and think of the consequences of what we were doing. I knew if I started thinking about all the reasons we shouldn't do this, I would panic.

Outside, the wind picked up and the room darkened. A downpour followed, and the roar of the rain against the roof and windows drowned out the minister. As soon as he pronounced us man and wife, Adrian's mother began to sob.

Then it was over. The wedding and the rain.

Papers were signed, and the minister was paid.

Outside, my grandmother tossed rice, laughing at her own cleverness, oblivious to the hostile undercurrents surrounding us.

Introductions were made, followed by brief, awkward conversation. An uncomfortable glance passed from mother, to father, to son, and I had to wonder at the scene that must have taken place hours earlier on the farm. Shouting? Begging? His mother pointing out the ways a marriage to me was wrong and foolish? And what did he say in return? What did he tell her?

Regardless of the exact words, he'd apparently told her no.

A few stray raindrops fell from a blue sky. Adrian grabbed my arm, and we ran for the truck. A turn of the ignition key and we were on our way, heading for the farm over roads strewn with leaves and small branches. The air smelled like rain-soaked earth.

"I need to check on the wind damage," Adrian said once we were in our little house.

I hadn't even thought of the trees. "Do you want me to come?"

"Stay here. I'll be back in about an hour."

While he was gone, I showered and changed into jeans and a T-shirt. I thought about going to visit Adrian's mother, but that didn't seem like a good idea considering her behavior at the wedding.

The sky was beginning to darken, and Adrian still hadn't returned. I opened a couple of windows to let in fresh air. I smoked and waited.

Two more hours passed, and my annoyance turned to worry. I grabbed my car keys and hurried out the door. I had no idea where to begin looking, but I had to search.

I heard a truck. Then Adrian was pulling up next to the cabin behind my car, shutting off the ignition. He tumbled out the door, catching himself before he hit the ground.

"Where have you been? Are you okay?"

"Fine. I'm fine." His words were thick. *Drunk.*

He shot for our little house, and I followed him inside, closing the door behind me. "You've been *drinking?*"

He dropped down on the couch. "A wedding celebration."

"Without me?"

"Just one drink."

"You've had more than one."

He tugged off his tie, then pushed himself to his feet and launched himself toward the bedroom, unbuttoning his shirt as he went. The shirt hit the floor, and he fell across the mattress. "It was supposed to be just one, but people kept buying."

I pulled his dress shoes from his feet and dropped them to the floor. He didn't budge. I slipped out of my jeans and got into bed beside him. "How were the trees?"

"Trees?"

"The *apple* trees. You went to check on them, remember?"

"A few small limbs broken, but that was it." He rolled to his back and put his arm over his eyes. "I feel sick. I'm not used to drinking. Not serious drinking."

I turned off the lamp. "You picked an odd day to go pro."

No answer.

A short time later, his voice came out of the darkness, sad and forlorn. "Everybody's pissed off at me."

"Who? Your mother? Your father?"

He didn't answer my question. "What are we doing?" he said.

I didn't know if I should laugh or cry. I wanted to hit him, but I restrained myself. "Go to sleep," I told him.

"Maybe. If the room ever stops spinning."

What had I done? What had *we* done?

Same people. Same world. Yet nothing felt the same. *Nothing.*

The air had changed. The mood had changed. The color, shape, and texture of my life had irrevocably changed.

My car was outside. I could leave right now.

No, I'd sleep on it. See if things were different tomorrow.

A few minutes later, Adrian began to snore.

Miami, Florida, and Burlington, Iowa, 1961

MY PARENTS divorced when I was six. One day my world was perfect; the next day my father sat down at the foot of my bed and told me I'd never see him again. We lived in Miami, Florida, and he was in charge of a deep-sea fishing boat, working for a divorcée who'd been married to the prime minister of the Bahamas. She was twenty years older, enjoying a lifestyle my father, in his early thirties, had only dreamed of. She lived in a mansion, had servants, a Rolls-Royce, and a swimming pool. He traded us for her.

The wounded always return home, and shortly after the divorce and two weeks after my mother gave birth to my younger brother, Uncle Jim paid for airline tickets and picked us up at Chicago O'Hare. His downtown apartment was unlike anything my young eyes had ever seen. Spotless, with shiny black surfaces and polished glass that displayed pieces of art. The closet in his bedroom was full of white dress shirts, dark slacks, and leather shoes lined up in a neat row. I inhaled the scent of clean, ironed shirts and aftershave.

He gave my mother his bed, and he slept on the foldout couch while my older brother and I took the floor. My new baby brother was put in a drawer that had been removed from a dresser.

Two days later, Uncle Jim drove us to Burlington, Iowa. My mother insisted we go past the house she and my father had once shared. A house he'd built shortly after their honeymoon.

"We were living there when you were born," my mother said from the passenger seat, baby in her arms, my uncle at the wheel. "Do you remember it?"

I shook my head. Nope.

"I liked that house," my brother said.

Our mother sighed. "We should never have moved to Florida."

For a brief time, our life seemed to stabilize. My mother got a job teaching at a Catholic school even though she'd only briefly attended a community college. Every weekday morning, a sitter took care of the baby while the rest of us packed into the car and headed for school. I wore a blue plaid jumper with white knee socks, my brother a white shirt and navy-blue slacks. Our mother dressed in a stylish skirt suit, and she pulled her hair back into a smooth French twist. The boys and girls in her class adored her.

One day she was called to the office and told she must pack her things and leave immediately.

She'd lied to get the job.

"You have to tell white lies to survive," she said as she drove us back to our apartment. "I was doing it for us. Doing it for you kids."

"Will you go to hell?" I asked. The Catholic school had given me a newfound concern for all of our souls.

"It's not a lie if you tell someone something," our mother said, "then, in your own mind, finish with this line: 'As far as you're concerned.' "

I was on her side, because everybody talked about what a good teacher she was. Many of her students' grades had improved under her guidance, and one boy who couldn't read a word had quickly moved from first-grade to second-grade readers.

"You can't go back there." She stopped at an intersection, then gunned the car, transmitting her anger to the gas pedal. "We'll have to find you a new school."

That day marked the true beginning of our nomadic lifestyle. Within a year, we'd lived in an apartment, a house, a trailer, another apartment. We went from public school, to Catholic school, back to public, while remaining around Burlington. Our mother got a job as a desk clerk at the Holiday Inn. Her coworkers and the salesmen who arrived from exotic locations became her new family.

It almost seemed our apartment had a revolving door, the men came and went so quickly. Some were nice, but many were loud and scary. Babysitters could no longer be afforded, and I was often left in charge of my younger brother, our mother coming home when the sun was rising. Days consisted of drama and rage and tears, of cheap engagement rings thrown as far as they could be thrown, of broken promises and men who lied, claiming to be single when they were really married. *As far as you're concerned.*

Every man proposed, and every one was a wedding that never happened. Most of the men lasted weeks, but a few lasted months.

"We're getting out of here," my mother

announced one day. These were words we were used to hearing with such regularity that most of our belongings never made it out of boxes that had become soft from our repeated moves. "To Albuquerque, New Mexico."

Since the divorce, we'd never ventured beyond the boundaries of Burlington. Now she was talking about moving far away.

"Boyd lives in New Mexico, so we'll move there."

I'd heard this kind of talk before, enough to know it wouldn't happen, and Boyd, the newest boyfriend, would one day disappear to be replaced by someone else. But this time was different. This time my mother rented a U-Haul trailer and had a hitch welded to the bumper of our green Rambler. Once we realized a big move was truly in our future, we became excited. Even my baby brother, who was now three, felt the thrill of a new adventure. But I was sad to leave my grandma Florence, the only person who came to see us off, still wearing an apron, hands clasped tightly in front of her.

She and I had grown close, and our relationship was one more thing my mother found an intolerable reminder of the man who'd left her. I'd never seen Florence show much emotion, but I detected tears in her eyes as the Rambler pulled away from the curb.

A trip by wagon train couldn't have been much harder. Instead of outposts, we traveled from one roadside motel to the other, the journey interrupted by flat tires, a faulty hitch, an uneven load, an overheated engine, and a hysterical woman at the wheel of the car and at the wheel of our lives. And when the landscape turned alien and the sky became huge, my brothers and I watched from the backseat in silence and awe. No trees, no grass, just a vastness that was impossible to comprehend, that made me feel untethered.

On day five of the adventure, our mother made an announcement: "We're out of money." It was another common line, but this time she really meant it. "Even if we don't have another breakdown, even if we go without eating, we won't have enough money for gas."

We were at a Stuckey's, parked in the shade of a Greyhound bus. The Rambler's windows were down, and our damp hair was plastered to our foreheads, our cheeks red from the heat.

She grabbed the steering wheel with both hands and began to sob. "I wish I were dead!" she wailed.

"Can you call Boyd?" my brother asked.

"No! He doesn't know we're coming. I wanted to surprise him!"

I waited a few moments, then ventured: "I have money."

The sobbing stopped. She turned and looked over the seat at me. "How much?"

"I don't know. Birthday money. From Grandma." My brother was smart; he always spent his gift money. I saved every dime. My mother had a notebook of all the money she'd borrowed, money she said she would pay back someday *with interest.*

But I'd finally started lying about how much I had. *As far as you're concerned.* I was sure I would never get any of it back.

"Where?" she asked.

"Packed. In the trailer."

"Is it change? Is it just pennies?"

"Some pennies and some dimes and quarters and paper money." It would all be gone once I gave it to her. I knew that. But this was important. I was coming to the rescue.

We unloaded the trailer right there in the parking lot. Everything we owned. There were only a few boxes left in the trailer when we found it. Twenty-three dollars. Money I'd squirreled away for years.

Now that our mother had it in her hands, there was no more talk about writing it down in the notebook she kept for her debts. Even though it was hot and we were physically miserable, her mood improved now that our fortune had changed. "Look at this." She surveyed our belongings scattered around us in the parking lot. She laughed, and we all joined her. Even if I never saw the money again, the evaporation of her black mood was worth every cent. With joy and hope and renewed energy, we repacked the trailer. We would make it to Albuquerque.

Boyd was going to be so surprised to see us. I tried to picture him, but his face blurred in my mind with the other boyfriends'.

"Why are we going so slow?" my older brother asked. "Everybody's passing us."

The Rambler labored to pull the trailer up

the steady incline, cars and semis roaring around us. "We're in the Rocky Mountains," our mother said. She pointed. "Look. That must be Sandia Peak. There's snow even though it's summer. Boyd told me about it. He wants to take all of us there. We'll go skiing and snowshoeing."

Her excitement was contagious, and we all stared out the window at the strange surroundings. When she was happy, we were happy. That's what our lives were about, ever since the divorce. Trying to keep her happy, trying to stay out of her way, trying to be good.

I thought New Mexico was ugly, but I would never say so out loud. Maybe it was prettier in the mountains.

We finally reached an area where the road leveled out and the little car no longer labored to pull its load. And then we were heading downhill. Below us a city spread from horizon to horizon.

At the edge of town, we pulled into a gas station, stopping a few feet from a phone booth. Even the gas station was ugly, with broken glass and weeds growing from cracks. Our mother shut off the engine and opened her door. "Wait here while I make the call." She dug in her purse and pulled out some coins. "Fifty cents. That's all we have left. Can you believe it?" She laughed in delight. We were here. We'd made it with enough money to call Boyd.

All three of us bounced up and down.

She gave us a ravishing smile, left the car, and stepped into the phone booth, closing the door behind her. We saw her drop the money in the slot and dial the number. She grasped the receiver, looked out the door, spotted us, and waved, her eyes sparkling.

It had taken us five days, but we were here. Tired and dirty and hungry, but we were here. I imagined the next few hours. We would eat, and we would be taken to a nice house. Would I have a bed of my own, or would I have to share with my brother? That would be okay for a while, but my mother had promised me a room of my own. I wanted a canopy bed. Pink, with ruffles. Cozy and safe. I would unpack my stuffed animals, and they would join me there.

We could see that someone had answered her call. She was talking. We saw the smile falter and the light in her eyes vanish. There was more talking, fast now, angry. She was shouting and crying, but we couldn't tell what she was saying. She slammed down the receiver, then jerked open the phone-booth door. All three of us sank down in the back-seat, trying to make ourselves as small as possible. The driver's door opened, and her rage and despair filled the car as she slid behind the wheel, sobbing deeply now.

"He lied to me! He's not getting a divorce. His daughter answered the phone! Everything was a lie!"

"So we aren't going to his house?" I asked.

"No!" She swung around to glare at me, her teeth gritted in anger. "How can we live at his house? He's married! His wife and kids live there! He lied. He lied to all of us. Dirty, stinking creep!"

No food. No bed.

My younger brother had been struggling to keep his tears to himself, but now he let loose, sobbing in terror. "I'm hungry!"

"Shhh," I said, pumping his little stick arm, trying to get him to stop crying. "We'll be okay. See if you can find a dime under the seat. If you find a dime, I'll buy you something at the gas station."

He stopped sobbing and began his hunt.

My mother wiped her face, pulled a tube of lipstick from her purse, turned the rear-view mirror, applied one, two, three swipes, and capped the lipstick. "He's coming," she explained, dropping the lipstick tube back in her purse. "I told him we didn't have any place to stay and nothing to eat. He's going to put us up in a motel."

"Do you think he'll really come?" I asked.

"He'd better. Otherwise I'll call his house and tell his wife everything."

He came. It took forever, but he finally showed up. He looked worried and sick, his shoulders hunched, the armpits of his shirt soaked with sweat. He didn't talk to me or my brothers, but I caught him looking at us with an expression of horror and guilt.

Boyd lived in an area of Albuquerque called the Heights. He found us a place to live in the Valley, as far from his house as possible. He stocked our refrigerator with food, paid for a month's rent, helped my mother find a secretarial job, then disappeared.

Chapter Four

A HONKING horn woke me from a restless sleep.

It was a Cadillac horn, which is similar to a barge horn. You know these things when you've lived near the Mississippi River.

Outside the small house, the horn honked again and sleep fell away completely. I was in bed, my new husband beside me.

Adrian started to get up, then fell back against the pillow. "The shower. I forgot about the shower."

The bedside radio said six o'clock. *In the morning.* I tried to figure out what a shower had to do with the car outside our house.

"I forgot to tell you my mother is having a shower this morning. It's something she and her friends do whenever one of their kids gets married."

"A shower? You mean like a wedding shower? She doesn't even know me."

"I'm sorry." He sat up. "I was supposed to tell you. Doesn't matter if she doesn't know you. My mother is all about tradition and keeping up appearances."

I used to think my life was really messed up and that there was this whole world out there of normal people that I would never be a part of, that I would never understand. But I was beginning to wonder if I'd had it backward. I swung my legs over the side of the bed, reaching for my jeans. "I'm not going to any breakfast shower."

"My God, you're beautiful."

I looked over my shoulder to see him staring at me all dreamy eyed and hungover. "You're just telling me that so I'll go." Or was he saying it so I'd forgive him for last night?

He lightly touched my back with calloused fingertips. "I would never do that."

I put on a green top with long flowing sleeves. "Well, I'm not beautiful, so you can quit trying to sweet-talk me." I squeezed around to his side of the bed to peek out the window, pulling the muslin curtain aside a fraction of an inch. I groaned and dropped the fabric. "The car is full of people."

He grabbed my hand, and I turned to look at him. He was propped against the pillow, covered to the waist with the sheet. I should have been in bed too. We should have slowly woken up together.

"Come on," he said. "Just go."

"What kind of person doesn't even ask someone if she wants a shower?"

"A controlling person."

If I didn't go, his mother would hate me forever. She might hate me forever no matter what, but not going left no wiggle room.

"In three hours it will all be over," he said. "Three hours."

I'd already forgiven him. I was still smitten, and it would take more than one screwup to change my feelings.

Sandals and a finger-brush of my cropped hair, grab my shoulder bag, and I was out the door.

Giant white Caddy in the driveway.

The sun was barely up. Dew dampened the hem of my jeans, and a blue haze clung to grass and cornstalks in the nearby field.

I love that smell. The smell of corn. Not kernels of corn but the plant, the leaves. That humid, organic scent that wraps around your head and comforts you. It's heavy and rich, like nothing I've ever smelled in my life. If perfume smelled like that, I would wear it.

The car was packed. Four people in the front seat, three in the back. Too late to change my mind; they were all looking at me.

I'd never seen so much pastel and polyester packed into one vehicle in my life. White slacks with sharp creases. Floral perfume and hair that had just come out of hot rollers.

I squeezed in back with three girls who were probably a few years older than I was. I could tell they were shocked by my unkempt appearance. The girls gave me an uncomfortable hi, and one even shot me a look of sympathy.

My new mother-in-law made introductions as she drove, very badly.

They talked about wedding things and babies. Ruth explained to them that I hadn't registered my pattern yet, but I would soon.

My *pattern?* I wanted to say that my pattern was Kmart melamine with a little pawnshop thrown in, but I was pretty sure nobody would think it funny. This was serious married stuff.

It was thirty minutes to Burlington. Mothers and daughters gave me sly, sidelong, hopeful glances.

Oh, they were enjoying this. Not because they were enjoying torturing me. I meant nothing to them. No, they were enjoying the pain my very existence brought to my new mom. Interesting.

A few tentative questions came my way— shy attempts to start conversations. All topics I knew nothing about that had to do with taking care of the home, and cooking, and thread counts, and monogrammed towels. How to hang curtains and who was at church last Sunday. There was talk of baby showers and 4-H.

Much of the conversation from the front seat was gossip disguised as concern, and once it was obvious I would be no help in any of it, my presence was ignored. I dropped into observer mode while trying to sort out the mood in the car.

We approached my uncle's bar, and conversation died.

If there had been any train tracks in the vicinity, the bar would have been on the wrong side of them.

As we passed, all heads turned. I could feel my mother-in-law's shame and the combined horror and pleasure of her friends.

The car moved on, away from that uncomfortable situation within an uncomfortable situation. A turn to the west and we were off the bluff, dipping into the bottoms where the soil was black and fertile and where the river had once been miles wide. Tilled soil flashed past windows until we reached a metal span that connected Illinois to Iowa. We crossed the bridge and were in Burlington.

It used to be magnificent, with beautiful Victorian homes clinging to majestic bluffs overlooking the Mississippi River. But most of that was gone. People had decided to rip out the heart of the small city, bulldozing hundreds of historic homes to put in a new road that led to sprawl, strip malls, and the rest of Iowa. The people who stayed got to witness a death rattle that would last a century, and the people who came would never know what they'd missed.

The total disregard for the beauty of the past hurt me deep in my soul. Why don't people stop? Just stop?

But who was I to judge or complain?

THE breakfast took place downtown at Hotel Burlington. The hostess ushered us to a small banquet room with a white tablecloth and white napkins folded in wedges and placed on fine china.

We ordered. We ate.

It was even more awkward than I'd anticipated.

People gave me gifts. Complete strangers gave me gifts.

Things that left me baffled as to function. A silver tray. A crystal vase. A lot of crystal. Shiny stuff. Someone gave me a set of pretty etched plates with glass teacups that fit into outlines on the plates.

Seeing my perplexity, one of the girls explained, "They're for homemaker parties. They hold your dessert and coffee."

I didn't have homemaker parties. That would never be me.

But it seemed a mandatory part of this new life, and I could already feel the tedium of it sucking the soul right out of me. Here a woman's role was to take care of the house and have babies. And the women didn't resent it. They embraced it.

On the return trip, we passed my uncle's bar again. This time Uncle Jim was outside puttering, waist-deep in weeds and junk cars. And I suddenly caught a faint whiff of my mother-in-law's horror. Just for a fraction of a second, I almost understood her.

My uncle—someone I'd always seen as an eccentric genius—changed as I imagined him through her eyes.

White trash. He was white trash.

I suddenly saw the situation from Ruth's perspective. Her son had married an outsider, someone beneath him. White trash.

Stunned, I swallowed and looked away, and a seed of doubt was planted. That's how easily it happens.

Less than twenty-four hours into this new life, my self-perception was shifting. Already I was wondering if my world had really been what I'd thought. Already I was wondering if I was the one who was messed up. Maybe all of the crystal and silver trays and talk about curtains was the way real people were supposed to live.

A crop duster buzzed a nearby cornfield.

When the pilot reached the highway, he shut off the cloud of yellow spray and throttled up, the plane roaring skyward to circle for another approach. It was a beautiful ballet, the yellow plane against the blue sky, the music of the engine, the green of the corn.

The spray hung suspended in the air, then drifted toward us.

The heavy odor of pesticide crept in through the car vents. It touched white slacks and hair that had been set on rollers. It fell against soft cheeks and dark, shy lashes.

The mothers and daughters carried on as if nothing unusual were taking place anywhere outside or inside the car. They were caught up in talk of babies. Talk of family. Talk of the future.

THE next afternoon, I answered a knock to find a stocky female dressed in jeans and a gray T-shirt standing on the front step. She looked about twenty-five, with a sunburned face and shoulder-length brown hair.

"You must be Adrian's new wife." Like somebody hitchhiking, she pointed over her shoulder with her thumb. "I'm your neighbor, Connie. I run my parents' farm now that they've retired."

"By yourself?" She became instantly more interesting.

"By myself."

There seemed to be two main types of farm women. The homemakers who had little to do with farming, and the women who worked right alongside the men.

"I know you had one of those boring breakfast showers," Connie said. "I would have come, but I wasn't invited. Here—got you a little something." She handed me a package wrapped in yellow tissue paper, tied at both ends with white, curling ribbon.

I tried to imagine Connie packed into the car with us, but couldn't. "I'm sorry you weren't invited to the shower, but it was pretty awful."

Following me inside, she laughed, and the sound was deep and robust. "I'll bet." She nodded toward the gift. "Go on. Open it."

The paper tore easily. "Oh, a rolling pin." Heavy and wooden.

"Do you already have one?"

"No." It had been years since I'd used a rolling pin. "Thank you," I said.

"If you live on an apple farm, you have to have a rolling pin."

It was understandable that the locals were curious about me, and she was staring in a way that made me uncomfortable. I wasn't sure if I wanted her to sit down, so I lingered near the front door.

"I heard Adrian married a girl he hardly knew," she said, getting directly to the point. "The whole county is buzzing about it. But Adrian isn't a spur-of-the-moment kind of guy. He thinks things through, then thinks them through again."

"So you're trying to figure out why he married me?" What a horribly rude person. She should have thought twice about giving me a rolling pin.

She tipped her head and examined me. "You're kind of interesting. Cute in an innocent way. That might have appealed to Adrian. Have you ever lived on a farm?"

"No, but I've lived near them."

She shook her head and smiled. "This is just so odd. I mean, I've known Adrian all my life. This is totally out of character." She paused, examining my face again. "You won't last. If you haven't grown up on a farm, you won't make it here. One day you'll pack your bags and be thankful to put this place behind you."

I wadded up the wrapping paper. "Did you ever date Adrian?" I asked with suspicion. She might be a bitter old girlfriend.

"Growing up, we were more like brother

and sister. Although I have to confess to having a crush on him back when we were in middle school. Who wouldn't? The guy is gorgeous."

I wasn't buying that she didn't still like him.

"But honestly?" Connie said. "You aren't his type."

I managed to make it to the couch, setting the rolling pin and wrapping paper aside, company briefly unimportant.

I'd known. Good things didn't happen to me, but couldn't a girl pretend a guy loved her?

Connie followed and sat one cushion away, her cheeks flushing bright red under the sunburn. She looked distressed. "I'm so sorry," she said. "Please forget everything I said."

Forget? "Hey, I appreciate the information." I reached for a pack of cigarettes and lit up, surprised that my hands weren't shaking. "I'd like to know more." I inhaled deeply and blew out a cloud of smoke. It wasn't enough to take the edge off, but it was something to fiddle with while I pulled myself together. Gradually I became aware of

Connie's voice. I think she'd been talking a long time.

"He was dating a girl . . . supposed to get married. I'm not sure what happened. Adrian was crazy about her."

"Was her name Melinda?"

"I think so. Now that I think of it, his old girlfriend looked quite a bit like you, and she worked at a bar. Didn't you and Adrian meet at a bar?"

"Yes." I didn't want to believe her, I wasn't ready to believe her, but she'd set in motion a lot of doubt.

"Everybody is talking about the marriage."

"You already said that."

"Well, I'm saying it again because that could be a motive behind this stunt. Nothing Adrian's mom would hate more than everybody in the county gossiping about her son's marriage and new wife."

"Maybe he cares about me," I heard myself say. "Maybe we'll move away from here and find our own place."

Connie shook her head and chuckled. "That will never happen. Never. That's what I mean. If you haven't grown up on a farm, you don't understand how it works. He won't leave. He *can't* leave. He's the eldest son. He was born here, and he'll die here."

I couldn't decide if I liked Connie or hated her. I knew I should hate her, but there was something oddly refreshing about her directness, even if I was unsure of the motive behind it.

"You certainly aren't what I expected—I know that," she said.

"What did you expect?"

"Someone with a lot of curves. Blond hair and a ton of makeup. The kind of girl who blinds a man for a while. Until he gets his fill of her and wonders what he was thinking. But you . . ."

She didn't say it. She didn't have to. I was a mouse. A little gray mouse. And why would Adrian marry a mouse when he could have the pick of any woman in the area?

"Maybe Adrian *is* crazy about you." She gave my arm a quick, reassuring squeeze. "Maybe it was love at first sight."

"Yeah. Maybe." But Connie had tapped into my own repressed concerns, and my response was hollow.

"Adrian can be a self-centered workaholic," she said. "If you need a night out, give me a call or just stop by. We could bake an apple pie, and you could bring it home to Adrian as a surprise. He used to love Granny Smiths. He loves cherry pie too."

She knew more about my husband than I did. She could have answered my grandmother's questions.

Connie got up and headed for the door. "You'll come?"

Before her visit, I'd been able to fool myself into thinking everything would be fine. But she'd filled in blanks that I hadn't wanted filled. She'd brought a blunt truth, and along with that truth a darkness that might never lift. And in that moment I understood that I'd stepped into a world I could never be a part of.

Connie was in the doorway now. "One mile if you go through the fields. Walk out your front door and turn left, cross the hard road to the lane that runs along the creek. Follow that until you hit a rusty DeKalb sign. Turn south and go a quarter mile. You'll come right up in my backyard. If the dog is out, don't pay any attention to her. She'll bark, but she won't bite."

How could I have imagined being able to

step into this strange life? Farm wife. I'd never thought about the consequences. I'd never thought about a year from now, or even a month from now. And I'd been infatuated. I was still infatuated.

But this was real. These people were real. This life was real.

Not my life. It would never be my life.

I WOULD stay. For a while. At least that's what I told myself, waiting to see if things improved or got bad enough to justify a packed suitcase. I spent days alone. Evenings alone. I would wait and wait, and he would never come home. Not until I'd gone to bed and turned out the lights. And there he would be, fumbling for me in the dark. He would rise before dawn, gone before I woke up.

Where did he go? What did he do when he wasn't at our house?

I'd never had any desire to be a wife. Ugh. A horrid word. *Wife.* It implied ownership. And now I was acting like a whiny wife. I'd seen it on television. Where the wife was always nagging the husband. *Husband.* Another unappealing word. But in those stories, the guy was usually up to something. Like having an affair. How had my life become such a cliché, and in such a short time?

If there was another woman, it would mean they'd hooked up right after he and I were married. How was that possible?

Unless it was someone he'd known before . . .

Yes. The girl he'd almost married. Or another old flame.

"Where have you been?" I'd asked him several times in our short marriage when he would show up with a bundle of clothes tucked under his arm. He'd never moved in. All of his belongings were still at his parents' house. "How can you farm in the dark?"

He'd dismissed me with words and a look of disdain. "You don't know anything about farming."

That was true, but something wasn't right. A lot wasn't right. I felt it in my belly—a darkness and a sense that if I peeled away what was on top, I would find something I didn't want to find.

I heard his truck.

Already my ears could distinguish it from

the other vehicles that rolled past. The engine was steady, the exhaust loud.

It didn't stop. Didn't pull into the driveway.

Sitting on the bed in the dim light, I kept my ears tuned. The sound of the truck faded, then grew a little louder. It slowed, then shut off.

Not at our house.

I waited, expecting to hear the crunch of boots on gravel, expecting to hear the kitchen door open and close.

Nothing.

Dinner was on the table. It had been on the table for an hour. Just like every other night.

I would see if I could find him. I would venture from the house into his world.

Outside, the sky was black and the air was cool against my bare arms. Across the road at the big two-story farmhouse, lights burned in windows. I moved closer. When I hit the grass, my footsteps silenced. I cut through bushes and ducked under the clothesline.

There was a little patio outside the kitchen. I clung to the deeper shadows of trees and bushes. From there, I could see through the window. There they were, like a Norman Rockwell painting, sitting at the kitchen table. Mother. Father.

Son.

Sitting at the table eating supper. Talking and smiling.

I couldn't process what I was seeing. I just stood and watched, thinking that I had to be having some kind of hallucination. But no. There was my new husband, sitting and eating with his family.

This is where he went every night. This is why I never saw him. Yes, there was another woman. His mother.

If I returned to our little house, he would eventually show up and poke around at dinner, never admitting that he'd already eaten.

Playing house. That's what he was doing. What we were doing. Because I couldn't blame him for everything. After all, I'd married a guy I didn't even know. My uncle had warned me. My grandmother had warned me. And now I was witnessing his real life through the kitchen window.

The only times I'd been inside the house had been when Adrian was with me. On the few occasions when I'd attempted visits without him, I hadn't been invited in. Why had Adrian married me? I didn't get it, and I needed to get it. Needed to understand.

I stood staring at them for a long time.

Had it been hormones and sex? I hated to think there had been no other connection. But it seemed that was the case. And yet I couldn't help but feel cheated. He'd represented the most normal of existences to me. The kind of normal I'd craved my entire life.

I had no desire to confront them. I just wanted out. I don't know why I hadn't left before. Maybe because I actually cared for him. Or maybe because I was young, foolish, and romantic, even though I hated to admit to believing in love and romance.

One thing I knew—a guy had no business getting married when he was still on the teat.

Chapter Five

I RAN back to the small house. Inside, I pulled out my suitcase and tossed in my clothes. I slammed the suitcase shut, grabbed the handle, my purse, my keys, and ran out the back door.

I shoved the suitcase behind the front seat, jumped into the car, and turned the ignition key. I had two exit choices: sneak away quietly with no lights or fly out of there like the devil was after me. I wanted to choose number two, but with my heart slamming in my chest, I restrained myself. Instead of tromping down on the accelerator, I coasted past the big farmhouse, wincing at the sound of tires rolling over gravel. I turned left on the blacktop surface. I wasn't sure where I was going. *Away* was the only thought I had. Away from Adrian. Away from the farm.

When I reached Highway 34, I hit the headlights and made another left. In less than a minute, I was in third gear doing sixty.

Until that moment I hadn't realized I was shaking.

Where was I going? My uncle's? No, I couldn't face him right now. Not when he'd tried to talk me out of getting married in the first place. I could go to my grandmother's, but I'd shown up on her doorstep too many times. I just wanted to drive and keep driving.

My entire world was the interior of the car. I didn't want to think of anything beyond the doors. Everything he'd said, every gesture, every touch, every smile, had meant nothing.

I suddenly realized I was driving. I'd forgotten I was behind the wheel until I caught a dark movement in my right peripheral vision. At that same moment I felt a violent impact, followed by the sound of metal scraping across the surface of the road.

The windshield shattered. The hood crumpled.

The car spun in slow motion, the rear sliding, sparks flying until it came to a jarring halt. I sat there, hands gripping the wheel. Gradually I became aware of the smell of antifreeze, gasoline, and motor oil. The hiss of hot water. I became aware of my ragged breathing and the darkness that surrounded me.

Get out. I fumbled for the handle. Pulled. Nothing. I slammed my shoulder against the door. Nothing.

I rolled down the window and dove out, falling to the ground, gravel cutting my palms and knees. Beyond the roar in my head, beyond my own thundering heart, came another sound.

A horrible sound. An animal in agony.

I could see a darker shape on the shoulder of the road. Deer?

No, it didn't sound like a deer. Cow?

It was suffering.

Someone please come and help.

My arms and legs shook uncontrollably, but I managed to shove myself to my feet. Two cars drove past, slowed, then sped up. Several minutes later I heard a siren. The gawkers must have called the police. Flashing lights appeared around the bend, pulling to a stop in front of a tangled mass of guts. I turned away.

The officer checked on me first. "Are you hurt?"

"No. I don't know. I don't think so."

Everything had happened so quickly that I suppose I could have been hurt, but I didn't feel anything. Nothing but the violent, almost comical shaking. I realized my mouth and fingers were numb, and when I talked, my tongue felt weird. Frozen and thick. "You h-have to h-help th-that animal." I pointed but didn't look.

"Was anyone else with you?"

"No."

Two more police cars showed up. One officer pulled out a handgun, approached the thrashing animal, and fired three times. The cries of agony stopped.

He put away his weapon and walked back to where the other officer and I stood along the road. "What a mess." He sounded sick.

"A cow?" I asked hopefully. I don't know why it seemed less horrid to have killed a cow, but it did. I guess because cows were slaughter animals.

"Horse."

A horse . . .

He pulled out a notepad and began taking down information. Without even thinking, I gave him my maiden name.

"We should call an ambulance."

"No, I'm okay."

I'd had a lot of practice pretending I was okay, pretending I wasn't messed up when I really was, so I was able to convince the cop that I hadn't been seriously injured. I would assess myself later.

"Then a relative or friend."

I gave him my uncle's name and number.

Tears burned my eyes, and I blinked rapidly to clear my vision. I was crying about the animal I'd killed, and I was crying about my uncle and our damaged relationship. I was crying about Adrian.

Another cop car showed up, lights flashing. Officers began setting up emergency lights and directing traffic. Someone wrapped a blanket around me and led me to a police car and helped me into the passenger side. "Wait here."

I lost track of time, uncertain if minutes or hours had passed.

My uncle would be here soon. He would take care of me. I thought about going back to the bar, opening my sofa bed, crawling between familiar sheets. Home. But it wouldn't be the same. After what had happened, how could anything ever be right again? But things hadn't been right for a long time. Things hadn't been right since long before I'd eaten the mushroom.

The door opened and the policeman stuck his head inside. "I called your uncle, but he said to contact your husband."

I looked up through the windshield. A truck was pulling sharply to the edge of the highway, gravel spewing, headlights momentarily blinding me. A man got out, and I recognized a familiar stride coming toward me. Adrian.

I SAT in the cab of Adrian's truck, shivering even though the night was muggy and warm. In the headlights of the police car, the cop passed my battered suitcase to Adrian. I couldn't see his face, but I imagined his surprise, maybe even embarrassment.

Confusion clouded my brain, and I struggled to recall what had precipitated my drive. *The kitchen window. The kitchen table.*

Yes. That was it. As soon as the memory entered my head, it floated away and became irrelevant. The poor horse, the wrecked car, other times when death had come knocking—those were the things right in front of me. Those were the things I focused on.

And the man walking toward me with the suitcase.

For a moment I couldn't place him. *Who is that?*

Then I realized it was Adrian. *My husband.*

He hefted the suitcase into the bed of the truck. The driver's door opened, and he slid behind the wheel. "Your car is totaled." His voice was devoid of emotion. I had no idea what he was thinking.

Just a car, but it had special meaning to me because it had been a gift from my uncle, something he'd won in a bet. A Mustang. A horse hitting a horse. "What will happen to it?" I asked.

"A junkyard will tow it away."

Adrian turned the truck around, and we headed back in the direction of the farm. I felt a flutter of panic at the thought of returning to a place I'd left for good. I could feel my world shrinking. And this time it would be smaller than it had been before, because I would have no car.

"You were leaving without even telling me," he said. "Why?"

From his point of view, I'm sure my flight had no apparent trigger. I should have confronted him and told him I was going, but I can be a coward at times. Even now, I could only blurt out the most direct and limited words necessary to get the message across. "I don't know why you married me."

He made a strange sound of shock and surprise. "Maybe I care about you."

"You still live at home. You still eat supper with your parents. *I saw you.*"

He acted as if the whole arrangement were perfectly normal. "That's what people do on a farm. They eat together and talk about the day. And honestly, I don't like the food you cook."

After getting married, it had surprised me to find that he'd grown up eating packaged and processed meals that could quickly go from the freezer to the oven or fryer, heavily seasoned with salt, pepper, and ketchup. I'd had no exposure to most of the food he liked. Having lived in New Mexico, I was more familiar with tamales and enchiladas, chiles rellenos and refried beans. My childhood may have been messed up, but the food I'd eaten had been prepared from scratch and had involved creativity. I'd brought that tradition to our meals, with disastrous results.

"You're just picky," I said. "Not liking my cooking is no reason to eat at your mother's. I really want to know why you married me, because what we have is not a marriage. Am I a breeder? Is that it?"

He let out a snort. "Why can't you believe I care about you?"

He didn't mention love. "Then let's leave." I shifted to face him. "Let's go somewhere and start our own life. Together."

"That's impossible. The farm is my home. It's been in the family for over a hundred years. I'm not walking away from my heritage."

"It's not my heritage." I hadn't understood how my lack of roots would alienate me on a daily basis. "Turn around. Take me to my uncle's." I had the feeling that if I didn't leave now, I'd never leave.

Our speed didn't change.

I reached for the door handle. "Stop the truck or I'll jump out."

He laughed as if he found me incredibly amusing. "I'm sorry. It's just that you sound so melodramatic. Come on. Let's go home. Forget about tonight. I'll draw pictures of you when we get back."

Draw me? He was treating me like a child. "I don't want you to draw any pictures of me. That would mean nothing now."

"But I married you. Doesn't that count for anything?"

He was confusing me. Making light of something I'd taken seriously. Was I over-reacting to his eating dinner with his parents? "I was your protest. That's what I think."

He'd broken my heart; that's what he'd done. That's why I'd run away. I hadn't been able to face the thought of his not caring for me. Of just being some stray dog he'd brought home and then quickly forgotten.

"So what if you're my protest? Not saying you are, but so what?"

"So what? That's mean! You're mean." I couldn't think straight. I'd just wrecked my car and killed a horse. He should have hugged me, told me how worried he was. How glad he was that I was alive. He'd done none of those things. Instead, he offered to draw me.

"Maybe I don't fully understand why I married you. There. Is that what you wanted to hear?"

"Of course not, but it's better than a lie." Were we nothing more than two mixed-up people who'd unwisely chosen to pool our confusion?

"The farm is number one. The farm will

always come first. I'm sorry. That's just the way it is."

A farm. I hadn't understood the rules that came with this new life. I'd been looking for tradition and family and security. And yes, love. Was that so shameful? "What about Melinda?"

"Who?"

"Melinda. The girl you almost married."

We were home now, pulling into the gravel and grass driveway. Adrian shut off the engine before the truck stopped rolling. "Her name was Matilda, and we were never engaged. She was a psycho, and when I dumped her, she stalked me for months and told everybody I'd broken off our engagement."

Those certainly weren't the words I'd expected to hear.

I TOOK a hot shower, and when I was done, I slipped on a pair of flannel pajama bottoms and an old T-shirt. In the medicine cabinet mirror above the bathroom sink, I could see a bruise on my forehead, and I thought about my earlier confusion and how I hadn't recognized Adrian. I remembered when a neighbor had fallen and hit her head on the sidewalk. She'd acted very strange for a few days, with dizzy spells and memory problems.

In the living room, candles burned. A small lamp glowed in the corner. The windows were open. From outside came the sound of crickets and the scent of damp earth. Ivory curtains billowed softly, made of fabric that changed according to movement and light.

"Here." Adrian handed me a small package. "Sorry about the way it's wrapped."

I peeled the newspaper aside. A vintage nightgown. Long, off-white, thin straps, made of silk.

"I got it as a wedding present, but I didn't know if you'd like it, so I didn't give it to you. I know you don't wear things like that—" He looked uncomfortable, as if the inappropriateness underscored how little he knew about me. But I loved vintage even though I rarely wore it. He reached out to grab it back. I pulled it away.

"No, I love it. And you wanted to draw me."

In the bedroom, I put on the gown. I let the fabric slide over me, the hem falling to my knees. Adrian was right—it was unlike anything I would ever wear. I could smell the fabric, like something that had been tucked away in a drawer for a long time, with hints of lavender and dust.

My brain felt cloudy, and confusion washed over me again.

Did it matter? Did any of it matter? Why did I care where he ate dinner? I struggled to figure out why any of it made any difference.

Everything was cast in shadow. The floor under my bare feet was uneven, hand-hewn from pine trees. The faded flower-print wallpaper could hardly be seen in the dim light, but I could smell the paper and old glue. One day I would scrape it off, and I would paint the wall with something fresh.

Or not.

Maybe I wouldn't change anything. Maybe I wouldn't put my touch on the place at all. Maybe I was the one who needed to adapt. Maybe the secret was to accept and acknowledge the past, the history, the heritage, without bringing myself into the picture. Maybe I didn't want or need to know what was under the wallpaper.

I touched the gown. I loved the way it felt against my body. So foreign and unfamiliar.

Yes, so unlike me. Like putting on someone else's skin.

In the living room, Adrian was waiting. He sat in a wooden chair, floor lamp behind him to illuminate the sketch pad on his leg.

When Adrian saw me in the gown, I think he wanted to reach for me, pull me to him, but I walked by to curl up in the armchair on the opposite side of the room. Two candles burned on the table, near enough for me to feel their heat and smell the melting wax.

My head hurt, but not badly. I was more aware of the air on my arms and the cold fabric that caressed my body. Silk was so impractical. And why wouldn't it be? Something made by worms?

I touched the cloth. "This is silk." Yes, I think the bump on my head was making me stupid.

He started drawing. "There are almost seventy species of silk moths."

I had the notion that when Adrian held a pencil, he connected with who he was. He fell through a hole in the paper and entered another consciousness. And me? I was all about old wallpaper.

Maybe I was looking for romance, but I wasn't a romantic person. That might be because I'd witnessed the men who'd come and gone in my mother's life. I'd seen the parade and knew that none of them cared about her. I think the man she married after my father was the only one who'd truly loved her, but I'm not even sure what he'd felt was love. It was more of a desperate obsession, a clinging to something he knew he could never hang on to.

But somehow Adrian seemed able to stage romantic moments that didn't make me laugh. He made me feel like someone else.

What a mystery for me to see his head bent over the sketchbook, see the shimmer of light on his hair and his face cast in shadow while the pencil lead softly scraped across the rough surface of the paper, with no idea of the image materializing on the blank sheet.

"Do you know I used to be left-handed?" he asked.

"How does a person go from being left-handed to right? Did you have an injury?"

He offered me a cigarette. I shook my head. He lit up and tossed the pack aside, blowing a cloud of smoke toward the ceiling before going back to the paper resting on his leg. "My mother tied my left hand to my side every day until my right hand became dominant."

A wave of dizziness washed over me, dizziness that had nothing to do with my knock on the head.

"I was already drawing by that time. Just houses and those people with nothing but heads and legs that kids like to draw."

"You can remember that far back?"

"You tend to remember things like that, even if you're three. So I had to learn to use my right hand. It took a while, but I did it."

"Did she do it because she didn't want you to be different?"

"My mother has some strange notions. She's not the only one around here who thinks being born left-handed is the sign of evil. She thought she was protecting me."

"If you had a left-handed kid, would you tie his arm down?"

He looked up from the sketch pad. "No." He took a drag from the cigarette, pinched it into his mouth, and squinted against the smoke. "I'm done." He unfolded himself from the chair and handed the tablet to me.

A simple yet elegant line drawing. My legs tucked under me, a wistful hand beneath my chin, elbow on the table as I looked, not at Adrian but out the window into the night. The woman's face was thinner, the lips fuller, the hair wispier. But the drawing was me.

"It's lovely." I passed the tablet back. "But you didn't sign it. You should sign it." I could tell he didn't want to, that a signature meant he was taking himself too seriously. "Please."

He signed his name in the corner, very small, then passed it back.

"I'll frame it."

His face fell. "Don't do that. It's not good enough. I've never framed any of my drawings. I don't want them framed."

"Okay." But I would do something special with it. I wasn't yet sure what.

In the bedroom, we undressed.

"I thought you'd vanished tonight," he said. "I came home and you weren't here. I thought you'd left. And then your car was gone, and the police called." His voice caught. "They wouldn't tell me anything over the phone, and when I saw the car . . . the blood on the road . . . I thought you were dead."

I wondered why I'd ever been upset enough to leave. *Don't think. Just don't think and everything will be fine. Everything will be wonderful.*

Adrian's world wasn't a place for thinking. And I have to admit that when he touched me, I lost track of who he was and who I was. We were just two people, two bodies coming together in the dark.

And in that dark, maybe I *was* someone else.

An HOUR later, I could feel his thoughtful silence in the dark beside me. I sensed that he was mulling something over. Finally he spoke, and when he did, his words proved I wasn't being paranoid.

"I almost didn't go through with the marriage," he confessed. "My parents and brother tried to talk me out of it up until the last minute. They came close to convincing me I was making a mistake. That night, after we were married, when I left to check the trees, I stopped at the farmhouse. I was upset, having second thoughts, and my mother assured me we could have the marriage annulled."

"So you went drinking."

"Yeah."

"Why didn't you come back here and talk to me?"

"I was trying to sort it out in my head. Talking to you, seeing you, would have confused me more. My mother said you tricked me into marrying you, and I started thinking maybe she was right."

"Getting married was your idea. I suggested living together."

"I know, but I started questioning everything, wondering if I'd been manipulated somehow."

The naïve country boy manipulated by the slick city girl. This was a role I couldn't tolerate. I tossed back the covers with the intention of finding my clothes. I would walk if I couldn't drive.

He grabbed my arm. Just enough to stop me, his fingers trailing away. "Come on. I'm being honest with you. That's what you wanted, wasn't it?"

I was beginning to grasp the full extent of the sheltered and isolated life he'd led, hardly ever leaving the orchard, having very little contact with people beyond the farm. His social skills were undeveloped, but maybe I was making excuses for him. His charm was rooted in the fact that he was unlike anybody I'd ever met, and much of that came from his lack of influence by the outside world.

I could now see that everybody had been right about our being a poor match and being too young, but I was stubborn. I found myself wanting to prove them wrong.

Chapter Six

Albuquerque, New Mexico, 1968

I WAS twelve and my younger brother six the year Robert Kennedy was assassinated. We still lived in Albuquerque. Not the Valley any longer, but a nondescript area of the Heights, part of the sprawl that would soon reach the Sandia Mountains.

My mother was disposing of us one at a time, and my older brother had been shipped back to Burlington to live with our grandmother. A man named Freddy Fontaine had become a permanent fixture in our lives. He'd moved from France as a child and was now a United States CIA agent, information he eventually shared with my mother with the request that she not tell anyone.

Like any decent secret agent, Freddy had a lot of guns, and we spent Saturday afternoons in the foothills shooting cans from rocks, going through boxes of bullets. His guns had intriguing names like Colt and Ruger. Some were revolvers, and some came with clips that Freddy loaded and clicked into place with professional efficiency. I preferred his rifles, because I could steady the butt against my shoulder for better aim. Freddy praised my skill.

My younger brother was enthralled with the idea of his mother dating a secret agent. A man with a badge. A man with guns. A man with a cool car, complete with a siren and bullhorn. We loved riding in the backseat of Freddy's big red-and-white convertible.

The man fed us well, and under Freddy's care we thrived. But the meals came with a price. Freddy loved causing public scenes, roaring with laughter at everyone's discomfort. He was loud and demanding, only happy when he was making some poor waitress miserable. Often the manager had to be called to our table.

"Do you know who I am?" Freddy would flash his badge, careful to reveal the gun he always carried in a holster under his jacket. The manager would become apologetic, and we would end up with free drinks and free food.

I could have almost understood my mother's devotion if Freddy had been a dreamboat, but he was fat, short, and ugly. But he adored her, and she needed to be adored. "Being a CIA agent is stressful," she told us, making excuses for his juvenile behavior.

"I don't know what his job has to do with anything," I said.

"The way he acts—it's a release valve. He's under a tremendous amount of pressure," she said.

They would drop me and my brother off at the movie theater, and when they picked us up, long after the movie ended, they were usually drunk, my mother's clothes in disarray, both of them giggling and hanging on each other. It was always a relief to see her happy, no matter that I knew the happiness wouldn't last.

One day at a grocery store, a man waved and shouted to Freddy from the opposite end of the dairy section. "Frederico! What are you doing in this part of town?"

"You must be confusing me with someone else." Freddy gave the man a hard stare, as if trying to transmit some secret information. But his friend didn't seem to get it and with a look of confusion said, "See you at the shop on Monday."

"Shop?" my mother asked.

"It's a cover," Freddy said. "It has to do with my job."

She nodded, understanding.

But finally my mother found out the truth about her CIA agent. His real name was Frederico Florez, and he was a car mechanic.

A week after she dumped him, he pounded on our front door. "Let me in! I have a gun!"

It was late evening, and my brother and I were by ourselves. We crouched down, away from the front window. "Leave us alone!" I shouted. "She's not here!" Going for the phone would have meant walking in front of the window. I didn't dare try it.

"I'm getting a screwdriver!" His words were slurred, and I hoped he was too drunk to follow through on his plan, whatever it was. I heard him stumbling around, crashing through shrubbery. A car trunk slammed; then he was back, working at the door handle.

"Let me in or I'll call the cops!" he shouted.

My brother and I both laughed, Freddy's words a comforting reminder of his foolishness. Maybe he was no real threat. Finally the noise at the front door stopped. A few minutes later, I heard him trying to force open a bedroom window, scratching and cursing like some crazy cat in heat. While he was occupied at the back of the house, I ran for the phone and dialed the police.

Freddy was nowhere around when they arrived, but he'd left gouges on the front door where he'd tried to force it open.

"At least he didn't do any real damage," my mother said when she returned home. She wasn't overly concerned. But the next morning she went outside to get her clothes from the line and discovered that her best bras and panties were gone.

"Bali bras are expensive," she said forlornly.

I didn't understand why Freddy would want bras and panties. Did it matter? He was gone. And hopefully he wasn't coming back. But I knew it meant another guy was just around the corner.

THE day after the car wreck and Adrian's confession, I decided to visit Connie. When I stepped off Curtis land, the terrain returned to what was typical of the area—flat ground and unbroken fields that went on forever. Nothing relieved by hills or ravines too steep to plant. If a tractor could pull a plow without tipping over, the ground was farmed. Every inch was utilized.

A mile or more in the distance, I spotted green tractors pulling sprayers across fields, heat from the soil creating a mirage so the vehicles appeared to hover above the shimmering ground.

Soybeans brushed my ankles. I've never been a fan of soybeans. Maybe I knew too much about them, knew they required a lot of chemicals to farm. Chemicals were even used to kill the soybean plant before harvest because the pulpy, spindly, stringy leaves and stems would otherwise plug up a combine after just one sweep. So when I looked at soybeans, I got the idea they were trying to look cute and harmless, when really they were one giant Superfund site.

And yet my heart still responded to nature even when that nature was no longer natural. Even when it had been forced into straight lines and miles of the same, because there was an incredible beauty in symmetry and control on such massive scale.

Modern farmers were artists, destructive architects of the land. I could appreciate the blackbirds that watched me from the furrowed fields and the hot wind that blew across acres stripped bare. Birds still sang the same song, even though their habitat was forever changed, even though the trees and prairie grass were gone.

Someone once told me that nobody really cared what happened in the Midwest, that nobody really cared about all the pesticide and herbicide, but I had to wonder what people would think if they could stand here where I was standing. If they could breathe and feel and taste this air.

I found the metal sign Connie had mentioned, an advertisement for DeKalb corn. In the distance, I spotted a grouping of trees that indicated a house. I turned and headed toward a large, sweeping backyard. A garden. Fruit trees. Clothesline with sheets and towels.

A border collie shot across the yard toward me, barking. I let the dog sniff me, and when it appeared it wasn't going to bite, I lowered my hand and let it investigate more thoroughly before I chanced a pat on the head. I didn't know a lot about dogs, but it looked like it was happy to have company as it trotted beside me.

The farmhouse was two stories tall, with a big front porch supported by wooden posts painted white like the rest of the structure. It sat on an elevated piece of ground, the yard shaded by a giant oak. The property felt private, remote, and peaceful.

The dog continued to bark and circle me, acting like a puppy even though it was gray around the mouth and eyes. A screen door slammed, and Connie stepped onto the porch. "Come here, Sophie."

The dog turned and ran to the porch.

"I've had her for years," Connie said as if my visit weren't the least unusual, or as if she'd just seen me five minutes ago. "I was just getting ready to have some iced tea. Come in and join me."

I thought Connie was actually glad to see me, but I couldn't be sure about that. I followed her inside.

Connie walked to the sink, turned on the water, and began washing her hands. "I've been cultivating corn all morning. Forgot my thermos, so I left the tractor in the field and walked back."

"I don't want to interrupt anything," I said.

"You aren't." She dried her hands on a red and white cotton towel. "I could use a little company. The radio on the tractor doesn't work, and I'm sick of being stuck with my own thoughts."

She opened the freezer, pulled out a container of ice, filled two glasses, then poured tea from a plastic pitcher. "You take sugar?"

"No." I stepped closer to the wall to examine a cluster of framed photos. One image was of a young Connie and a middle-aged couple posing in front of a colonial-style house. They were dressed up. The older woman was pregnant.

"That's my mother. She miscarried the day after that photo was taken. It was her fifth miscarriage in two years."

"How awful."

"There were a lot of miscarriages around here during that period. I blame it on drift from the fields, but we don't point fingers. Every occupation has its hazards."

"That's more than an occupational hazard." I was surprised by Connie's complacency. "I think people get used to life being a certain way. They accept things they shouldn't accept."

"You have no right to judge us."

Her defensive reply took me by surprise, yet at the same time, I knew what she meant. I could sense a twisted tangle of complexities that were tied to farming and generations and tradition, things an outsider like me would never be able to fully grasp. But it still hurt for her to point out that I wasn't one of them.

She got up and made a big production of turning on the box fan in the corner and arranging it so it blew toward the table; then she sat back down. The noise took away some of the awkwardness.

"What in the world happened to your head?" She leaned forward and touched the ugly lump. It was already turning yellow.

I told her about the wreck and about Adrian continuing to eat dinner with his parents. But that morning he'd brought arm-loads of clothes to our house, taking a step toward moving in, the public shift of belong-ings a statement to everyone on the farm.

"Good God." She tipped her head and pressed her lips together in a sad smile. "Do you care about him so much? Do you love him?"

My face must have reflected more than I understood, because her look of sympathy increased. "Do you know his mother tied his hand to his side to force him to become right-handed?" I asked.

"Doesn't surprise me. The Curtis farm is all about perfection. Perfect apples, perfect corn, perfect people, perfect life. Nothing flawed can exist there. But you also have to realize people around here are superstitious. They still believe a lot of old folklore."

Connie and I were on the same side again. "His mother seems driven by fear," I said. "Fear of being different." For someone like me, someone who'd never wanted to be like anybody else, I couldn't fathom that way of thinking.

The dog scratched at the door, and Connie let her in. The ticking of the plastic clock on the wall seemed to grow louder, and I finished my tea and got up to leave.

"Would you like a ride home?"

"Thanks. I can walk."

"Let me give you a ride. I need to run to town anyway, and it's getting hot out."

We rode back to the Curtis farm in her truck, and when we pulled into the gravel drive, Adrian stepped off the porch and strode toward us. At first his expression was anxious, and I realized he thought I'd run off again. Connie cut the engine and we both exited the truck.

"In the field today?" Connie asked, glancing at the orange and tan David Brown tractor parked along the main road.

"Mowing hay," Adrian said. "You?"

"Cultivating corn. Kind of wishing I'd gone no-till this year."

"I don't know," Adrian said. "Too risky and expensive. Chemicals have to be applied at the right time. And if it rains too much or rains too little, you might end up cultivating anyway."

Connie nodded while I stood on the edge

of their conversation, unable to participate. Connie was attractive. Smart. A hard worker. Her farm was nearby. She was part of Adrian's world. If I'd been a matchmaker, I would have paired them off.

"Maybe I could learn to mow pasture," I said after Connie left and Adrian was heading for the David Brown tractor.

He swung back around, an odd expression on his face. "Women don't drive tractors here."

I laughed. I thought he was kidding.

"Really. I mean, I know you could learn to mow pasture, but on this farm, women aren't allowed to drive tractors. It's a man's job."

"You mean your mother has never driven a tractor?"

"No."

"Could she drive one if she had to?"

"I'm not sure. I don't think so."

"And she's okay with that?"

"It's her rule."

I laughed again. Of course it was. The decree was ridiculous, but I had to wonder if it was less about sexism and more about a way to efficiently distribute the workload. And who was I to question the cultural boundaries established long before I showed up?

"Do your man thing, and I'll go in the house and do my woman thing." I was making fun of their silly rules, but at the same time I felt the pull of housekeeping and cooking. I thought about what I might prepare for dinner, and I thought about painting the kitchen a lovely pale yellow. These things would occupy my time and keep me content for a while, and a while was all I needed to think about.

A FEW days after my visit with Connie, the phone rang. At first I couldn't figure out who was calling. I finally realized the voice at the other end of the line belonged to my grandmother's sister. I didn't know my grandmother's relatives well, but over the years I'd spent a few Sunday afternoons at her sister's house.

"Your grandmother had a stroke." The sister sounded as if she'd been crying. "She's in the hospital and isn't expected to live another hour. You have to get here fast."

I couldn't find Adrian, but I found his truck, the keys in the ignition. I drove off, part of me anxious to get away without being stopped, the other fearful of arriving at my destination.

Twelve miles.

That's how far it was from the farm to the hospital. I took the bridge across the Mississippi. The water made me think of my grandmother. When you spent years on the banks of the Mississippi River, it became a part of you in ways you didn't understand. I imagined my grandmother's soul being swept away by the current.

At the hospital, I found an information desk and choked out my grandmother's name. The receptionist told me where to go, and I tried to follow her directions, winding around the hospital to end in a dark hallway that seemed like a basement.

I spotted my grandmothers' relatives, and from their faces I knew I was too late. She was dead at seventy-two. I had known when I crossed the bridge.

"Do you want to see her?" someone asked.

I shook my head. Someone hugged me.

I couldn't stand to stay there any longer. I turned and left, hurrying back to the truck. I drove where I always drove when things were bad. To her house.

I parked in the alley and dug in my bag for the skeleton key I always carried. I unlocked the back door, stepped inside.

I stared at my shaking hands. I wanted to tell someone, but she was the one I would have told. She was the one I would have called.

I walked to the buffet and looked for the tapered candle she'd shown me. There it was. Light blue. Faded. On it was a wedding band she'd quit wearing when her knuckles had gotten too big.

"When I die, make sure they bury me with my ring."

"Don't talk about dying," I'd told her.

I'd given her the assurance she'd wanted, while inside I'd told myself I'd never need to see it through. But still, I'd promised.

I wandered through the house. There was her bed. Her chair. Her hairbrush and hand mirror. In the bathroom was the toilet seat my father had given her for Christmas. Who gives someone a toilet seat? But she'd been thrilled. It was soft, and when her friends came over, she'd take them into the bathroom and show it to them.

"He gave it to me for Christmas," she'd

say with pride. They would poke it and laugh.

I HADN'T planned to return to my grandmother's house, but two days later I remembered the ring and drove back to Burlington. I ran up steps I'd climbed ever since I could walk. Through the kitchen that still smelled like ironed cotton sheets to the dining room.

"Where's the ring?"

Blank faces of my grandmother's sisters.

"Her wedding ring." Someone must have taken it to the funeral home.

"I don't know anything about a ring," one of the women said.

Frantically I went through the house, asking each person I came upon. "The ring," I said. "She wanted to be buried with it."

Nobody knew what I was talking about.

Did it matter? Did it really matter? She was dead.

Had someone taken the ring? I kept staring at the blue tapered candle, thinking the ring would appear.

If something could vanish, it could come back.

I went into the spare bedroom, shut the door, and sat down on the bed. This was my room. I'd stayed in it a lot. Sometimes for a day, sometimes for weeks.

"You always have a place here. You can always come here."

And I had. Come knocking in the middle of the night. Broke, dirty, hungry.

Somewhere in the back of my mind, I got the sense that my marriage had opened a door, and now this avalanche of bad was pouring in. I looked in the closet. One of my suitcases was still there, along with some of my things. I put the suitcase on the bed and began filling it.

I SENSED Adrian's shadowy presence on the edge of my grief, but he didn't say anything to me about my grandmother. Not a word. Not a touch that might have conveyed a hint of sympathy. His parents offered hollow condolences that were nothing more than social obligation, but I was too numb to care.

Days later, when I reran the funeral in my head, I had little memory of Adrian at the church, but I knew he'd been there.

She was gone. The ring was gone. That was real.

But it wasn't something I could grasp. And didn't want to grasp it, because I wanted to hold on to her a little longer.

PARKED in the driveway was an unfamiliar truck with a small white trailer attached. My new husband and two men stood in the yard with a horse. A young red thing with a shiny sleek coat, smooth muscles, and four black hooves. I stepped outside and immediately smelled the animal. Skin and sweat and hair.

One of the men broke away and took a few steps in my direction. "I'm sorry about your grandmother."

Adrian saw my confusion. "The horse is for you."

"You bought me a horse?" I felt a spark of life, but also disbelief and irritation. I mean, what the hell? A horse? My grandmother had been dead two weeks, and in that time Adrian had never offered a word of sympathy, yet he went out and bought me a horse?

I moved closer, and the horse got fidgety and nervous. "It's not broken?"

"No," one of the traders said. "But it won't

take long." To demonstrate the animal's gentle nature, he draped himself over its back. The horse tolerated the weight. The guy got brave, swung a leg over, and the rodeo began. Within two seconds, the man was on the ground. Everybody laughed.

They reloaded the horse into the trailer and drove it to a small pen near the corncrib where Adrian could keep a close eye on it. I returned to the house, baffled by his actions.

The next day, Adrian blustered in. "I've got a saddle and halter on her. She doesn't seem to mind it. No bucking at all. She's going to be a mellow thing." This was the most animated and communicative Adrian had been since the night I'd tried to leave.

I climbed in the passenger seat of the truck, and we headed for the crib. Halfway there, Adrian tensed. The truck shot forward, we flew down the road, and pulled to a stop in front of a set of pens. Adrian bailed out, vaulted over a fence. I followed and reached the fence in time to see the glint of a pocketknife.

The horse was hanging by the halter. Eyes blank.

Adrian sliced the tie rope and the horse

hit the ground with a rolling thud. Without pause, he began kicking the dead animal.

The strangulation of the horse was bad enough, but the violent scene playing out in front of me lifted a sad tragedy to another level of awful. Out of breath, Adrian finally looked up at me.

The horror I felt must have shown on my face. He was hard to read, but I could see the moment it occurred to him how enormously his gift had backfired, going from something to make me feel better to something that could only compound my grief.

And yet in that horrible moment, I at last understood that Adrian was unable to communicate his emotions verbally and the horse had been his way of telling me he was sorry about my grandmother.

The Family

Chapter Seven

THE skin of the early summer apple is thin, almost translucent, and the flesh is white. I was picking a variety called Transparent. Adrian's great-grandfather had planted two rows, but this broken, gnarled tree was the only one left. The rest had been bulldozed to make room for easier-to-pick dwarf trees.

I'd started early. Two hours later, the dew still clung to the grass, and a haze hovered above distant cornfields. I stood on a wooden ladder. The thick straps of the picking basket pressed into my shoulders as I filled the metal container resting against my belly. It was an ingenious and simple way to pick, leaving both hands free.

When the apples reached the rim of the container, I climbed down the ladder, unhooked the two sections of cotton rope from the picking basket, releasing the red canvas sleeve at the bottom, allowing the apples to roll into the wooden crates that waited in the grass near the base of the tree. Once the basket was empty, I wound the sections of rope over the hooks, securing the sleeve once more.

Picking had been Adrian's idea. I was still grieving, and it felt good to get out of the house. My grandmother's death had brought about another small measure of change. Adrian seemed to recognize our marriage as something to value. He was no longer eating dinner with his parents, and despite our un-defined relationship, Adrian, this newcomer to my life, was now the only close family I had. Such an odd thing to think about.

Adrian's mother had been skeptical about my picking, and she'd stood at the base of the tree to make sure I did it correctly. "Twist and pull," she'd instructed. "Nobody wants apples with no stems. And don't grasp them too firmly. Your fingers will leave bruises."

She'd been right about that. The first bushel was doomed to end up as seconds be-cause my fingerprints appeared an hour after picking, but now I was finally getting the hang of it.

I twisted and pulled but occasionally still produced an apple with no stem. I rubbed a stemless apple on the leg of my jeans as if I could wipe off the toxins. But an agent was added to the chemicals to make them adhere to the surface of the apple, and no amount of rubbing and scrubbing could remove it all.

I took a bite. The thin skin made a crisp, snapping sound, and my mouth filled with sour juice. Not your ideal eating apple. Most of the older locals used them for applesauce, adding a lot of sugar.

I finished the apple and tossed the core.

I moved the ladder to another spot, climbing higher to reach a cluster of fruit near the top. I could see ribbons of roads winding through green fields. Nearer, on Curtis land, I spotted what looked like the knoll with the pioneer grave Adrian had shown me that perfect day. I searched for the cabin in the woods. I spotted a cluster of trees that might have been the location. Nearby was the pasture, and beside it, dark timber and steep ravines. Familiar, but different because it was now overgrown. Different because I was different.

A death. A loss.

Somewhere far away, a tractor moved through a field. The sound of the diesel engine reminded me that I wasn't completely alone, but it also reminded me that what Adrian and I shared might never be real.

It began to rain. I climbed down the ladder, dumped the load of apples, and ducked out of the harness. I stood under the protection of an apple tree, listening to the patter on the leaves above me. I became aware of a tempo change and a hollow patter that was closer than the leaves above my head. I turned to see one of the red paper boxes used to monitor moths. The little tent was full.

I wiped the back of my hand across my mouth, tasting the pesticide being washed from the leaves. Adrian and his father kept spraying, but the moths still came.

New Mexico, 1969–1972

I WAS thirteen when my mother met David, a man who'd spent most of his life in a strict religious environment. At age twelve, he was sent to live at a monastery run by Christian Brothers. Twenty-five years later, just weeks before taking his final vows to become a Brother himself, he wanted to find out what he was missing. He wanted to know what it was like to have a girlfriend. In a vulnerable state and as randy as a teenager, he ran into my mother.

In order to be alone, they spent evenings at drive-ins, then came home drunk, tumbling into bed. David never stayed the entire night. That would have been inappropriate, but he would swing by early the next morning, a box of doughnuts in his hand. Later, they went to confession and the whole thing would start again.

I wasn't invested in the new guy, and I knew if I bided my time, he would soon be gone. Oddly enough, I was happy. I'd found my groove, and I knew these guys weren't important. In fact, they were my entertainment, my own up-close-and-personal study of dating and relationships. And my mother's secretarial job, combined with her obsessive involvement with men and dating, left me free to do whatever I wanted as long as I kept one eye on my younger brother. Stay up all night listening to the radio if I felt like it. Skip school if I felt like it. Eat whatever I wanted. Read all day long while eating candy. I was as content as a cat. No expectations, no pressure.

But David stuck around. He was a math professor at a new college in a little desert town in southern New Mexico. The College of Artesia was a party school, known for accepting anybody, no matter the grades. Rich parents sent their spoiled brats there, and the school was also a popular place for people who wanted to avoid the Vietnam draft.

It wasn't that I hated every guy my mother dated. I hated the ones who were so obviously wrong for her. I'd adored the shy painter who'd been madly in love with her, and I was heartbroken when she dumped him. My mother didn't love David. I was pretty sure of that. She hadn't loved any of them. They were her do-overs.

We made a few trips from Albuquerque to Artesia, and pretty soon there was talk of getting married, and they'd bought a house, and we moved to the middle of nowhere, and my younger brother and I were once again starting a new school.

People in Artesia had exaggerated Southern accents. Girls at the public junior high school wore saddle shoes and skirts that fell to their knees, and for lunch they dumped small packets of salted peanuts into a bottle of Pepsi, put their thumbs over the glass lip, and gave it a good shake. They said *y'all* and *ma'am* and told me I sounded like someone from television. Within a few months I was saying *y'all* and *ma'am* and dumping peanuts in my Pepsi. But I refused to wear skirts that fell to my knees.

David was malleable. He would do whatever my mother said, no questions asked. If she told him to beat me, he would do it with no expression on his face. If she told him to lock me out of the house, he did. Sometimes I thought he might be the epitome of evil, and at other times I felt sorry for him and saw him as a helpless victim. He didn't have a chance against her.

My mother didn't think of me as her daughter, but rather as a person who'd had a hand in ruining her life. "You look like him," she would tell me with confusion and hatred in her eyes, as if she'd gone back to Florida in her mind and was seeing the man who'd left us. She would never outrun that man. Deep down, my mother knew what a mess she'd made of her life, but there was no turning back. She was finally married. Her years of trying to correct something that had happened in the past had led us to this new existence.

A façade had been erected, not only for the people who looked at us from the outside, but also for my mother and her new husband, and even for my younger brother. They'd gotten on this train, and they weren't getting off, and they would ride it out and pretend it was going somewhere nice. And sometimes it worked.

My mother and the new husband and my

younger brother made an odd family. My brother had never had a father, and he embraced the new life with gusto. He and his new parent did things together. My brother began to use the word *Dad*. He was too young to realize he was a traitor, not to the father he'd never known, but to our way of life. He and his new father put together models, and the three of them took trips to the desert, returning with the treasures they'd collected. And sometimes I thought the new dad wasn't the person who didn't fit—*I* didn't fit.

Weekday mornings, David put on a gray suit and tie and pedaled his bicycle to school, proud as a peacock, saddlebags bulging with the textbooks he'd strapped above the back tire, his posture straight, ringing the handlebar bell for no apparent reason, just to announce that he was happy. From the window of the school bus, kids would point and laugh. "Look at that weird guy!"

As the months ticked away, my mother's unhappiness increased. I began to dread stepping in the front door. My younger brother managed to stay beneath her radar because he could charm his way out of anything and because he was still thought of as the baby.

I would arrive home from school to find her in a rage, and that rage was usually directed at me. Maybe I'd forgotten to put a spoon in a special, designated cup in the sink. Maybe I'd used the wrong washcloth. The infractions were small, her behavior masking the real problem: She was miserable in her new life, and I was a reminder of the man who'd left her. She may have been able to fool my younger brother, but she couldn't fool me; I was old enough to see through her act and her pretense.

What are you doing? What have you done? My eyes asked the questions. This place, this man, were more wrong for her than the secret agent had been. Her days were filled with preparing meals, grocery shopping, cleaning house, nothing that remotely spoke of her. She was like a horse kept in a confined stall. Always volatile, she became even moodier and more unpredictable.

People thought my mother was clever and beautiful and artistic—bohemian cool—and few suspected what went on behind closed doors. A handful of friends witnessed the rages and the irrational behavior. Those friends never returned, and they quit associating with me. They would give me sideways glances in the school hall or turn their backs and pretend to be concentrating on their lockers.

The marriage made me long for the days of the revolving door and the men who came and went. With them, I always knew the page would turn, and the guy would be gone and another would take his place. And for a brief time, my mother would be happy.

"I'M GOING to look for a job," I said.

It was evening, and Adrian and I sat on opposite ends of the couch, heads bent over sketch pads, me with a pencil and eraser, Adrian with pen and ink. Two months had passed since my grandmother's death. Every day was still tough, but the fog was lifting, and I occasionally caught myself laughing at something absurd or silly. Life held a hint of promise.

I swept eraser crumbs away and tucked my feet farther under me. "Maybe something in Burlington."

I'd painted the kitchen yellow and hung yellow curtains in the windows above the sink. I'd refinished the living room floor and put down linoleum in the bathroom. I'd immersed myself in all things domestic as long as I could, until I began to understand how pioneer women lost their minds locked up in tiny cabins all day.

He dipped his quill pen in the inkwell. That was followed by the sound of the sharp tip moving across rough paper. I'd already peeked and knew he was drawing a cowboy on a horse. He drew the most magnificent horses. "My mother is hiring part-time help," he said without looking up. "Apple baggers and sorters."

I laughed out loud at the idea of taking orders from his mom.

"No, really," he said. "You should work in the salesroom."

I didn't want to tell him his idea had disaster written all over it.

"She has to hire somebody. It may as well be you. And then you wouldn't be driving back and forth in bad weather. Or in the dark."

And we both knew how good I was at that.

"I'll talk to her," he said. "I'll let her know you want to work for her."

Work *for* her. Not work for the farm. Not work *with* her. But I also saw this as an opportunity to prove myself. To be a part of the farm. To be a part of Adrian's life. "Okay." And really. What could be so hard about sorting apples and putting them in crates and bags?

I had little time to think about the foolishness of our idea. The next morning, I headed out the door to work at my new place of employment under the critical eye of my mother-in-law. I'd done a stint at a Levi Strauss factory in Albuquerque, sewing pockets on jeans. I knew the drill of the tedious, and I understood the need for efficiency of movement and combining quality work with speed.

As I walked across the road to the sales-room, the rising sun hadn't yet warmed the air. Golden leaves from towering hickory trees drifted silently to the ground. The beauty of the morning raised my spirits, filling me with excitement and hope. Maybe this would work. Maybe this would even make everything okay.

As I circled the main house, I saw the view that greeted every visitor. A cluster of buildings, all painted a brilliant white. Adrian had told me the Victorian farmhouse with its gingerbread trim had once belonged to a preacher back when the farm was part of a small village, and wakes and viewings had been held in the parlor.

A circular drive with an entrance and exit. Two massive white barns and a long, low building that had once been a stable, carriage house, and blacksmith's shop but were now used for storage. In the center of the parking area stood an ancient windmill. A historical marker embedded in a rock reminded visitors that this was a place of history, a place with a past that stretched back generations.

The day was already under way, with pickups full of seasonal help heading down the road. Wearing a flannel shirt and jean jacket, Adrian waved to me from a tractor. He shifted gears, and he took off toward the orchard pulling a flatbed loaded with crates.

Most everything that had to do with apples was done in a giant barn that had been converted into a salesroom, cider room, and storage room. In the sorting room, apples rolled and bounced down conveyor belts to be ejected into areas designated by size, while women in sweatshirts, bandanas, and cotton gloves watched and removed damaged apples that would either be fed to cattle or made into cider. Sliding wooden doors big enough for full-size tractors stood open on the east and west sides of the building, a cold breeze blowing apple leaves from the sorter to the cement floor. Pallets were stacked with wooden crates, CURTIS ORCHARD stenciled in black below the handles.

I caught a glimpse of Adrian's father driving a forklift, moving pallets of sorted apples from the main barn to the storage area in yet another white building. Our eyes met. His were blank, offering no welcome or acknowledgment. I got the distinct feeling my employment had been thoroughly discussed and given the stamp of disapproval. I found myself thinking that I had to do a good job, that I had to prove my worthiness to both of my in-laws. And then I quickly caught myself. I didn't need to prove myself to anybody.

The smell of apples was so intense and so

sweet it almost seemed artificial. It soaked into hair and clothes and skin, and when the women in front of the sorter smiled and waved in greeting, they seemed a part of the soil and trees and fruit.

When the din couldn't seem to get any louder, someone opened the cider-room door where the high-pitched sound of apples being ground for the press caused alarmed children to scream and clap their hands to their ears.

Apples were best stored in temperatures a little above freezing. People dashed coatless from heated cars, plunging into the salesroom only to find the temperature no warmer within the closed doors. Inside they were quickly overwhelmed by variety. Apples for cooking, apples for eating, apples for pies, apples for applesauce. Apples that taste like wine, apples that taste like honey.

I was put to work placing Golden Delicious apples in peck bags, one piece of fruit at a time, without bumping or dumping or dropping. I knew that bruises wouldn't show up immediately, but in twenty-four hours a damaged apple would reveal imperfections.

At break time, everyone scattered. Some

went to their cars, turned on the radio, popped open a soda, relaxed, and soaked in the solitude. Others stood in the open barn doors enjoying a smoke or eating a previously pocketed apple, saved for that very occasion.

I joined the smoking crowd.

"This your first day?" The question came from a big woman dressed in baggy jeans, light-blue Windbreaker, and floral scarf. Earlier I'd heard someone call her Georgia. She pulled a large red apple from her pocket and took a bite.

I nodded, wondering if I should explain who I was.

"My mother worked here," she told me. "And I started when I was sixteen." She continued her visual evaluation of me. "Ruth don't usually hire help like you. She hires local."

I took a last drag from my cigarette, scraped it out on the ground, then tapped what remained back in my pack for later. "I'm local."

"Whose kid are you?"

I looked up to see Ruth glaring at me from across the parking lot.

"See what I mean?" Georgia said, noting the direction of my fixed stare. "You'd better not do any chatting while you work, and don't leave a second early. In fact, stay a half hour after your shift ends if you want to stick around here."

"Is she really so hard to get along with?"

"Her son got married, and she's had a bee in her bonnet ever since. We're all feeling the brunt of it, but she's a good woman. She really made something of herself."

"But she married into this place."

"She came from one of the poorest families in the county. No running water, no electricity. Her daddy was crazy. He didn't have a car or driver's license, and he used to drive to town on his riding mower, naked as a jaybird. But look at Mildred now."

"Mildred?"

"That's what we used to call her, but she changed everything about herself when she got married, even her first name. It's like she wanted to be a completely different person."

"How'd she meet Mr. Curtis?"

"A friend was doing bookwork for his daddy. Told Mildred Mr. Curtis had more money than he knew what to do with, and that pretty much started the wedding bells to chiming."

"That makes me feel a little sorry for her husband."

"You know he was with those other two kids when they died. Family vacation to Colorado. Three kids in the backseat. Two died from carbon monoxide poisoning. The other one almost didn't make it, but he pulled through. I heard his mother, who would be Adrian Curtis's grandmother, never forgave him for living because the boy who died was her favorite. Doctor told her to have another baby to get over the grief. That baby died two days after it was born. Sometimes I think this place is cursed, but it's been a blessing for me." She checked her watch. "Gotta get back at it." She gave her apple core a toss into tall grass along a fence. "Good luck."

"Thanks."

Two hours and eight crates of Golden Delicious apples later, it was time for the lunch break. Recalling Georgia's warning, I considered working through it, but my hands were freezing, my legs were tired from standing, and I was hungry. I headed home.

As soon as I stepped in the door, the phone rang. I answered it.

"You don't need to come back this afternoon," Ruth said.

I was surprised, but maybe we'd bagged enough apples for the day. "What time would you like me tomorrow?"

"You don't need to come in tomorrow or the next day. I won't be needing you. Turn in your hours and I'll pay you for this morning."

It took me a few seconds to completely get what she was saying. "Sure." Stunned, I replaced the receiver in the cradle on the kitchen wall. Automatically, I began dragging food from the refrigerator. But as I slapped mayonnaise on a piece of bread, I began to laugh.

A short time later, Adrian appeared, his hair wind-raked, his face sunburned. He dropped his jacket over a chair and headed for the kitchen sink, rolling up the sleeves of his flannel shirt.

"Your mother fired me," I said, pressing fingers to my lips to stop my grin.

He turned on the water and reached for the soap. "She did not."

"She did. I swear."

"She wouldn't do that." He shut off the water, dried his hands. "You must have misunderstood. Did she say you were fired?"

"She didn't use the word *fired*. She didn't have to. She told me she no longer needed me, and I know she's short on help."

"What did you do to make her mad?" He grabbed my sandwich.

"Mayonnaise!" I warned. I squeezed past him to retrieve a couple of glasses and plates from the cupboard. "It wasn't me. I thought I was doing a pretty good job. Didn't get as many apples bagged as workers who've been doing it a while, but I kept up."

He took a bite from the sandwich, grimaced, then handed it back. "I'm going to talk to her."

"Don't do that." She'd probably deny it anyway. There was a reason she'd called me on the phone rather than fire me in the salesroom where people would overhear.

I set the table, then sat down with the sandwich finally where it belonged, on my plate. "It doesn't matter. Working in the salesroom was a crazy idea anyway." Ruth wanted me to know I didn't belong in her world, that I had no place in it. "I'll find a job in Burlington."

He was making his own sandwich now, adding lunchmeat, cheese, pickles, lettuce, and sliced tomato. I could see he still didn't like the idea of my off-site job, so I changed the subject. "I heard some interesting family history while I was over there."

"Oh?" He sat down across from me. I told him a little of what Georgia had shared, leaving out the implication that his mother may have been a gold digger.

"Those sorters are a bunch of gossips," he said. "I can't believe they were telling *you* our family history."

I recalled Georgia, and my deception. "I didn't exactly tell anybody who I was."

He laughed. "Let's go over there right now. I'll introduce you to Georgia. We'll walk in and I'll say, 'I want you to meet my wife.'"

I smiled and shook my head. "There's no way I would do something like that to the poor woman."

But I couldn't help laughing along with him. Our glee at the idea of pulling such a prank reminded me that he was only a few years older than me. A kid. We were both kids. Because I was young, it was easier to brush off Ruth's treatment. It would have made things easier if she'd liked me, but I filed the day under adult disapproval, and I could even find her dislike slightly amusing.

I DIDN'T look for a job. Suddenly I had an idea, something I hadn't thought about in years. I dug out my manual typewriter, bought typing paper, carbon paper, and a new ribbon, and began writing. I kept it a secret for the first week, hiding the typewriter and my accumulating pages, but one day Adrian dropped by midmorning, a time that was unusual for him. He caught me sitting at the kitchen table, pawnshop typewriter in front of me. I quickly rolled the paper backward and rested my arm over it.

At the sink, he filled a glass with water, then turned around. "What are you doing?"

"Writing."

"Writing what?"

Oh, he would think it so silly. "A book."

"Book?" The glass in his hand stopped halfway to his mouth. "About what?"

"About a girl who leaves the farm to go to the Amazon."

"Why is she in the Amazon?"

"I don't know. I haven't figured that out yet. But it will have adventure and mystery and romance." My voice rose in excitement.

"What do you know about writing?"

"Nothing." I didn't even know if the pages should be double- or single-spaced. I had no idea where I would send it once I was done. "But I'll learn. I'll figure it out."

"It seems like a waste of time to me, but if you want to—" *waste your time* were his unspoken words. "I'll bet you type fast. You should be done in a couple of weeks, right?" The book was an intrusion, and I could see he was already looking forward to once again being the center of my world.

"It could take a year." I had to smother a laugh at his shocked expression. To point out that I was committed and he should get used to it, I added, "And when I get the first book done, I'll probably write another."

"I don't get why anybody would write one book, let alone two. What will you do with this book if you finish it?"

"Try to sell it to a New York publisher."

He might have thought it pure foolishness, but I could also see the wheels turning. I knew he was thinking about my getting fired by his mother, relieved to know that this writing project might keep me from driving back and forth to the job I'd talked about finding.

"You don't think I'll do it," I said. "You don't think I'll finish."

"It's not that. Stories in books aren't real. I don't know why anybody would want to read one, let alone write one. I don't know why you're doing it. People read fiction to escape. Are you writing to escape? To create something you don't have here?"

"I just want to tell a story. I don't know if I'll be able to sell it, but I'll write it."

He finished his water, put down the glass, and stood behind me, rubbing my shoulders as we talked. "What about drawing?"

"I'll still draw, but I'm never going to be very good."

"You will. You are."

I shook my head. "I don't think so." Doubts about my artistic talent had increased, maybe because of my exposure to Adrian. He was a real artist. Drawing came naturally to him. He loved it.

It occurred to me that I owed my new endeavor to Ruth, and I could already imagine the dedication page: *To my mother-in-law. Thanks for firing me.*

If she'd embraced me, if she'd welcomed me, if she hadn't fired me, I might not have pulled out my typewriter or thought about writing a book. Maybe Adrian's implications had some truth to them. Maybe my writing had less to do with the need to create and more to do with the need to carve out something for myself, give myself a sense of purpose. Something that reached beyond the farm and the apples that were arranged just so, five on the bottom so the plastic bag wouldn't tip over.

As the days and weeks passed, I worked steadily. I tried not to flaunt my new career path. I never left typed pages lying around. And if I stopped in the middle of a page, I rolled the paper so the text wasn't visible. But sometimes I would forget, and I'd catch Adrian reading a stray paragraph or a description. And he would look hurt and betrayed, like a jealous husband who'd come across a strange phone number in his wife's purse.

Chapter Eight

"COULD you be pregnant?" the doctor asked in a German accent.

I sat on the exam table, which was wrapped in thin crinkly paper. "No . . . I mean, well . . ." My stomach took a dive. Pregnant?

The period following my grandmother's death had been a strange combination of time moving quickly and time moving slowly. Yes, I'd been feeling sick and weak and sleepy, but I thought it was depression.

"I'll have the nurse draw some blood so we can rule out a few things. We'll run a pregnancy test at the same time."

The nurse tapped a vein and filled three small vials. "Go ahead and get dressed. I'll be back with the results of the iron test."

I was anemic. Vitamins and iron were prescribed.

"Call back in three days for the pregnancy results," the nurse said.

I returned to the farm, but I didn't say anything to Adrian other than to tell him about the anemia. Surely I wasn't pregnant.

I thought of the girls in the car, the wedding shower girls, and their talk of babies. How foreign it had seemed, how far from me as a life could be. I didn't know what worried me more, the idea of having an infant to care for or the idea of being a mother.

Three days later, I drove to Burlington to call the doctor's office. I went the twelve miles because I wanted to be alone when I made the call. I didn't want Adrian walking in on me while I was on the phone. I pulled into the Montgomery Ward parking lot to use the drive-up pay phone, which sat along the heavily traveled Mount Pleasant Avenue. Immediately after dialing, traffic noise picked up.

The receptionist answered. I shouted my name and told her I was calling to get my test results.

She was gone a moment, then returned with a clatter of heavy plastic. A pause, then a response I couldn't quite decipher.

"Positive?" Had I heard right? "Positive? What does that mean?"

A semi trailer accelerated in front of me. I breathed diesel fumes.

"You're pregnant."

"Pregnant?" I was still shouting.

"Yes."

I put the receiver back and rolled up the window.

Someone honked and I looked in the rearview mirror to see an angry face in the car behind me. I pulled forward a couple of vehicle lengths. Then I did what I always did in moments of high stress—I reached for my cigarettes. I lit up and took a deep drag.

And immediately realized I shouldn't be smoking.

Okay, calm down. It's not like a baby was going to pop out of me at any second. Nine months. But how far along was I? A month? Maybe two? I had no idea. I knew nothing about babies.

I couldn't handle being married; how could I have a baby?

Back home, I told Adrian about the pregnancy. He turned white, got up from the kitchen table, and left the house. I would have done the same thing. But to his credit, he returned an hour later.

"I'm sorry," he said. "It just took me by surprise. I've always wanted kids. I've always wanted to be a father."

But his mother didn't take the news as well.

"Don't tell anybody," she said as soon as she heard. She'd made a special trip to our house and sat on the green living room couch. "You might have a miscarriage."

"A miscarriage? What are you talking about?"

"You might not have a baby." She fixed me with a hard stare, as if trying to transmit something she couldn't say aloud. "Don't tell a soul. Once one person knows, the whole county will know."

"So?" Her odd behavior and odder directive both frightened me and irritated me. *Just say what you mean.*

"One day you might be pregnant, and the next you might not be pregnant anymore."

Her words certainly held a sinister quality, and I couldn't help but imagine her pushing me down a flight of stairs or some such nonsense, but I soon realized she was implying that pregnancies often ended in miscarriages, at least on the farm.

I'D NEVER GIVEN MY health much thought, and for the past year or so I'd lived on a diet of alcohol, beef sticks, pickled eggs, and Stewart's sandwiches. But shortly after finding out I was pregnant, maternal instinct kicked in. I quit drinking and smoking, and I began eating nutritious meals. I didn't experience any threat of miscarriage, and the pregnancy moved along uneventfully.

"MAYBE we should start looking for our own place soon," I said.

Harvest was over, the cider press was running, the air smelled like apples, and Adrian and I were sitting at our tiny kitchen table.

"You mean a place to live?" Adrian asked. "We have a place."

"We can't stay here forever, especially with a baby coming."

"This is where the hired man lives, and that's what I am."

"You're the son." I was surprised to find that a place so embedded in history was run like an impersonal business. "You've never had any plans to move at least into your own house? I'm not talking about moving away." We'd already had that conversation.

"Where would I move? *Why* would I move?"

"I don't know where. Up the road."

"My parents would never allow it."

"That's ridiculous. What about the East Place?" The farmhouse had a private lane and a huge yard. It was less than a mile from the main house but out of eyesight.

"A renter is living there."

Practically for free. In return he kept an eye on the place and paid for repairs. We could do that. "Can't he be given notice?"

He shook his head. "You don't get it. This is where I'm supposed to live."

"What difference does it make where we live as long as you show up when you're supposed to? And if this house were empty, there would be more places for the pickers to stay. I'd think your parents would like that."

"Come with me to talk to them. You'll see what I'm up against."

We crossed the yard and entered the big house. Adrian's parents sat facing each other at the kitchen table, a package of caramel rolls between them, his father in overalls, his mother in her signature gingham shirt and jeans. The kitchen smelled of strong coffee.

Adrian poured himself a cup and sat in the chair that was still his chair. I took the remaining seat.

There was some discussion about the plans for the rest of the day, and what apples were getting low in the salesroom, and what apples needed to be replenished from the underground storage area; then Adrian cleared his throat and broached the subject of our moving.

His parents looked at each other, and I could see that Adrian hadn't exaggerated their feelings about the subject. Adrian's father made eye contact with me, and I almost recoiled at the iciness I saw there. Then he turned to his son. "If you move, don't bother ever coming around here again. You won't be welcome." The older man got to his feet, chair scraping. "I'm going out to the cider room."

That was that. Final word.

He left all three of us sitting there. Ruth started clearing the table. "You know how he feels about that kind of thing."

Adrian shrugged and looked at me. *See what I mean?* He wasn't upset. No, he seemed a little relieved.

"That house is for you," Ruth told her son. "Why would you want to live anywhere else?" She gave me a hard look. "This is your fault. You're too independent."

"That's a bad thing?" I suddenly understood that Adrian's parents saw me as a threat to their way of life. Absurd. What kind of impact could someone like me possibly have on the future of the farm?

"Of course independence is bad," she said.

Adrian got to his feet. "Let's go."

We walked home in silence, and I sat down on the front stoop.

"I thought my dad would be more sympathetic." Adrian lit a cigarette. "He didn't want to stay here when he and my mother were married. He wanted a place of his own. I think my grandparents would have been okay with it as long as they didn't live too far away, but my mother talked my dad into staying."

"You're okay with living here?" I asked. "Honestly?"

"It's free. If we moved, we'd have house payments. This place is a big part of my income."

I'd been around long enough to know how

much money he made. Barely enough for a single person to scrape by, let alone a family. "You're basically their slave. Practically free labor." Adrian's tangled relationship with his parents and the farm was something I was just beginning to grasp and would most likely never understand.

"The farm will be mine one day." He shrugged. "But right now I'm just a worker bee."

"When will it be yours? In fifty years?" I knew I sounded like the outsider I was. I wasn't sure it was worth staying, but then I didn't understand having such a strong connection to a parcel of land, a connection that went back generations. Even if he moved, he'd have to live with the guilt of abandoning the farm and his parents.

For me, it was unfathomable to have your whole life mapped out before you were born. And here I was, soon to give birth to the next generation.

THE first Christmas was spent at the big farmhouse. Sunlight falling in the giant windows was unrelenting. A football game blared on the television, and everybody, including

Adrian's unmarried brother and sister, gave off an aura of wishing they were somewhere else.

Conversation was dull, and the food was bland—a lot of pastel side dishes made with Jell-O and Cool Whip. I found myself wondering if this was how normal people lived. I couldn't fully grasp why it was so awful. Maybe because it was just a group of people doing what was expected of them, with no surprises and no joy. The holidays of my life may have been volatile, but they'd come with good food and wine, music, introspective discussions, and laughter.

None of Adrian's family seemed to really know one another. They occupied the same space but seemed shut off, closed off, secretive, and repressed. The conversation was the conversation of strangers, with awkwardly introduced topics that fizzled out until someone came up with something else just as impossible.

Did they ever raise their voices? Did they ever shout? Or get excited? Did they ever share their feelings and emotions?

Even though Adrian's brother and sister no longer lived on the farm, they were still defined by it. Without the farm, would they exist? They were who they were because of the farm, because its soil and the generations buried in it bound them to life.

Conversation shifted to farming and a topic I didn't understand about purchasing chemicals with a special applicator's license. Once Adrian and I left the farmhouse, I brought up the discussion.

"Why was your dad so intent on buying so many drums of pesticide?" I asked as we walked back to our little house. The temperature was below zero, and the snow had a crust that would hold for a moment, then break.

"The EPA is always banning important chemicals, and we have to stock up while they're still available," Adrian said. "We all have a license so we can purchase several seasons' worth."

I looked at him in shock.

"Everybody does it. Do you know how hard it is to kill the codling moth? They can wipe out an orchard. Especially the old orchard, because those trees aren't as disease resistant. Once they bore into the trunk and lay their eggs, that's it. It's too late. Farmers know what works in their fields, and they know what doesn't. And there's a misconception that new products are safer. It's all bad. It's all dangerous. The new stuff just hasn't been banned yet."

I didn't like what I was hearing. I thought about the fields that began outside our door and stretched to the horizon.

"The Midwest has a higher concentration of insects than the East or West Coast," Adrian said. "And decades of pesticide use have created resistance. It's going to take stronger and stronger chemicals for farmers to stay in business, not weaker ones."

Inside, we hung our coats and stocking caps by the back door and kicked off our boots. "They should stop," I said. "Go organic."

He laughed at my unrealistic comment. "It can't be done. Maybe somebody with a few acres could go organic as a side project, but it's too labor intensive for a full-size farm. Plus, the codling moth would take over. And everybody would think we were nuts."

"You can't be concerned about that."

"It's too late," he said. "Farms are too big, and chemicals have created superbugs and superweeds. It's too late to turn around. The EPA might be looking out for the average person, but nobody is looking out for the farmer. It's us against them."

"Do you really believe that?" If anything, the EPA probably wasn't being strict enough. And how dangerous was it to have a child in the middle of such toxic saturation?

But people had kids around here all the time, I reassured myself. Adrian had grown up here. He was healthy. His father had worked around chemicals most of his life. Really bad things like DDT, and he was okay. How could you blame farmers for choosing to believe that they weren't poisoning the world and their own children?

Albuquerque, New Mexico, 1969

AT AGE fourteen, I ran away from home.

I'd been sent from Artesia to Albuquerque, New Mexico, to stay a week with people I'd never met so my mother and David could play honeymoon. I understood their desire to be alone. It had to be tough for newlyweds to have a teenager sleeping in a room a few feet away. The solution was to send me to a town I missed—Albuquerque. The strangers

I visited had a daughter my age, a beautiful girl with large gray eyes and blond hair that hung past her waist, a girl who came hand-picked by my mother—someone with a solid track record for latching on to the biggest loser in the room.

The girl, whose name was Jodie, turned out to be a soulless bitch who filled her home with drugs and equally soulless, sex-crazed boys while her parents were at work, and who talked about slicing her parents' throats while they slept. Jodie would have done Charles Manson proud.

After marijuana was discovered in Jodie's room, my mother and David arrived in Albuquerque to tell us that Jodie and I were being sent to a "home." I imagined masculine women with beige walking shoes making me get down on my hands and knees to scrub stone floors. Later, I would beg for gruel: "More, please."

While everyone slept, Jodie and I ran off, parting ways once we hit the city streets.

As the days passed without food or sleep, my judgment vanished and I ended up in a house full of junkies. To get to their place, I took a fire escape up the side of a weed- and trash-littered cement building, crossed a pea-gravel roof where sunlight steamed beer urine, to a door that opened to a room littered with mattresses.

Right away I could tell the professionals from the frauds. The professional junkies had slack jaws, thin arms, and desolate eyes. Then there were the shiny suburban kids who were visiting for a thrill—or maybe they'd arrived by accident. Heard about a place where somebody was old enough to buy beer. Maybe there would even be sex. They'd stepped inside and—whoa. Junkies everywhere.

I was young and confused, so it was no surprise that a guy talked me into letting him dilute some heroin with water so he could shoot me up and turn me on. Before he pulled the tourniquet from my arm, I felt the magic wash through me and fell back on a mattress.

Heroin junkies might look dead on the outside, but inside it's heaven. Inside it's the absence of everything bad. It's beautiful and perfect, and when you're inside, the last thing you think about is dying because you want that perfect moment to last forever.

But perfection is an illusion. Perfection has a price.

During those perfect moments while I was tethered to the bed by drugs, bad things happened to me. Very bad things that I will never talk about.

Once I was able to function, I left the junkie house. The lesson I learned was that some people will take what they want, whenever they want, with no guilt or thought of the consequences, and that evil people existed to prey upon the innocent. But I also knew cruelty wasn't always delivered by strangers. Sometimes abuse came from the people who should have cared the most. It could take place in the dark heart of any family.

I walked to a grim neighborhood drugstore, swiped a pack of razor blades, and found a quiet spot under a cement overpass.

Fourteen and I was tired of living.

I'd heard that bleeding to death was painless. I'd heard it was peaceful and you just drifted off. An absence of fear. And wasn't that what we all wanted? For the fear to stop? Isn't that really what it was all about? The drugs? The running away?

I thought about the plate of poison mushrooms, about how I should have died years ago. With the razor blade, I made a test slice. Even though it wasn't deep, a red line formed on the pale skin of my inner wrist. I found myself mesmerized by the white and red.

There was more than one way to escape what had happened to me. I tossed the blade away, and in that moment I made up my mind. I would never tell anybody about the heroin and the junkie house and the bad things that had happened there. There are things you don't want people to know because as soon as they know, you change. You become someone different in their eyes.

I wasn't sent to a home, and when my mother asked where I'd been all those days, I lied. I told her I'd hidden in a storage shed.

As far as you're concerned.

"Don't tell anyone about running away," my mother instructed. "David has a reputation to uphold in this town. If anyone asks about your weight loss, say you got food poisoning."

As far as you're concerned.

WINTER turned to spring, and I began to accept farming risks as a part of life. Like coal miners who know their job is dangerous or artists who work with lead. Every occupation can impact a person's health. These were the excuses I made, and the fact that nobody was dropping dead lulled me into a false sense of security.

As the land awakened around me, I saw the farm as something to cherish, as something beautiful and timeless. Even from my close vantage point, it sometimes seemed a little short of paradise.

When summer came, I photographed round hay bales resting against the light and shadow of softly rolling hills. Giant orange suns setting over hazy cornfields. I captured the pattern of the mowed fields, but I could never capture a green so deep it hurt or the organic scent of the ground when it's been sliced open with a plow blade. That couldn't be captured with a camera lens or a pen. That sweet ache of nature and time that kept invisibly moving, no matter how much you wanted it to stop.

A YEAR after starting my new life with Adrian, we had a baby boy we named Alexander.

The birth of a grandson brought about a change in my relationship with Ruth. I was suddenly tolerated because I'd supplied the farm with an heir. When I knocked at the back door, Ruth invited me inside, but I was always treated like a guest she didn't want around, ignored unless we were discussing the baby.

The farm and the ground and Alexander's heritage must have reached him in utero, because the first word he spoke was *apple*. I initially thought it an odd coincidence—I'd simply applied the obvious to his baby sounds. But, no. While the two syllables weren't exactly correct, they were close enough, and tests with images and actual apples brought the same results, almost as if he'd arrived with an awareness of his destiny. "Ap-pah."

Ruth beamed and bounced my baby on her knee. "Bless his heart. He already knows he's going to be an apple farmer."

As further evidence of Alexander's defection, his favorite toy was his grandmother's gift of a big plastic apple with an obnoxious smiling face. The toy rocked and chimed. Alexander latched on to it the way other children latch on to stuffed animals and blankets.

I WROTE while Alexander napped, and when the manuscript was finished, I put it in a typing-paper box and mailed it to addresses I found printed in the front of books. Months later, the manuscript would return with a rejection letter, and I would rework the material and send it out again. This process was repeated over and over.

Three years after typing that first page, I received an offer from a major publishing house.

Artists seek validation and approval. Unlike Adrian, I would never have been satisfied to leave the manuscript in a drawer. It wasn't enough to have written it; my words had to be read.

There was no celebration of my sale, no wine or champagne or dinner. Adrian was skeptical of the contract, and even when a box of paperbacks arrived, he was unimpressed. Adrian was an artist, yet he could never fully embrace art. Art for him was a secret thing, a shameful thing, done in privacy.

I put the money in the bank, because there was nothing we needed. We had it already. A nearly perfect life on a beautiful farm.

SOMETIMES there are people you must forget because of the damage they cause—blood ties or not. My mother was one of those people.

Months would pass with only a select few knowing her whereabouts; then at unexpected moments, a gift I'd given her as a child would show up in the mailbox. No return address, always postmarked from a new area of the country, accompanied by a cruel letter or by nothing at all.

"From her?" Adrian would ask if he saw me holding the unopened package, my face blank.

We rarely talked about my family or my past. But he showed amusement at my mother's mailbox intrusions into our life, possibly because the proof of my dysfunctional family made his own seem less abnormal.

Being a single mother and having your life derailed by children you resented must have been hard. If my brothers and I had been dogs, she would have dumped us on a back road far from town in the hopes that we would never find our way home. But she'd been stuck with us, and I almost felt sorry for her.

I kept in touch with my brothers, usually one or two phone calls a year, those conversations tempered with caution and oddly mixed with pain, as if we knew too much about each other's past. We compared notes on who'd heard from our mother last, what the package had contained, did it come with a twenty-five-page letter that revised our history but blamed us for ruining her life? Was there a return address? This last was almost always no.

"Open it," Adrian coaxed as we stood in the road near the mailbox.

"No."

Later, after he'd returned to the field, I opened the manila envelope. Inside was a piece of artwork I'd given my mother for Christmas. It was a photo of an apple cut from a magazine.

I remembered lying on my mother's bed while I pasted the image to a piece of green construction paper, fascinated by the beauty of the apple. I could almost smell the crayons, almost feel how hard I'd pressed against the paper. To fashion a frame, I'd used the lid from a box of silk stockings. The crude craft was supposed to be a Christmas card, and I'd worried that the choice of an apple would annoy her, because what did an apple have to do with Christmas?

The arrival of the childhood artwork made me wonder if my life was as preordained as Adrian's, just in a less obvious way. A photo from a magazine. An apple.

THREE years after our son was born, we had another child. A daughter we named Lucia. Being female and not the firstborn, Lucia didn't arrive with a designated role. She could be whatever she wanted to be. Her first word was *Momma*, her second *Dada*. And it was a long time before she could say the word *apple*.

Adrian and I embraced parenthood, and we both discovered that children were very easy to love. The four of us were inseparable. From the time they were infants, Alexander and Lucia spent every moment with us whether we were inside or out, the hours filled with silly talk, laughter, and private jokes.

Ruth rarely ventured past her yard. She never visited the fields or timber, so the entire farm felt like our private world. The pond behind our house especially felt like our place. I would pack a picnic basket, and we would spend afternoons fishing and evenings sitting in front of a bonfire. We started Alexander and Lucia on ice skates before they were three, and winter evenings were spent skating and playing pond hockey.

In the summer, we planted, mowed, baled, and put up hay with the children beside us. We fed cattle together; we ate lunch and dinner together. After dinner there were more chores to be done. Sometimes I remained behind to write, and when the three of them returned, the door would open on a burst of laughter.

"Will you draw with me?" a six-year-old Lucia asked later in the evening. And she and Adrian would lie on the floor and draw on separate sketch pads, Adrian offering advice while I typed in the corner and Alexander pored through my record album collection.

Alexander was infatuated with '60s and '70s music. He spent hours studying album artwork and asking about bands and wanting to know what the world had been like when good music and entire albums were played on regular radio stations. Drawing frustrated him, and music gave him a foothold in the creative world.

Every evening, I read Alexander and Lucia a bedtime story in their shared room, kissed them, and turned out the light.

"Good night! Sleep tight!" Lucia would call sweetly, smacking her lips against her palm.

"Adios! Adios, amiga!" Alexander finished.

As OUR children grew, the Sweet Melinda trees grew with them. The trunks became thick and sturdy, the branches strong enough to tolerate high winds without breaking. Each spring a few random blossoms appeared, but the buds refused to set. Each season marked another year of waiting for yet another spring and new blossoms. I began to fear that Adrian's trees weren't hardy enough for our winters. Maybe the blossoms would never set. Maybe the trees would never produce a single apple.

For Adrian, the Sweet Melindas were his and his alone, and I wanted him to succeed. They were a chance for him to establish his place on the farm, a chance to prove he was more than just hard labor and a worker bee. They would prove his worth in a place where worth shouldn't have to be proven.

MY GRANDMOTHER always said the best time to find morel mushrooms was when lilacs weren't yet blooming and oak leaves were the size of squirrels' ears. Every old-timer had a different theory of how and where to find the spongy morsels, but everyone agreed on one thing: Morels took a good rain, quickly followed by warmth and sunshine, to make them pop through the soil.

It was early spring, and our little family of four left the house on foot, plastic bags tucked into the back pockets of our jeans, to hike through timber that bordered the orchard and surrounded pastures. On this particular afternoon, the ground was soft from the previous night's rain, the sky was a brilliant blue, and the temperature was in the mid-seventies. Perfect mushrooming weather.

Unlike the skeleton canopy above our heads, the timber floor had already awakened. Near narrow, twisting streams, moss-covered rocks hid in a carpet of green. After a deep winter, the air smelled of last fall's leaves, decaying trees, and awakening spring growth.

At some point in the past, nature had tumbled giant trees to the ground, accidentally creating bridges that spanned small ravines. We tested the fallen trees and then crossed to the other side.

After two hours, our plastic bags still empty, we broke out of the winter-chilled timber into a warm field of rolling pasture. In the distance, Adrian's horse, Mr. Red, spotted us and whinnied. Hooves beat on soft ground as he raced across the open pasture to greet us. He still wore his shaggy winter coat, and he looked like a giant teddy bear. Mr. Red wasn't kept in a barn and was allowed to roam the pastures and timber at will. Adrian checked on him daily, feeding him oats and corn in cold weather, making sure he had access to shelter if needed.

Adrian made a stirrup with locked fingers and hefted a ten-year-old Alexander onto the horse's back. "Grab his mane," Adrian instructed. Then he lifted Lucia up behind her brother. "Hang on."

Even though she'd only just turned seven, she was independent, and I could tell she would rather be on the horse by herself.

"How old is Mr. Red?" Alexander wanted to know. Our son had dark hair and dark eyes, looking more like me but acting more like Adrian—introspective, with a clever sense of humor.

"Probably around fifteen," Adrian said.

"How long will he live?" Alexander already understood that death was a part of farm life.

"Fifteen is getting up there," his father told him. "Horses don't live as long as people."

"I don't want Mr. Red to die!" Lucia wailed.

"Some horses live thirty years." Adrian didn't add that those horses were probably in the *Guinness Book of World Records*.

With Adrian on one side of the horse and me on the other, we strolled through the pasture, pausing on a knoll that marked the highest point of the farm. In the distance, the bluff ended and the bottoms began. Ten miles across that flat, treeless expanse was the Mississippi River, and before the river, my uncle's bar. I'd been thinking of him a lot lately, and right then and there I decided I would visit him soon, regardless of the reception.

Mr. Red stopped with us, hung his head, and closed his eyes, the weight on his back and the sun making him sleepy. Adrian and I helped the kids down. Once their feet were on the ground, I stuck my nose in the horse's coat and inhaled. "I love the way he smells."

Adrian laughed and shook his head.

If I'd been a betting person, I wouldn't have expected our marriage to last. We were too different. But in some ways we were very much alike. I could look at Adrian's face and easily read his thoughts, and we often said the same thing at the same time. We shared a respect for nature, art, and creativity, we both wanted a peaceful home life, and we had two sweet children.

I still wasn't sure what married love was all about. Just saying you loved someone didn't make it so. But I thought maybe Adrian loved me. And I thought maybe I loved him. I wondered if this day was what love felt like. Not about words, but about time and peace and contentment. About trust and children, about reading expressions and finishing each other's sentences.

Adrian sprawled out on the ground, and Lucia and Alexander tumbled on top of him. Adrian reached out his hand for me. I grasped it and lay down beside him while the children held a serious and silly conversation that had nothing to do with adults. Sleepy, I closed my eyes and became aware of bees, birds, and Mr. Red's blunt teeth rubbing together as he bit and chewed grass. A few minutes later, Lucia woke me up, tickling my neck with clover.

"We haven't found any mushrooms!" she said.

Adrian braced his hands under her armpits and lifted her in the air above him, her long, blond curls bouncing. "You don't even like mushrooms," he said.

"I like to find them."

Lucia was bold and fearless, eager to embrace the unknown.

"Will you eat any?" Adrian asked.

"No."

"I won't either!" Alexander said.

"What about you?" Adrian asked me.

"I had kind of a bad experience with mushrooms."

The sun was going down. We got to our feet to head home.

"I want to show you something," Adrian said.

The children followed their father to the flat stone he and I had visited that afternoon before we'd ever talked about marriage.

"It's a grave," Adrian told them. "A teenage girl is buried here. She was a pioneer."

"She died of something called diphtheria," I said, finishing the legend but leaving out the more disturbing aspects. One day the story would be passed to the next generation. Alexander and Lucia would have children. Adrian and I would take them mushroom hunting, and we would bring them here and show them the grave and tell them the story.

"It's such a sad spot," I said. As soon as I

said it, I wondered at my words, because it wasn't sad at all. It was beautiful, but an odd sensation had washed over me—an unfounded fear of something I couldn't see.

"Sad? This is exactly the kind of place I'd like to be buried," Adrian said. "Close to nature, not in some flat, treeless cemetery."

Alexander and Lucia put their hands on the rock, thinking about a mysterious girl who'd lived long ago. Adrian and I smiled at each other across the dark and light heads of our children.

Chapter Nine

THE next morning I baked an apple pie and drove to my uncle's. I knocked on the trailer door. Uncle Jim answered and stared at me a second, his expression shifting from cautious to pleased.

I lifted the pie pan covered with clear wrap. "It's still warm."

Inside, we sat at the kitchen table and ate pie on paper plates. The trailer smelled like dust, stale laundry, and whatever was cooking in the Crock-Pot.

"I never thought your marriage would

last," my uncle said. "Mainly because of the mother." His hair had turned gray, but his eyes were as intense as ever.

"You were right about her," I said. "And right about my having no clue about what I was getting into."

"This is good." He pointed his plastic fork at his slice of pie.

Crumble topping flavored with cinnamon and nutmeg, sprinkled over a combination of Jonathan and Winesap apples, plus a few Golden Delicious for natural sweetness. Over the years, I'd learned how to bake an amazing apple pie.

"I know how one bad choice can change a person's life," he said.

"You're talking about what happened in Chicago. The murder." He'd never discussed it with me.

He nodded. Then, surprisingly, he elaborated. "My car was packed, and I was leaving for your place in Albuquerque. The guy who'd committed the murder showed up at the last minute, said he wasn't doing anything and wanted to help drive. Get out of the city for a few days. As simple as that."

They came for the visit, but I hardly remembered his young, quiet friend. They stayed a couple of days before heading back. On the return trip, Uncle Jim's photo hit the front page of the *Chicago Tribune*. Both men were arrested, my uncle immediately fired.

I wasn't sure what kind of job Uncle Jim had in Chicago, but at one time he'd been part of a team that had designed spacecrafts for early Apollo missions. I'd seen photos of him standing next to a command module, the kind that dropped into the ocean.

"Have you ever thought about selling the bar?" I asked, then immediately regretted my question. Who was I to come up with rash solutions to problems that couldn't be solved and would only make things worse. He'd grown used to this life, and sometimes the familiar was better than the promise of something better.

"What would I do?" he asked.

"Travel?"

"I don't need to go anywhere. And the customers—they're my family."

I nodded, understanding, and we both took another bite of pie.

"I've been reading about you in the paper," he said. "About your writing career. Books on the bestseller list. Awards. A lot of people dream about becoming a writer, and you just quietly did it."

"I won't accept defeat, that's all. That's the biggest secret to making it in the writing world. Being stubborn."

"But the talent has to be there."

I smiled. "Maybe."

Artesia, New Mexico, 1972

THREE years after moving to Artesia, the college where David worked lost its accreditation and folded, and my mother and stepfather and younger brother moved on to a new adventure while I stuck around in order to graduate. Once I had my high school diploma, I moved into a little rental house and began working as a waitress at a hotel not far from the oil refinery that spewed fumes day and night. I was seventeen.

"You need to get out of here," my friend Mark told me. He was home from college for the summer. We sat on a picnic table in a park at the edge of town, our feet on the seat, watching the sun go down. In the desert, the wind always blew. The fine dirt got in your eyes and your teeth; it crept into your clothes and left a layer on everything. But it also created beautiful sunsets. "You're a good artist," he said. "You should be in college."

"I can't even afford a bus ticket out of here."

Like Mark, most of my friends were gone, off to chase their dreams, many off to college. A few had stuck around, taking jobs at the refinery. Mark was right. My life wasn't in this dying town.

"Have you ever thought about writing a book?" I asked. Mark was a big reader, and over the years we'd discussed a lot of fiction.

"A novel?" He sounded excited. "How long would that take?"

"If I wrote a page a day, it would take a year. A really long time."

"But a book. That would be amazing. I know you could do it."

"It's a silly thing to think about. Like saying I want to fly to the moon." But men did walk on the moon, and one moon-visiting astronaut had been from Artesia.

"I know where you can get a car," Mark said. "For nothing." At my puzzled expression, he continued: "A friend of the family has a car they want to get rid of. A student abandoned it in their yard when the college folded. He's never coming back. It's an MG. The top is missing, but I guess it runs."

The whole thing seemed too good to be true, but it wasn't. I got the car, and within a few weeks I quit my job and told my landlord I was moving. Mark came to see me off.

I ended up back in Albuquerque where I worked at a Levi Strauss factory sewing back pockets on jeans until I could no longer take the mindless drudgery. From there I went to Santa Fe where I worked as a secretary. I had high hopes for Santa Fe, a good place for an artist. I would save my money; I would go to school. But at the same time, I missed the Midwest. I missed my grandmother.

When the letter arrived from my uncle inviting me to come and work with him at the bar, I was on my way, never guessing that his hastily scribbled note would prove to be the most important thread in my tenuously strung-together life of cause and effect.

I COULD read Adrian much better now, but not all of the time. I still felt he harbored a secret self none of us would ever know. In the middle of the night, I would wake up and lie very still, and I would feel his sadness in the bed beside me.

I thought the path his life had taken, I thought his inability to stand up for himself and be his own person, weighed heavily on him. He could have been much more.

One night he must have heard my breathing change and realized I was awake.

"I'm never going to grow old," he said.

Fear shot through me before I reassured myself. Strange notions came in the middle of the night. "Why do you say that?"

"I just know."

"Don't you feel well? Is something wrong?"

"I feel okay."

He was young. He was healthy. "Then why would you say such a thing?"

"I just know. I'm not even going to reach middle age."

I would have dismissed it as a lingering mood left over from a dark dream, but he seemed to have some strange connection to things I couldn't see or feel. His voicing a prediction of his future made it seem more real, and I worried that the words would somehow make it true. He didn't say anything else, but I sensed that he was already missing us. Already sad to be leaving us behind.

ON SATURDAYS, I took Alexander and Lucia to Burlington for music lessons. They both chose to play electric guitar, something that mortified Ruth. One day after practice, the children wanted to stop by their grandmother's house to show her what they'd learned.

Lucia removed the purple guitar from the gig bag, and Alexander plugged in the amp. They both sat down on the gold couch, while Ruth and I sat across the living room in matching recliners. Winter sunlight poured in windows that stretched from ceiling to floor, and I tried to imagine what the room had looked like when dead bodies had been laid out for wakes. People said the house was haunted. I'm not sure I believed in such things, but Adrian still acted odd whenever I asked him about ghosts, as if he knew something he didn't want to admit.

As usual, Adrian's father wasn't home, and I sometimes forgot he lived there. He was a shadow that lurked in the orchard and in the outbuildings as he spent his waking hours hiding from his wife. I'd spoken less than ten sentences to him the entire time Adrian and I had been married.

The performance was brief, one song each, with feedback that left Ruth clapping her hands over her ears.

"Why don't you play the piano?" she asked. It was about the thirtieth time she'd mentioned switching instruments. "What can you do with a silly guitar?"

"We could be in a band," Alexander said. At thirteen, he had an uncanny way of pinpointing a person's dislikes and driving them a little bit crazier because of it.

"A band with matching uniforms?" Ruth was hoping for the best of a bad scenario.

He laughed. "A rock band." The only thing worse would have been if he'd told her he was going to work for the Environmental Protection Agency.

"Oh, no!" she said, horrified. "You don't want to be in that kind of band! But a marching band would be okay."

Alexander frowned. "I'm not going to be in a marching band."

Even as an infant, he'd been hardheaded. He knew what he wanted, and nobody could dissuade him. Unlike Lucia, who was a social butterfly and couldn't wait until she'd started school, Alexander was introverted and had spent every morning of first grade clinging to the kitchen wall, screaming that he couldn't walk. No amount of cajoling could convince him there was nothing wrong with his legs, but he'd always made a miraculous recovery evenings, weekends, and holidays.

"Farmers aren't in bands," Ruth said.

"Maybe I won't be a farmer," Alexander told her.

"Come on." I got to my feet, hoping to divert the drama that Alexander was intentionally trying to create. "Let's go home."

"You *will* be a farmer," Ruth said. "An apple farmer. This farm will be yours one day."

"I might not want the farm," he said.

Ruth looked at me, then pushed her feet against the floor to start her chair rocking. "Guitar playing is wrong. I'll buy them a piano if you don't want to spend the money."

"Even if they wanted to take piano lessons, we don't have room for a piano." A year ago we'd added on to our house. Alexander and Lucia now had their own bedrooms, but the house was still tiny and we were still living on top of one another. There was no room for another toy or another piece of furniture, and we'd taken to storing our excess belongings in one end of the old salesroom, an area that had once been the blacksmith's shop.

"And if I'm not in a band," Alexander said, "I'm going to be a professional hockey player." He didn't like the idea of his life being dictated by his grandmother, and he never missed the opportunity to let her know she couldn't boss him around.

Ruth was full of fear, and I felt sorry for her because of it. I couldn't imagine being so frightened of everything. She'd once confessed that the wind scared her. And everything we said, everything we did, upset her. It was almost as if she saw a tomorrow we couldn't see and was constantly trying to change it.

At ten, Alexander had still been infatuated with the orchard. He'd followed his grandfather everywhere, he'd gone on trips with both grandparents to visit apple orchards around the country, and he'd worked alongside his grandfather and father to plant new trees. But Ruth had pushed him too hard, and she'd reminded him of his responsibilities to her and the farm too many times.

"Don't worry, Grandma." Lucia, now ten, zipped the soft guitar case while Alexander unplugged the amp and wound the cord. "I'm never leaving. I'll take care of the apples if Alexander won't."

"You'll get married," Ruth said, failing to understand that she'd been grooming the wrong person for orchard duty. "Hopefully you'll marry a local farmer. You can stop by to see me every day."

"I'm not getting married," Lucia said. "I'm staying here forever."

As if to prove her point, Lucia spent the following year leaving her stamp on everything. She scraped moss from giant slabs of rock, creating letters three-feet high so her name could be seen from the road. She left her signature on barns. She scratched her name in apple trees, and printed it on apple crates, sometimes adding a little daisy or heart. If cement was poured on sidewalks, her name was there, making sure everyone knew she wasn't going anywhere.

ADRIAN'S FATHER developed a case of pneumonia he couldn't kick. He was sent in for a series of tests. Lung cancer that had metastasized to his brain.

"People will say it was spray from the orchard," Ruth said.

It was always the farm and the reputation of the farm that was more important than the individual. The farm no longer existed to support and sustain the owners; it had become something owners guarded and protected. It wasn't working for them; they were working for it, keeping its secrets, building it up, making it more than it was because their self-worth and identity were tied to it. Without the farm, the owners would cease to exist.

People who've never lived on a farm romanticize farm life. But people who grew up on a farm and perhaps still live on a farm romanticize it more. They guard it and protect it. They hide its dark secrets. They don't think about the future.

This is how we live. This is how we do things. It's how we've always done things.

They're lulled by the gentle and harsh passage of years. They're hypnotized by the way the wet slabs of black earth fall away from the sharp edge of the plow blade, and the way the pattern of the cuts follows the contours of the land. Even the chemicals that saturated everything became in some strange way a part of the poetry. A succession of days that were never questioned. Animals to be fed and cared for. Crops to be grown. Rain or sunshine. Life or death. The ground was always there. A promise and a curse.

There was immeasurable comfort in knowing that this would be the rest of your life. And there was immeasurable sorrow in knowing that this would be the rest of your life.

In knowing that when you were gone, the plow would still cut deep into ground you once planted. Things that had been everything to you would still exist after you were gone.

Farmers spent their days planning a year ahead, yet at the same time, there was this feeling that they all lived in the desperate moment, with no regard for the past or the future. When something broke, they came up with a new fix. Once the topsoil and subsoil were gone, they used twice the fertilizer.

There was a national crime going on in the heartland, and nobody cared.

We might have been breathing and eating and drinking poison, but so was the rest of the country. They just didn't know it.

In an odd way, the people who lived far from farms, the people who idealized farm life, were also to blame. City dwellers didn't want their romantic notion of farm life shattered. They wanted to believe that the farms of their grandparents really existed.

During apple season, families came in sweeping waves so that children could see where apples were grown. Parents wanted their children to experience nature. And I'm sure on those sweet fall days, they weren't thinking about farm chemicals.

In the salesroom, apples were sliced and offered as samples, but workers weren't allowed to wash the apples before cutting them. That might taint the warm fuzzy feel of a trip to the orchard. Nobody wanted to be reminded of why their apples didn't have spots on the skin or worms inside. They just wanted an unblemished and beautiful apple.

But weren't we all after the sublime?

DOCTORS OFFERED no cure for Adrian's father's cancer, but over the next two years he underwent two complete rounds of chemotherapy and radiation, spending blocks of time at the Mayo Clinic in Rochester, Minnesota, coming home and resting before the next visit. Sadly, he could no longer hide from his wife.

I baked pies for him. Apple pies and chocolate pies and lemon meringue, lemon meringue being his favorite. His memory had been damaged by radiation, and he forgot he wasn't supposed to like me. On afternoons when I kept him company in order to give Ruth a break, we chatted about the children and the farm and the always-popular topic of weather.

"How's your grandmother?" he asked one day.

Fifteen years had passed since her death. "She's fine," I said.

He nodded, pleased to hear it. "She's quite the character."

It wasn't as if he'd had a lobotomy, because the core person was still there. Anxiety and stress and worry had been lifted from him. He was content. He was nice to me; he was nice to his grandchildren; he was nice to his son. Not because he knew he was dying and thought he'd better shape up. No, at some point during the radiation, he'd forgotten about his impending death and that the treatments were a temporary fix, and nobody told him differently.

I LAY in bed and listened to the sprayer. It roared like a jet engine. So many nights I used to hear the sprayer and visualize Adrian's dad out there by himself in the orchard.

Now it was Adrian.

When he reached the end, the sprayer shut down. I imagined the tractor turning in the dark, getting into position for the next row. The sprayer engaged and the roar began again.

Odd that I found the sound of the sprayer comforting. The windows were open, and I caught a whiff of pesticide. It had a garlicky odor that was as familiar as the scent of fabric softener.

Fortunate son. There was a deep dread in my heart, a dread that was always worse in the middle of the night.

I heard the sprayer getting closer.

The chemicals were all around us. In the clothes I removed from the line. In the air we breathed and the water we drank.

We were all Lily.

ADRIAN'S father died in late summer, two years after his initial diagnosis and a few weeks before harvest.

The funeral was held at a nearby church, and the burial was in a treeless cemetery surrounded by fields and backed by a hog lot. During the graveside eulogy, I heard hogs snorting and metal feeders clanging while the smell of manure drifted over the crowd.

I found myself wondering if the hogs would always be behind the cemetery. Maybe someone would rotate them out and put in crops. That would be nice. Well, not nice, but at least less awful.

THE death of Adrian's father left Ruth in complete control of the farm. Adrian took on most of the orchard responsibilities, but he wasn't in charge, and every decision was okayed or vetoed by his mother, usually vetoed. He worked eighteen-hour days. He went to bed exhausted and got up exhausted.

He bailed hay and vaccinated cattle during the day; at night, he sprayed the orchard.

"You can't go on like this," I told him. "The farm is at least a three-man operation."

We stood in the middle of a hay field, the tractor and bailer a few feet away. I'd brought him a thermos of water. He'd already made twenty-five large bales, with about the same number to go.

"You need to hire someone to take care of the orchard."

"Who? Someone with a degree in orchard management? That would be worse than training a person from scratch."

One mistake could ruin the trees forever. Right now Adrian was spraying for codling moths. In a few days, he would apply something that inhibited rust and mildew. Next week, it would be something else. Even if someone could be found to help, the concern—which nobody would mention—was whether it was ethical to allow an outsider to spray these chemicals. To bring someone in, pay them minimum wage while they bathed in toxins day in and day out—it was wrong.

Alexander toiled alongside his father whenever he wasn't at school and the job didn't involve pesticide. Lucia and I helped, too, but the largest part of the labor fell upon Adrian. He lost weight, and lines appeared on his face. He smoked twice as much, and in his fatigue he disregarded what little precautions he normally took.

He was in his late thirties, but it was hard to see the beautiful boy in the exhausted man. Even a normal amount of farming caused people to age at an accelerated rate. Hair turned gray overnight, and teeth fell out. The physical and mental stress never let up.

Every day farmers got out of bed because animals were waiting to be fed. No matter how brutal the weather, no matter it if was a weekend or Christmas or twenty below zero. No matter if you had the flu or broken ribs or a fever.

Every day was a marathon with never a chance for the body to heal or recover. It made old men out of boys, and eldest sons worked for pennies a day with the promise that the very thing that had made them old before their time, the very thing that had killed their fathers and grandfathers, would one day be theirs.

The Orchard
Chapter Ten

THE spring after Adrian's father died, our luck seemed to change. The Sweet Melindas bloomed, and their blossoms smelled sweeter than the blossoms of any other apple trees. Bees were trucked in, the white hives stacked and lined up behind a row of young trees. Would they produce apples this year? They had blossomed before, and they had smelled sweet before. . . .

I spent hours walking through the Sweet Melindas, willing the bees to pollinate the fragrant blooms. The trees were over fifteen feet tall, their size a visual testament to the passage of time. The blossoms eventually faded and dropped, the beekeepers returned to collect their bees, and we waited. And we watched. Below the dying blooms, tiny green apples appeared.

The curse had lifted.

The darkness that had dwelled in my heart was gone, replaced by hope. The days had a new buoyancy. Throughout that summer,

Adrian brought fruit from the Sweet Melinda trees home until the kitchen windowsill was lined with green apples picked at various stages of growth. At bedtime, Adrian unzipped his jeans and apples would fall from the pockets, hitting the rug with muffled thuds.

"You won't have any apples to pick once they're ripe." I spoke softly because the children were asleep beyond our closed door.

"There's no need to worry about picking them all." Adrian tugged his T-shirt over his head, dropping it on a chair. "I've never seen so many apples for a first-year crop." He tried to sound casual, but he couldn't mask his excitement. "I'm really just thinning. If I don't thin, the branches will break. If we don't have any big storms, we should have a bumper crop." He turned out the light.

"What color will they be?" I asked. Color was related to temperature. I'd also learned that soil unique to locale gave apples a distinct flavor. Two identical trees, one in Washington State and one in Illinois, would not produce apples of identical flavor. The apples from the Curtis farm had more flavor than apples grown in most other parts of the country. The flavor contained hints of so many things, and describing it could be compared to describing red wine. Words like *earthy, flowery, woodsy,* and *loamy* came to mind.

"Red." The mattress dipped. In the dark, Adrian reached for my hand, linking his fingers with mine.

"What shade of red?" I was aware that I sounded like an eager child, curious about the world. I felt young again, new again.

"Color is tricky. You want the temperature to briefly hover above freezing about a week before harvest. Just a kiss. If that doesn't happen, the color won't be as rich. A good apple crop also depends on the right amount of rain. You don't want a lot of rain before harvest. The apples grow too quickly and will be mushy."

"What kind of red would make you happiest?"

Adrian and I often talked about the orchard, about what we would do if we were running it. Maybe it was because he was now a father, but over the years he'd come around to thinking that organic might be the way to go. We read everything we could read about organic farming and dreamed of a farm where we would grow apples that weren't without flaws and where toxins didn't drift in open windows.

Over time, Adrian had implemented what subtle environmental measures he could get away with. Planting waterways to stop soil erosion, creating wildlife habitat with brush piles, leaving saplings and hedgerows for migratory birds, fencing off streams and ponds so cattle couldn't pollute. Small measures, but important ones.

He unlinked his hand from mine, shifted to face me. "I like a true red. A solid, unbroken red."

"What about shape? Round? Oblong?"

"Round like a Winesap, but with shiny, thin skin."

"Isn't thin skin bad?"

"On an insect level, but it's a risk I'm willing to take for skin that's flawless."

"Does everything always have to be perfect?"

"Do you have something against perfection?" Adrian asked.

The window was open, and humid air

drifted into the small bedroom, carrying with it the thick scent of green fields. The night nature hypnotized me. Lulled me into thinking everything would be okay, that it was there to protect and nurture. That instead of being vast land and sky that went on for miles, it held us close; it sheltered us.

THE weeks passed, and with every storm we held our breath. Once the rain stopped, we rushed to the orchard to make sure the entire crop wasn't on the ground. Storms weren't our only concern. Some apples required a longer growing season, and we didn't yet know if the Sweet Melinda was a late apple that would be threatened by frost.

In early September, Adrian appeared in the kitchen, pulled an apple from his pocket, and announced that they were almost ripe.

The fruit wasn't quite full-size and hadn't yet reached the deep red we were both hoping for. He rummaged in a drawer and found a paring knife, grabbed a cutting board, and sat down at the kitchen table. I took a seat opposite him, elbows on the wooden surface. This was the way to do it. With ceremony.

He placed the apple in the center of the cutting board. We watched it for a while, committing the moment to memory. And then, with steady fingers, Adrian tipped the apple on its side and made the slice, separating the fruit into a top and bottom half.

Reverently, he opened the apple. The meat of the apple was almost luminescent, the white outlined with a thin line of red. I don't know if I'd ever seen anything quite so beautiful. He offered me the top half. I accepted it and raised it to my mouth.

"Wait." He looked alarmed by my impatience. "Smell it."

He demonstrated, lifting the other half to his nose while closing his eyes. He inhaled. I did the same.

It smelled sweet and earthy. We opened our eyes.

"What do you think?" he asked.

"Lovely."

"We have to wait another minute. See if it stays white."

And so we waited.

Later, he examined his piece. "A little yellowing, but not bad. Now smell it again."

I lifted the apple section to my nose. "It has more of a floral scent now."

"That's because it's already breaking down."

We both took a bite, laughing at the dual sharp snap as our teeth broke the crisp skin. The apple wasn't quite ripe, yet it had an incredible flavor, like a combination of wine and cherries.

"Oh my God," I said. "The best apple I've ever eaten."

He smiled and nodded, then quickly finished his half.

And then we both got to our feet. He wrapped his arms around me. "You know the whole country is going to be talking about these apples. Maybe we can build a log home in the woods."

"Or move away? And start a farm of our own?"

He pressed his lips to mine, then looked at me. "That too."

But I could see the hesitation in his eyes.

It actually made me sad to think about going somewhere else with the Sweet Melinda trees. Planting them in some foreign soil in

Michigan or Wisconsin. I don't know why that felt so wrong and made me so sad, but it did. Like Adrian, the trees belonged to the farm. We all belonged here.

"THEY'RE ready."

Adrian came bursting into the house, radiating heat from the sun, smelling of diesel and fall leaves and late grasses.

He'd made a satchel from the flannel shirt he'd removed once the day had warmed up. Now he untied the sleeves and tails, letting six apples roll across the table. Two metal picking baskets were stacked in the corner. Once we determined that the apples were ripe, Adrian and I planned to strap on the baskets and harvest the trees ourselves.

I grabbed the cutting board and handed a paring knife to Adrian. They were his apples; he should make the first slice.

"Wait." I'd almost forgotten the wine I'd picked up for just this occasion. I removed the cork from the bottle, then poured the burgundy liquor into two glasses that we raised and touched together. "To us and the Sweet Melindas," I said. The pure and delicate chime of glass against glass echoed in my head, seeming to predict a future that was clear and bright.

Adrian placed the knife next to the stem and sliced down through the core. The two halves separated and rolled apart.

We both stared at the sliced apple. At the dark, rotten core and the worm shifting in a brown tunnel. I can't explain the kind of dread I felt in that moment. It was similar to the day when I'd eaten the mushroom and thought I was going to die. Fear. It was fear. But not the kind of fear you feel when something startles you. This fear was deep. This fear went all the way to the bone.

"Codling moth," Adrian said.

I picked up one half and examined it. I thought of all the nights spent spraying, all of the nights Adrian had carried pesticide home on his skin and clothes, crawling into bed too exhausted to shower.

He grabbed another apple and sliced it open. Same thing. One by one, he sliced open the remaining apples. They were all damaged.

Tears burned my throat and eyes. I remembered what Adrian had told me long ago. *Once the codling moth takes over an orchard you're pretty much screwed.* "Can they be saved? Is it too late?"

He shook his head. "I don't know. Maybe. Maybe not."

We got in the truck and drove to the Sweet Melinda trees. We slipped into the picking baskets and we began to harvest the infested crop, hoping to find at least a few undamaged apples.

Adrian pulled out a pocketknife and began slicing open random apples as he tugged them from the tree. Every one was infected.

He slipped out of his harness and tossed the metal basket to the ground. "Stop picking," Adrian said. "The trees have to go."

I looked up in alarm. "No."

"They'll infect the rest of the orchard."

He had to be overreacting. "Can't you spray?" I couldn't believe I was suggesting spray. "With something stronger?" Maybe the secret spray he had hidden away that his father had stockpiled.

Now I finally understood how it happened. The desperation to save something you've worked so hard to create. The length you find yourself willing to go, the compromises you're willing to make. Just this once.

I ducked my head as he helped me remove the basket from my shoulders. He dropped it to the ground, and apples spilled at our feet. Beautiful apples, red against green.

I looked up at him through a haze of tears. "I'm sorry."

He reached for me, pulling me close. "It's okay. They're just apples."

But they were more than just apples. We both knew that. "You have to spray," I said. "Now. Right away."

I felt his fingers in my hair. "No. I've done enough spraying."

Back at the house, I poured the wine down the drain and it stained the white sink. How long before the stain went away?

Adrian appeared with a shovel. "I'll bury them."

He dug a hole in the backyard, tossed in the apples with their rotten cores and writhing white worms, then covered them with dirt.

The next day, he bulldozed the Sweet Melinda trees and used the blade to push the trees into a giant pile in the middle of the orchard. He doused the trunks and branches and beautiful red apples with gasoline. Then lit a match.

The fired burned almost twenty-four hours. By morning, all that was left were a few smoldering embers, but the sweet scent of burning apple wood permeated our clothes, our hair, our house, and I wondered if it would ever go away.

Over the next few days, Adrian and I didn't talk about the trees, and we tried to find pleasure in small things. On Sunday afternoon while the kids were visiting friends, I packed a picnic basket and we went fishing in the pond behind the house. Maybe if we forced ourselves to engage in a relaxing activity, joy would follow.

THE bobber vanished. Adrian jumped to his feet and turned the crank, reeling in the line. A week had passed since the bulldozing of the apple trees, and time hadn't yet done much healing, at least not for me. It wasn't the failure of a dream that left me feeling stricken; it was knowing the trees would have been Adrian's claim to the farm. They would have given him a voice, given his ideas weight and validation. His mother had humored his experiment, but now he needed to get down to the business of real crops.

But I didn't want to think about the politics of the farm. I wanted to enjoy the afternoon and the feel of the sun on my face. I was a lazy fisherman, more interested in everything that went along with fishing than I was in catching a fish. I watched sleepily from a blanket, hoping my hook no longer had a worm.

Adrian snagged the fish with his free hand and brought it close.

It was covered with oozing sores. Tumors.

The loss of the Sweet Melindas seemed suddenly insignificant. If a moment could define a life, this was Adrian's moment. And if a moment could forever change the way I viewed the world, this was mine. In that instant, we both felt the future pressing down on us.

He removed the hook from the deformed mouth and tossed the fish back in the water. He looked across the pond to the orchard. "Chemicals are getting in the pond."

Proof. Finally proof.

They'd lost track of why they were farming. It should have been about making a living and supporting your family, but along the way, that core reason had become buried. It was more about big business and success on a large scale, no matter what the cost, no matter how it impacted the very people it was supposed to support.

Silently we packed up everything. Adrian gathered the poles, and I grabbed the picnic basket.

It was like the moment you found out someone had died. Before the bad news and after. You were occupying the same space, but everything looked different and was permanently altered.

"We can't stay here," Adrian said. "As soon as the crops are in, we'll start looking for new ground."

"Where?" I was no longer the person with outsider ideas who couldn't exist on a real farm. We both understood that something had to be done. Things had to change. But as long as his mother ran the farm, we believed, change would never happen.

"Up north. Minnesota or Wisconsin."

A place where the land was less contaminated, the air purer. A place where an organic movement was taking hold. I thought about our children and about Adrian and me. Hopefully it wasn't too late.

Even though we were deep in harvest, Adrian and I found time to pore over farming magazines and the monthly newspapers that arrived advertising farms for sale. We found three possibilities, all small acreages, two in Wisconsin and one in northern Illinois.

"Let's drive up and look at them as soon as the apples are picked," Adrian said. "I should be feeling better by then." He'd been running a low-grade fever, and he was on a second series of antibiotics.

I was surprised that he was actually initiating his plan, and I had to wonder if he could really make himself go through with a transplant and the guilt that would come with leaving. I doubt he'd thought it through, and once he did . . . well, he might see there was no satisfactory solution. He might see that he was trapped. Leaving his mother alone with the orchard would be a lot of guilt for a first-born son to carry. But there was no harm in looking. "We'll make a vacation out of it," I said. "We could visit House on the Rock."

"And maybe Frank Lloyd Wright's Taliesin in Spring Green."

Adrian called the listing numbers, and I

made motel reservations. But two weeks
later, when the apples were in crates and
stored in hillside bunkers, when the cider
press was running and the corn hadn't yet
been picked, everything changed.

Chapter Eleven

THE eldest son is born into two things: a life
sentence and a death sentence. The fall harvest had just begun when Adrian's doctor
told him he might have cancer. He was next
in line; this was his destiny. But it was too
soon. Years too soon. Four years had passed
since his father's death, and Adrian should
have had more time.

FEAR is bigger in the predawn hours.

I think that's when our emotions are most
vulnerable. In our sleep, a door opens to allow the dreams inside, and along come the
emotions that play such an important role in
our sleeping life.

I set the alarm, but there was really no
need. I think Adrian and I were both awake
most of the night.

It was a two-hour drive to Iowa City and

medical specialists, and the sun rose as we headed north. Farmers were in the fields picking corn, trying to beat the rain.

THE diagnosis ended up being what we most feared. Cancer.

"Was it caused by smoking?" Adrian immediately asked. He didn't want to think he'd done this to himself and his family.

"It's almost unheard of to see throat cancer in someone who just smokes," Dr. Wagner told us. "There's always a second toxin."

"Pesticide?" I asked.

"No research has been done on the connection, but we're seeing more and more farmers with this type of cancer."

Upon learning that Adrian was an apple farmer, Dr. Wagner had been full of questions, and the two men quickly bonded over talk of the apple trees the doctor had recently planted. Even doctors seemed to need to embrace apples as a symbol of family and the perfect life.

"Operating is the only treatment," Dr. Wagner told us. "But the cancer is advanced, and your chances of a cure are low. I'm sorry."

ADRIAN CHOSE TO HAVE the surgery, but
before he was out of the hospital, we both
sensed it had been unsuccessful, and we soon
had confirmation of our suspicions.

Dr. Wagner took us to his office and asked
us to sit down in the matching chairs on the
other side of his desk. Behind him on the
wall were framed magazine covers proclaim-
ing his department to be the best in the
country.

Dr. Wagner fiddled with his pink tie, and
Adrian and I could both see that he was
struggling for composure in order to give us
the test results. I think he'd become fond of
us and had connected in ways he probably
shouldn't have.

"The cancer is still there," Adrian said,
helping the doctor along.

"Yes. I'm sorry."

"What do we do now?" I asked.

"In forty percent of cases, chemotherapy
slows down the growth for three to six
months," the doctor told us. "Then it be-
comes ineffective. There is no cure, and in
sixty percent of cases it will do nothing but
make the patient sick. That's all I can offer
you."

His words sucked the air out of my lungs and caused the room to shrink to a pinpoint. I was aware of my heart slamming in my chest.

"I'm not going to get the chemo if there's no chance of a cure," Adrian said, his words no surprise. "How long do I have to live?"

"Two weeks to two months."

Two weeks. I'd been expecting a year, maybe two or three. "Fourteen days? How is that possible? He seems fairly healthy." Just that morning he'd fed cattle and repaired a broken fence.

"Part of the tumor is wrapped around the carotid artery. That artery could burst at any time, and if that happens, the patient bleeds to death. It might sound unpleasant, but it's fast and painless. If the artery doesn't burst, the tumor will slowly poison the patient."

I'd known this day was coming, but that made it no easier. Adrian had known too. Almost a lifetime, it seemed.

From him I sensed an initial fear, followed by acceptance and relief. He'd been in such a hurry to marry and have children. For years, he'd felt the shadow of his short life looming over him. I thought of the occasions when he'd alluded to his own death. *"I'm not going to grow old. I'm not even going to reach middle age."* And now here it was. The end that he'd been waiting for.

"How are your apple trees?" Adrian asked, breaking the silence that had fallen over us.

Dr. Wagner blinked in surprise. "Great. Had a little trouble with rabbits, but we wrapped the trunks and that seems to be working."

Adrian nodded, glad to hear it. "Do you know the apple tree is part of the rose family?"

"No," Dr. Wagner said. "I didn't."

We got up to leave. Dr. Wagner stood too. I could see the pain in his eyes. I think he thought he'd let us down. "I wanted to go into research," Dr. Wagner said. "But my professors told me I could do more good as a surgeon." He was doubting his choice. As a researcher, he would never have had to tell someone he was dying.

"Good luck," Adrian said. And he meant good luck with the apple trees, and good luck with his family, and good luck with the next patient he couldn't save.

They shook hands. "Good luck," Dr.

Wagner said, and he meant good luck with dying.

I was too upset to drive; Adrian drove us home. Calm. At peace. As if a weight had been lifted from his shoulders. He reached across the seat and took my hand. "I'm sorry."

I threw another tissue on the floor, adding to the pile growing at my feet. "Doctor Wagner made it clear it wasn't caused by cigarettes alone." I didn't know that many farmers, but I knew four who'd been diagnosed with throat cancer in the past few years.

Adrian gave my hand a comforting squeeze before letting go. "No matter what caused it, I'm sorry."

I knew he meant he was sorry for leaving us, sorry for smoking, sorry for not being able to fulfill our dream of moving. The idea of our own farm was what had kept him going, but I don't think he could ever have left the Curtis Orchard and his birthplace. I think that's where his sense of peace and relief came from; dying solved a lot of problems. Moving wasn't the only way to leave a place.

That day he became more than the farm, more than his mother's son. He took a step toward something none of us could see. He'd finally reached a point where nobody could force him to do what he didn't want to do. He'd never been in control of his own life, but by forgoing the chemotherapy, he would be in control of his death.

Once we were home, we told Alexander and Lucia the news.

"You're not going to die on my birthday, are you?" Lucia sobbed. "Don't die on my birthday!"

In two weeks, she would be fifteen.

"Does that really matter?" Alexander asked. He wore brown coveralls, and his face was red from hauling hay on the tractor.

"I don't want to think of it every year on my birthday," Lucia explained as she struggled to stop crying.

"She has a valid point," Adrian said with a smile. I could see he was trying not to laugh. "Okay, I won't die on your birthday."

"Oh, I don't care!" she said. "I don't want you to die at all!"

"Come on." He put his arm around her. "It'll be light for another two hours. Put on boots and we'll all go for a walk in the woods."

As THE four of us walked through the woods, we were thinking that this was the last time we would walk these paths together. And somehow the knowledge made the moss that bordered the streams that much greener and made the air that much sweeter. And it made the day the saddest day on earth, but also the most beautiful.

The sun was going down by the time we broke out of the dense timber, ending up in the north end of the orchard where the branches bowed with the weight of the fall apple crop.

"This is one of the original plantings," Adrian said. We stood at the foot of the towering and twisted tree where I'd harvested Transparent apples years earlier, after my grandmother had died. From where I stood, the orchard represented five generations of Curtis men, two of them standing beside me.

Adrian pulled off a piece of bark and showed us where the codling moth had bored into the trunk of the ancient tree. "The old orchard needs to be destroyed," he said. "All of it. It might be too late, but it's the only way to possibly save the newer dwarfs."

"I'm not staying," Alexander said. "Once you're gone, I'm not staying. I'm here for you and Mom, not her." Of all of us, Alexander had suffered the most verbal abuse from his grandmother over the years. Her bullying would have been forgivable if it had been an isolated incident. But Ruth's insults had never stopped.

"Once I'm gone, all of you have to leave," Adrian said. His words were something we knew, but he needed to remind us, to make sure Alexander, Lucia, and I would do what had to be done.

We'd been remiss in not establishing our own life, our own home from the beginning. It could have helped carry us through this hard time, but instead we were squatters, stewards, with twisted roots that had never taken hold the way they should have.

"Does anybody have a pocketknife?" Lucia asked.

Alexander pulled a knife from his overalls and handed it to her. She opened the blade and carved her name in the trunk of the tree.

At first I didn't understand why she still felt a compulsion to leave her mark on everything, especially when we would soon be gone. But then I realized she had every right to leave it wherever she wanted. This place belonged to her as much as it belonged to anybody. And I thought how right for all of us to carve our names in a dying tree that had been part of the original orchard.

RUTH didn't take the news of Adrian's untreatable cancer well. In fact, she unraveled before our eyes.

That's the sad thing about a life of pretense designed from magazine ads. The people in those ads didn't die from cancer. It was all Tupperware parties and cupcakes and cigarettes that were good for you. Innocent children could drink herbicides with no consequences. Bad things didn't happen in her world, and death was the first thing Ruth had come across that she couldn't control.

WHEN word got out that Adrian hadn't long to live, people stopped to see him one last time. The visits were awkward as guests wrung their hands, stared at the floor, and struggled to find the right words to say to a dying man. One of the visitors was Connie.

Standing outside on the front step, she didn't look much different from the day she'd appeared at the door with the gift of the rolling pin. She'd gained weight, but her hair was the same, and she could have been wearing the same clothes—a testament to how nothing ever changed here.

She looked at me with mild affection. "I never thought you'd last a year, yet here you are. Shows what I know."

"We never made that apple pie," I said.

"People are saying Adrian isn't going to be buried with his father and grandfather," Connie said. "They're saying he'll be buried at South Henderson. That can't be right. Nobody's been buried there in years. As far as I know, they don't even allow burials anymore."

Yes, nothing changed. Like Connie's first visit, she'd once again ridden in on gossip. She was here to get the scoop.

"We found a plot owned by Adrian's ancestors," I told her. "There were two empty spaces." The cemetery was isolated and serene, with hills and huge shade trees, surrounded by timber. "I got in touch with the board, and they gave us their okay." Adrian and his mother had been fighting about it ever since. Where he would be buried was his one and only real act of defiance.

We went inside, and Connie kept her visit light. She was one of the few who understood that she was there for Adrian and that he was living moment to moment. It wasn't his place to reassure and soothe or tell her everything would be okay. He could no longer talk, and he kept a pad within reach, the rasp of pencil lead moving across paper another reminder of what could have been.

He and Connie joked about grade-school escapades, and when he grew tired, Connie got up to leave. Her eyes never filled with tears. She smiled, blew him a kiss, and walked away. Moments later, I looked out the window to see her sitting in her truck, forehead against the steering wheel.

Once she was gone, Adrian flipped the tablet to a fresh sheet. He wrote with intensity and mystery, and when he was finished, I took the tablet from his hand.

A confession. Written with a pencil that had sketched people and animals and trees, now telling a different story, a detailed story of the pesticides Adrian and his father had applied over the years and, the most chilling of all, how his father had disposed of the canisters.

Everybody does it.

As far as you're concerned.

At last I knew the secret Adrian had carried for so long, and by entrusting me with it, I knew he loved me. He was leaving it up to me to reveal what he'd shared if I so chose. He was leaving it up to me to do the one thing he could never have done even if he hadn't become ill. Death would give him a voice.

I put the tablet away and handed him a new one.

ADRIAN lived four months, long past Lucia's birthday. Doctors said the unexpected length of those final days was most likely due to his years of hard labor. His body wouldn't shut off.

But one night after Adrian had been moved to a Burlington hospital room, his breathing changed. Long and deep, with only a few inhalations per minute.

I wanted to take his hand and talk to him, but I was afraid the slightest touch, the slightest shift in air, would call him back.

Fly away. Just fly away. Leave that rotting body and fly, beautiful, perfect boy with the golden curls. Fly far, far away.

I held my breath, afraid to move. From somewhere came the faint sound of a television. I could hear voices from the nurses' station.

It seemed that only a single growing season had passed since the day Adrian had walked into my uncle's bar, and yet we had two beautiful children. A son. A daughter.

The passage of time is ephemeral. You wrap it up and put it in that place where memories go. And when you pull it out, it doesn't matter if it's one year or eighteen. It feels the same.

As I watched Adrian's slow, labored breathing, I remembered the day he'd finally spoken up, not for himself, but for his son.

There had been talk about Alexander joining his grandfather in the orchard to learn how to spray and how to make perfect apples.

"Absolutely not," Adrian had said. "He can't spray apples or corn."

"He has to learn someday," Adrian's father told him. "He can't be a farmer if he doesn't know how to spray crops."

"I don't want him around any chemicals."

"You're babying him."

Then Adrian had taken his young son aside. "If your grandfather tells you to spray, don't do it. He's not your father. I'm your father, and I'm telling you not to do it. You don't have to."

Alexander had looked at his father with relief. And he'd looked at his grandfather with shame. But he didn't spray.

Love doesn't happen overnight. It doesn't happen in the first months of attraction and infatuation. In that moment when a father finally takes a stand, not for himself but for his child, that's where love is shaped and re-defined in a way I could finally understand.

Adrian took one long breath and slowly exhaled.

A minute passed.

Another breath. Another exhale.

At the nurses' station, two dark heads were bent over a book. Moments later, a lovely woman in yellow beachcombers entered the room and offered Adrian a plate of mushrooms. Or was that a dream? And were they apples?

He ate them all. Because that's what good boys do.

And then he was gone. A life unfinished.

He hadn't accomplished what he'd wanted to accomplish, always thinking he had time. Always thinking his turn would come.

Don't wait. Don't ever wait.

TWO hours later, after all the paperwork was signed, I drove home. The moon reflected off the river, and when I reached the bottoms, I could smell the cornfields on both sides of the road.

The house was dark, the children asleep.

Inside, I lay down on the bed and waited for dawn.

I PACKED. Adrian's belongings filled a few small boxes. That was it. His books and his sketch pads full of drawings. I'd saved most of the tablets he'd used when he was dying. Maybe someday I would read them again.

As much as he'd hated it, his world had been the farm. Not the house. Not even us—not really. He wouldn't have bought a farm up north. Death was the only way he could leave.

Now that he was gone, the farm was different. Lifeless and empty. Just ground. When he'd been alive, it had held possibilities. Now it was just a farm. Just the place that had killed him.

THREE weeks after the funeral, I found us a place to live, a house outside Burlington with a barn and four acres for Mr. Red. We couldn't possibly leave him behind. A few days before moving from the farm, I stopped the truck in front of what used to be the stable and blacksmith's shop to deal with something I'd been dreading—retrieving our stored belongings. I'd deliberately chosen a time when the salesroom was open and people were around, hoping to get in and out without Ruth knowing I'd even been there. Thankfully, the door was unlocked, and I began carrying boxes to the truck.

Five minutes into the task, Ruth materialized from behind parked cars. "What are you doing in here? Get out!"

I suppose I should have called her, but I was afraid a phone call would give her enough warning to make sure the door to the storage area was locked. "I'm just getting our stuff."

"*Stuff.*" She mocked me by exaggerating the word, a word that, to her mind, belonged to hippies and bohemians and uneducated morons. "You don't have any *stuff* here." The disgust and hatred in her face reminded me of the day she and I had first met in this very driveway. Her opinion of me hadn't changed in eighteen years.

"I do have stuff here, and I'm getting all of it."

Her thoughts shifted from her dislike of me and my vocabulary to Adrian. "I didn't do anything wrong!"

When her son had needed her most, she'd said horrible things to him, things no mother should say to her dying child. "You're a coward!" she'd screamed at him. "You're dying on purpose! You're dying to get away from me and the farm!"

He'd been the bravest person I'd ever known. But the words she'd spoken had held a seed of truth, because dying was the only way he would have ever left. He'd felt some measure of relief knowing it would all be over soon, and that had enraged her.

She tried to block my way; I stepped around her.

"Let me see what you're taking!" She pawed through the boxes in the truck, making sure I wasn't stealing anything of hers.

Ten minutes later, Ruth changed tactics and began dragging large items out of the building. She was a pack rat, and she'd salvaged a lot of my old junk over the years, most of it ending up in the storage area. "Take all of it!" she said. "I don't want anything of yours!"

An audience was growing in front of the salesroom; workers and customers had come outside to see what the ruckus was about. Ruth was aware of the audience, too, and began to put on a show.

"Oh, you've been so cruel to me!" she wailed. "I've done nothing to you! I was always good to you! I treated you like a daughter!"

True, I thought, thinking of my mother. I put the last box in the truck bed, slammed the tailgate, and opened the driver's door.

Behind me I heard something heavy dragging across gravel; I turned to see Ruth standing near the tailgate, a wooden headboard in her hands. "Take this!" she shouted.

"That's not mine," I told her. "I gave it to you."

"What am *I* going to do with it?"

I fixed Ruth with an unblinking stare. I no longer had to tolerate her. I no longer had to take anything from her for the sake of keeping the peace, for the sake of her son.

For some people, things happen in threes. For me it was twos. Two crazy mothers. The first one taught me that family ties meant nothing without love and mutual respect. Blood or marriage was no reason to endure mental or physical abuse. From now on, I would surround myself with people who loved me, not people who hated me. People like Ruth would no longer be a part of my life.

By her smug expression and her confidence in the moral support gained from the witnesses in front of the salesroom, I could see Ruth fully expected me to obey her by loading the headboard, but I stayed where I was. "What should you do with it?" I asked conversationally. She leaned closer in anticipation of my submission. And then I followed up with the last words I would ever speak to her: "Shove it up your ass."

The audience let out a collective gasp. I hopped in the truck and drove away, Ruth and the headboard and her gaping mouth framed in the rearview mirror.

WE DROVE away and didn't look back. Had Adrian married me because he knew I was not like them, that I would find the strength to do just this if the time came? I'll never know. But I couldn't shake the feeling that we'd left him there.

Nobody knew the land the way he did. He'd known every curve, every dip, every glen, every stream, every tree. Nobody in his family loved it and cared about it the way he had.

Sometimes I think he's still roaming through the timber, and sometimes I imagine him riding Mr. Red or driving the tractor through a field. But mainly I imagine him walking through the woodland that he loved. And I think about what could have been.

THE codling moth won. And I've been told the entire old orchard was bulldozed, the trees burned. I wouldn't know, because I haven't been back. I've heard that the only trees left are the more disease-resistant dwarfs. I've been told that fences have been ripped out and the waterways Adrian struggled so hard to maintain were plowed. The fields eroded so that now plantings and green waterways have washed away to reveal gaping wounds that will never heal. Trees and migratory habitat are gone, and the wind constantly blows across miles of barrenness, carrying away the remaining topsoil. Most of Adrian's small environmental efforts are gone. Wiped out.

The farms of our grandparents no longer exist. People don't want to hear that, but farms are big business. They are no more warm and fuzzy than a factory is warm and fuzzy. Somewhere in the seventies and eighties, people got off track. It was uncool to worry about the environment. It was uncool to worry about chemicals.

Our children won't be farmers, but they will be what Adrian couldn't be. Artists. Teachers. World travelers. Because they did what Adrian couldn't do. They left. But they will always remember the smell of earth cut deep with the sharp edge of a plow blade.

And they will remember the sound of the wind in the corn.

If you drive down Highway 34 and see a narrow lane that drops away from the main road, you'll have found the old highway. Locals called it Bogus Hollow because counterfeit money was once made there. But now it's just broken buildings covered in tangled vines. An old rope swing. Decayed barns, abandoned wells.

Silent and secret. Don't slow down. Don't even hesitate.

Just keep driving. Past the place where the sprayer still shoots chemicals over the apple trees and where, on hot, humid nights, corn still smells like dark, mysterious perfume.

A place that goes on without us.

Minneapolis, Minnesota, 2003

I TURNED off the interstate and took the exit ramp to downtown Minneapolis. Seven years had passed since we'd left the farm. After Adrian's death, Lucia and I moved to the place I'd found for us in Burlington, and Alexander left for college.

The writing money I'd squirreled away for years supported me, and new book contracts came along. Once Lucia entered college, once Mr. Red was gone, Alexander and Lucia talked me into leaving Iowa. I followed them north to Minneapolis, land of the Spoonbridge and Cherry, Weisman Art Museum, and Bob Dylan.

I'm a city girl again. I ride the light rail, and I sit in cafés and drink lattes. I don't like to leave the city. Beyond its boundaries are cornfields and pastures and orchards, painful reminders. And I won't eat apples or drink cider. It's not the spray; I can't bring myself to ingest a symbol of a failed life.

I turned into Dayton's Ramp, pushed the red button, and pulled the parking ticket from the automated machine. The arm raised and I circled up, parking on the fourth floor. I took the elevator to street level, then made my way along the wide sidewalk. It was Saturday night and couples were everywhere, heading to restaurants and bars.

I crossed the street to First Avenue, the club Prince made famous in *Purple Rain*. I passed the main door and slipped into 7th Street Entry, First Avenue's smaller venue.

"I should be on the guest list," I said.

The tattooed door girl checked her paper and found my name.

Inside, as my eyes adjusted to the dark, I found a spot in the corner and watched the room fill. Two young guys settled to my right, and their conversation was easy to overhear.

"Do you know anything about this band?" one of them asked.

"They're brother and sister," the other guy replied. "Can you imagine being in a band with your sister? That would suck."

I smiled to myself.

And then Alexander and Lucia took the stage. It was their first gig. Lucia had just graduated from college, and Alexander was a sought-after recording engineer. Beautiful children, the last of the Curtis line. They'd waited a long time for this moment, but no one in the room knew how long or how far they'd traveled to get here.

Many of the song lyrics were about the farm. Strange how we'd wanted to get as far away from that life as possible, and yet all three of us were using art to express and re-create and revisit the past.

Heritage. The farm would always be ours,

even if we were no longer there. We could claim it in writing, in music.

Fear makes you brave. Fear makes you fearless. We left our terror back there in that old life, and here in this world everything was new even though it didn't ring with the same brutal and beautiful authenticity of soil and crops.

Alexander and Lucia finished their set and put down the guitars. With a bouquet of red roses in my hand, I squeezed through the cheering crowd and headed for the stage.

KEVIN ALAN MILNE

Kevin Alan Milne did not aspire to be a writer. He switched majors numerous times in college, finally graduating with a degree in psychology. The only thing he did not study as an undergrad, he says, was business. Therefore, he went to graduate school and earned an MBA at Penn State.

So how did Milne begin writing? "I did it the only way I know how: I sat down at the computer and started typing." That typing resulted in his first novel, *The Paper Bag Christmas,* which was published in 2008.

His biggest challenge? "Jobs have come

R. L. Doyle

and gone since high school," he says, "but along the way nothing has been quite so satisfying—or scary or downright frustrating!—as marriage and parenthood."

THERESA WEIR

Theresa Weir has written nineteen novels, from romances to mysteries to paranormal tales, under her own name and as Anne Frasier. In 1988, she sold her first book, *Amazon Lily*. Early editors rejected it because they found her hero unlikable. But early editors aren't always right, and the book went on to win *Romantic Times*'s Best New Adventure Writer Award.

The Orchard is essentially true, but some names have been changed, and some characters are composites. "The Sweet Melindas' story symbolizes the old and original orchard," Weir says, "hand planted by my husband's great-grandfather and eventually destroyed by the codling moth. All those scenes were drawn from real life."

Tony Nelson

Helping to enrich the lives of thousands of visually impaired individuals every day
www.rdpfs.org

Reader's Digest Partners for Sight is a non-profit foundation established in 1955 by DeWitt Wallace, co-founder of Reader's Digest. Originally created with the purpose of publishing high-quality reading material for the visually impaired, the Foundation has helped to enrich the lives of thousands of visually impaired individuals.

Now, through its program of carefully directed charitable grants to qualifying organizations, the Foundation is also a vital source of support on local, regional, and national levels for the blind and visually impaired community. **Partners for Sight** is also the cosponsor of the helpful online resource VisionAware.org.

If you would like to contact the Foundation, write to: **Reader's Digest Partners for Sight Foundation, Inc.,** 44 South Broadway, White Plains, NY 10601.